Handbook of Steel Drainage & Highway Construction Products SECOND EDITION

Prepared under direction of
the HIGHWAY TASK FORCE for
Committee of Galvanized Sheet Producers
Committee of Hot Rolled and Cold Rolled
Sheet and Strip Producers

Published by
AMERICAN IRON AND STEEL INSTITUTE
1000 16th Street, N.W., Washington, D.C., 20036
1971

Second Printing, 1973
Third Printing, 1976
Fourth Printing, 1977

The Lakeside Press
R. R. Donnelley & Sons Company
Printed in U. S. A.

Preface

THE SECOND EDITION of the *Handbook of Steel Drainage and Highway Construction Products* brings to the Engineer the benefits of fresh results of research on structural design. Greater economy is the result. Steel pipe and construction products have also been updated by new fabricating methods and new coupling devices.

Rearrangement of some of the contents of the Handbook has resulted in fuller discussion of the applications of storm drainage and special drainage problems. And there is a new simplified approach to hydraulic design and the selection of materials to meet various service conditions.

Greater safety features have been added to guardrail, barrier beams, bridge railings and break-away supports for signs and luminaires.

Acknowledgment for the present edition is due the various steel producers cooperating with AISI's Committees shown on the title page. (*Galvanized Sheet Producers and Committee of Hot Rolled and Cold Rolled Sheet and Strip Producers.*) An AISI Highway Task Force (made up of representatives from various steel companies) gave generously of their engineering talent, time, data and illustrations. Special appreciation is acknowledged to the National Corrugated Steel Pipe Association (NCSPA) whose Publications Committee reviewed and approved the latest revised text.

Thanks are offered to the various practicing engineers and associations, research organizations and government sources, most of whom are listed in the bibliography. Particular recognition goes to H. L. White and T. F. deCapiteau for their contributions. Commendation is due Consultant W. H. Spindler, P.E., who served as editor-in-chief on this and preceding editions.

Suggestions for improvements for future editions are welcomed.

American Iron and Steel Institute

1971

Contents

5

Fig. 0-1. Typical corrugated steel culvert under moderately high fill.

PART **I**

Applications

INTRODUCTION

Modern engineering construction for the "space age" is the challenge for engineers, consultants, contractors and public officials.

Flexible steel conduits play an important role in the form of culverts, storm sewers, subdrains, spillways, underpasses and service tunnels—for highways, railways, airports, municipalities, recreation areas, industrial parks, flood and conservation projects, water pollution abatement and many other programs.

PROGRESS THROUGH RESEARCH

Engineers and contractors are an imaginative lot in seeking improved ways of designing and building their projects. Steel manufacturers and fabricators have cooperated, by aid of their research and manufacturing staffs, to provide engineers and contractors with better materials, products and installation methods.

Manufacturers' sales staffs and associations are made up largely of experienced professional engineers, knowledgeable of the construction industry's problems, who constitute a prime information source on applications, specifications and installation of their products.

Fig. 0-2. Maintenance-free twin structural plate pipe-arch culverts serve to replace a small bridge. They are "first cousins" to the shop fabricated culvert pipe sections on the truck-trailer.

SIZES AND SHAPES

Steel conduits are available for many applications, in a wide range of sizes and shapes—round pipe in diameters of 6 inches to 24 feet and more, elliptical pipe, pipe-arches, horseshoes, arches and other shapes.

STRUCTURAL STRENGTH

Mechanical properties of steel are controlled in the mill, and the finished product is fabricated to exacting specifications. The strength and integrity of "soil/steel" structures is almost unlimited as the result of much current research in laboratory and field installations.

LOW MAINTENANCE

Costs of maintaining installations are effectively controlled through modern design criteria for corrosion factors. By proper use of materials for specific locations or applications, utmost economy and optimum service life are assured.

TIME SAVING

Contractors with their vast investments in equipment and high-cost labor are constantly seeking materials and products that avoid costly delays and help to speed up construction. Strategically located steel pipe fabricating plants and storage yards make for prompt deliveries. Because shop-fabricated steel conduits are but little affected by temperature extremes and by precipitation, these products can be adequately scheduled and installed with minimum

Fig. O-3. Installing a corrugated steel pipe sewer with full-spun lining on a large military base.

Fig. 0-4. Battery of 84-in. diameter corrugated steel culvert pipe under 25 ft of cover on a mainline railroad. This shows the confidence of engineers in this type of structure.

delay. Installation is rapid and often enables the contractor to more promptly operate over the structures with earthmoving equipment. This very real "savings" is often overlooked in evaluating corrugated steel vs. other materials.

ACCEPTANCE OF STEEL

Steel is universally recognized, specified and used as a construction material for corrugated conduits and other products. For many years, such products have been included in the standard specifications of the American Association of State Highway Officials, the Federal Highway Administration, the American Railway Engineering Association, the Corps of Engineers, the Federal Aviation Agency, the U. S. Forest Service; also state, county and city departments, and well-recognized consulting engineers.

MAXIMUM VALUE

Analyzing the foregoing factors while keeping his own problems and conditions in mind, the engineer, contractor or official can determine his own evaluation of their importance to the successful completion of his projects.

Fig. A-1. Carrying runoff from winter's snows is an important function for a culvert.

Fig. A-2. Installing a twin 85 x 53-in. helically corrugated steel pipe-arch sewer with a total length of 7800 ft.

Section A—STORM DRAINAGE

CULVERTS

A culvert is a conduit for conveying water through an embankment. Fig. A-1. It is a "grade separation" for water and the traffic or facility above it. The embankment may be for a highway, railway, street, industrial roadway, spoil bank, dam or levee.

Distinction is made between culverts and *storm sewers*, mostly on the basis of length and the types of inlets and outlets. Distinction is also made between culverts and *bridges* in that the top of a culvert does not serve as a road surface, whereas a bridge is a definite link in a roadway surface.

NEW CONSTRUCTION OR REPLACEMENT

Culverts may also be classified by use as for new construction on a new alignment or in supplementary, repair, replacement or relocation applications.

Supplementary. An existing culvert may be supplemented by an extension because of road widening or erosion troubles. Inadequate capacity may require adding another culvert alongside an existing one. In such case, adequate space should be provided so fill around the new culvert can be well tamped. Under suitable conditions, the new culvert can be jacked or tunneled through the fill without disrupting traffic.

Repairs. Repairs to an existing culvert are aimed at perpetuating its service life. Repairs may consist of (1) re-paving the invert, (2) threading a corrugated steel pipe through an existing culvert and grouting the annular space, or (3) using expanding collars and gaskets to seal leaking joints in short-sectional pipe.

Replacement-Emergencies. Culvert replacement may be a routine part of a realignment or required by emergencies created by floods, washouts, slides, structural collapse or other "acts of God" that require prompt return to service. Corrugated steel structures are particularly adapted to these emergencies.

STORM SEWERS

A storm sewer carries storm and surface water and street wash, exclusive of domestic and industrial wastes. Such water is little if any more corrosive than rural watershed runoff. Erosion by the hydraulic traffic may be a factor but normally is less than in culverts.

Corrugated steel storm sewers have a service record of well over half a century. The strength, flexibility, positive joints and installation economies of steel sewers are assured by the use of rational corrosion design criteria and readily available coatings and linings. Steel sewers are also used to reline failing sewers of all sizes and shapes, with a minimum reduction in waterway area.

Many growing communities have been faced with the need for rapidly expanding their storm sewer facilities to accommodate housing, commercial and industrial developments. Steel sewer pipe with its inherent advantage to contractors and its long-range economies for budget-conscious cities is enabling them to provide the critical drainage facilities which they sorely need but otherwise might not be able to build. (The "open materials competition" factor makes it possible to get more favorable bid prices.)

OTHER TYPES OF SEWERS

Although the principal use of corrugated steel pipe is for storm drainage, there are some classes of domestic, commercial and industrial effluents which may be economically handled by corrugated steel pipe sewers. The corrosivity of the effluents is a prime consideration. However, pretreatment of effluents, service structural conditions and required service life may also be pertinent factors. With adequate special coatings, linings and couplings, corrugated steel pipe has in many instances given a notable record of economical and satisfactory service.

Examples of recent sizeable storm sewer installations

Example 1:

Fig. A-3. *Large Enclosed Shopping Center, Six Miles of Sewers*

Monroeville Mall, a $30 million complex on the east side of Pittsburgh, Pa., consists of 125 stores covering 1.75 million square feet of space on 240 acres of land. One hundred acres of this, on two levels, is capable of parking 7500 automobiles.

Formerly a non-descript collection of buildings and activities, it has become what is believed to be the country's largest enclosed shopping center.

Storm sewers required more than 6 miles of pipe, including:

12,940 ft of coated and paved corrugated steel pipe—15″ to 60″
1138 ft of 84-in. structural plate pipe
104 corrugated steel manholes and inlets, plus fittings.

Example 2:

Fig. A-4. *Speedy Installation and Lower Costs*

Phoenix, Arizona, in the heart of a metropolitan area of more than one million people, was troubled with seasonal storms and flash floods that over-taxed the capacity of its storm sewers. A substantial answer to the problem consisted of installing storm sewers along two main thoroughfares. More than 23,000 ft of helicaly corrugated steel pipe, ranging in diameter from 12 to 72 in. was used for these projects. The pipe was coated and lined with asphalt to produce a smooth interior and a life of at least 50 years.

The consulting engineer firm on this job reported that the contractor completed the one job in about half the allotted time. Also, that traffic interference was held to an absolute minimum on both jobs, with public relations favorable to the city.

Example 3:

Fig. A-5. Retention "Basin" Solves Flooding Problem

Ann Arbor, Michigan, found that among the problems of an inadequate sewer system in one of its subdivisions was flooded basements. This was especially true during peak rainfall periods when infiltration of ground water aggravated the situation.

The solution consisted of an underground "ponding" area where excess runoff could be retained until it could be released into the sewers. The storage requirement was determined to be 17,000 cu ft. For this purpose a 94-in. by 58-in. coated and paved steel pipe-arch, 600 ft long was designed by the city engineering department. Installation of this line through a nice residential area is illustrated above.

Section B—SUBDRAINAGE

INTRODUCTION

Subdrainage is the control of ground water—in contrast to surface water or storm drainage.

Subdrainage is a practical, economical way of maintaining firm, stable subgrades and structure foundations; eliminating wet cuts and preventing frost heave; preventing sloughing of fill and cut slopes; keeping recreational areas dry; and reducing saturation of backfill behind retaining walls. Fig. B-1.

The civil engineer considers soil as an engineering material of construction in such works as foundations for buildings, backfills for retaining walls, embankments, cut sections for roads, highways and channels. He therefore is concerned about the basic characteristics of soils, the presence of ground water, and whether subdrainage is practical for the soils on his jobs.

With a little study and experience, many soil and ground water problems can be recognized and solved with subdrainage pipe. For the more difficult cases, the soils engineer and laboratory are indispensable.

HIGHWAY APPLICATIONS

Basically, a dry or granular soil makes a more stable embankment and a better foundation and subgrade for a road surface. Consequently, engineers resort to subdrainage wherever needed to assure maximum service and

Fig. B-1. Standing water contributes to soft foundations. Practical drainage helps to reduce maintenance and early replacement problems.

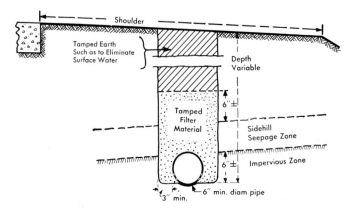

Fig. B-2. An intercepting drain placed in the impervious zone is effective for keeping free water out of the roadway and subgrade.

long life of the embankment or pavement with minimum maintenance and disruption of traffic.

Conditions requiring subdrainage include (1) wet foundation soils, especially under shallow and very high fills; (2) fills made of unstable soils; (3) seepage zones within a cut slope or at a depth below grade where free water and harmful capillary water can weaken the subgrade under the pavement; (4) side ditches with ledge rock that may hold water pockets; (5) transitions from cut to fill section where ground water above an impervious stratum can flow onto pavements; (6) the soil under a pavement where surface seepage

Fig. B-3. Fig. B-4. Two highway projects showing before and after joining 20-ft lengths of perforated steel pipe. Job at left used two-piece bolted couplings; job at right, sleeve couplings.

can be trapped, causing instability and loss of bearing power, and (7) areas subject to frost damage.

The solution in most cases is a subdrain trench to a suitable depth, provided with a perforated subdrain pipe and outlet, and a pervious backfill (or filter) for trapping silt while promptly draining the water into the pipe. See Figs. B-2, B-3, B-4.

Perforated corrugated steel pipe is widely used to control these ground water conditions. Advantages cited are long lengths, light weight, flexibility, strength, simple joints, ample infiltration but with exclusion of most solids.

RAILWAY APPLICATIONS

Railway subdrainage problems are much like those of highways. In addition, there is a tendency for water pockets to form from ballast being driven into soft subgrade, causing "rough track." Multiple tracks complicate the drainage problem, as do highway-railway grade crossings. Proper subsurface drainage in combination with surface drainage can help to minimize roadbed maintenance at these locations.

MUNICIPAL APPLICATIONS

City streets differ but little from rural highways with regard to pavement foundations and traffic loads. When free water exists in the subgrade, it should be intercepted in a pipe subdrain to assure long pavement life.

Other wet areas in cities that can benefit from proper subdrainage are parks, golf courses, athletic fields, race tracks and cemeteries. Steep hillsides and other areas subject to landslides can often be stabilized by proper subdrainage.

AIRPORTS

An inadequate drainage system can seriously hamper or endanger air traffic at airports. Poor drainage can result in saturation of the subgrade and subbase, causing loss of bearing power of the paved surfaces, erosion of slopes

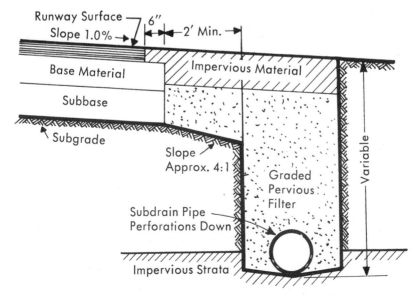

Fig. B-5. Subdrain and base drain along edge of runway.

Fig. B-6. Installing helically corrugated perforated steel pipe for subdrainage on O'Hare International Airport, Chicago, Illinois. Inspection holes are of non-perforated pipe attached to metal stubs.

and excessive ponding of water. Corrugated steel pipe and pipe-arches have been used extensively as airfield storm drains, stream enclosures and pavement subdrains. These structures offer resistance to crushing under impact and vibration. They come in long lengths that resist disjointing and clogging by the entrance of surround fill. Figs. B-5, B-6.

LEVEES AND DAMS

The use of perforated steel pipe subdrains for the stream side of levees and the downstream slope of earth and rock dams is considered good engineering practice. The purpose is to relieve the ground water pressure of accumulating seepage. A special type of toe drainage or relief well for use in major river levees is shown in Fig. B-7.

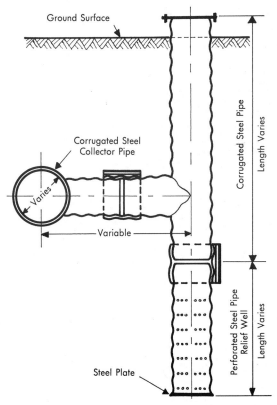

Fig. B-7. Vertical section of relief well and collector pipe as used on river levees. Perforated steel pipe is used extensively for toe drainage on dams and levees.

ABUTMENTS AND RETAINING WALLS

Undrained fill behind an abutment or retaining wall can cause bulging, over-turning or other troubles. Bridges, underpasses and grade elevations are

Fig. B-8. Perforated steel pipes extend through and drain the backfill behind this highway underpass on an interstate highway in Connecticut.

protected and stabilized by subdrainage. See Fig. B-8.

For a railway bridge with closed deck, water seeps through the ballast towards a depression on the center of the deck. There a perforated corrugated steel halfcircle deck drain can be installed to collect the water and conduct it to an outlet.

Fig. B-9. Perforated steel underdrains around the foundation of a research laboratory.

BUILDING FOUNDATIONS

Uneven settlement of building foundations due to high ground water or flood conditions often results in unsightly cracked walls, machines or heavy equipment out of plumb or alignment, and requires expensive and continual maintenance. Residential, commercial and industrial construction are all susceptible to these problems. Adequate subdrainage is usually the best preventive. Fig. B-9.

SLOPE STABILIZATION

Cut slopes and embankments of all kinds are frequently subject to seepage, causing instability and sloughing. Intercepting the water by means of well-placed subdrain trenches, as previously described, is generally the most effective and economical remedy. Fig. B-10. Rugged steel pipe assures long-lasting results.

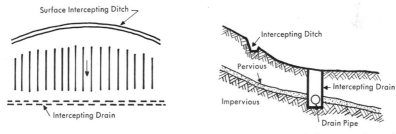

Fig. B-10. Intercepting drain at toe of slope keeps valley floors and other areas dry and useful.

Fig. C-1. Median and shoulder spillway drain of curved structural plate steel on an express highway.

Fig. C-2. Slotted steel pipe drain for intercepting and removing surface water from highway median.

Section C—SPECIAL DRAINAGE PROBLEMS

EROSION PREVENTION

Soil erosion by water is a common and destructive force that plagues many engineering works. It makes unsightly gullies on roadways, cut slopes and embankments. It gouges out side ditches and cross streams. It endangers road foundations and structures. It clogs ditches and culverts with sediment and is a costly nuisance.

There are three basic ways of preventing erosion. The first is to treat the surface—by paving, riprap, or erosion-resistant turf, vines or other vegetation. Second, reduce the velocity of the water by means of ditch checks. And third, intercept the water by means of slotted steel pipe drains, Fig. C-2, and conduct it in corrugated steel flumes, Fig. C-1 and C-3, pipe spillways, stream enclosures or storm drains. Larger streams may be controlled by steel sheeting, jetties or retaining walls.

Corrugated steel pipe with long lengths, positive joints and flexibility to conform to shifting soil is a most dependable means of solving erosion problems.

For design suggestions, see Chapter 6-A.

Fig. C-3. Spillway of corrugated steel pipe anchored by a rod around the pipe, attached to small pipes driven into cut slope.

DAMS AND LEVEES

Earth dams, levees and many other types of embankments require culverts or outlets for intercepted or impounded water. Corrugated steel pipes are particularly advantageous and have enviable records for this type of service. See Fig. C-4.

Fig. C-4. Levee culvert showing (1) diaphragms, (2) flap gate, and riser or manhole.

Small dams are used extensively for soil conservation and to supply drinking water for livestock. Large dams may impound water for public supplies, irrigation, power, recreation or navigation.

Soil conditions at these locations are seldom ideal. Hence the need for strong, flexible pipes to resist disjointing, settlement and infiltration of the surrounding soil.

For design suggestions, see Chapter 6-B.

POWER PLANT COOLING WATER LINES

Power plants require vast amounts of cooling water. Structural plate steel pipes up to 16 ft in diameter have been used for water intakes. These lines are typically subaqueous, requiring special underwater construction by divers. Corrugated steel is especially suitable for this type of construction and has been used for such lines in the Great Lakes region.

Thermal pollution is a major problem with discharge water from power plants. In large deep bodies of water, long discharge lines or structural plate pipe can carry the heated effluent to sufficient depth for dilution or tempering. In shallower waters a unique approach is to use multiple lines of perforated structural plate pipe. The Tennessee Valley Authority has used the latter design at Brown's Ferry, Alabama.

Fig. C-5. Three structural plate pipes serve to carry lake water to power station.

Fig. D-1. Giant sized vehicular steel underpass being constructed under an express highway.

Section D—UNDERPASSES AND SERVICE TUNNELS

GENERAL CONSIDERATIONS

Steel conduits serve many practical purposes other than for drainage, sewage and water supply. Some of these are:

Underpasses or tunnels for safe movement of people, livestock and vehicles.

Materials handling in conveyor tunnels and aerial conduits or protected by conveyor covers; and storage bins for aggregates and other materials.

Utility conduits for protecting pipe lines and cables; also entries, escapeways, ventilation overcasts, and air ducts.

UNDERPASSES FOR PEDESTRIANS AND LIVESTOCK

Pedestrian underpasses find their principal use in protecting people, including school children, who would otherwise be forced to cross dangerous railway tracks, streets or highways.

Safety is not the only advantage. Where a business, industry or institution is divided by a busy street or railroad, a structural plate underpass is often the most convenient, economical and direct means of access. Fig. D-2.

Large farms and ranches are frequently divided by a highway or railroad, requiring livestock to make repeated dangerous crossings. An opening or stock pass under the road is the most satisfactory solution to this problem.

VEHICULAR UNDERPASSES

Large underpasses serve as grade separations for automotive and railway traffic. For example, a county or local road can be carried under an Interstate Highway or railroad often at less cost than by building a bridge. Fig. D-1.

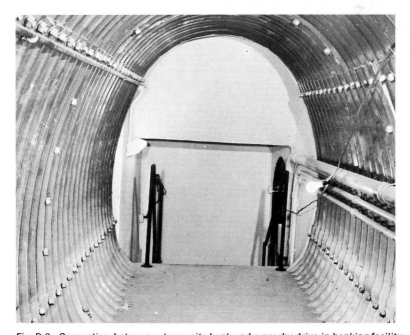

Fig. D-2. Connection between a large city bank and a nearby drive-in banking facility and parking lot is provided by a structural plate steel underpass.

Fig. D-3. Giant structural steel plate reclaim tunnel houses belt conveyor equipment on large western dam construction. It is 1600 ft long, with a span of 16 ft 7 in. and a rise of 18 ft 3 in.

MATERIALS HANDLING

When a plant property is divided by a roadway or other barrier, a tunnel or an aerial bridging conduit may serve to join the property economically. In some cases a conveyor cover for short or long distances can serve to protect the products from the elements while en route. Tracks, conveyor belts or walkways are used in these tunnels and bridging conduits or conveyor covers. Conveyor tunnels of heavy gage corrugated steel pipe are commonly used under storage piles of aggregates and other materials. Fig. D-3.

Storage bins of heavy curved corrugated steel plates are used on construction jobs as well as in plant material yards.

Fig. D-4. Combination service tunnel of structural plate pipe and conveyor cover of corrugated steel sheets.

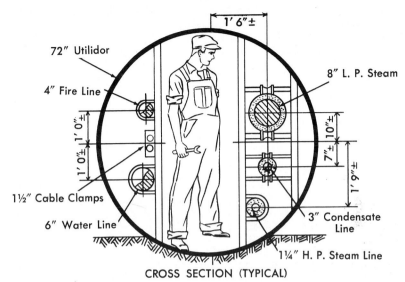

CROSS SECTION (TYPICAL)

Fig. D-5. **Cross-section of corrugated steel "utilidor" or service tunnel equipped with brackets and clamps for supporting various utility lines.**

UTILITY CONDUITS

Water, steam and gas lines, sewers, or power cables must often pass between buildings or beneath embankments or other surface obstacles. Good engineering practice calls for placing them within a conduit to protect against direct loading, impact, corrosion, temperature extremes, and against sabotage or vandalism.

For encasing sewers or high pressure lines, a corrugated steel conduit, in case of sudden breaks, helps to minimize damage to the fill and surface installations. A conduit sufficiently large to walk through provides better access for inspections and repairs. Brackets, hangers or cushioning bases are easily installed. Fig. D-5.

Utility conduits or tunnels may also double as air ducts. In the case of mines, munitions plants and other hazardous activities, these conduits may serve as ventilation overcasts and as escapeways. See following Section E *Aerial Conduits*.

Existing utility lines can be encased with two-piece flanged sections of corrugated steel conduit bolted together.

Fig. E-1. Aerial "bridges" of structural plate between adjacent buildings of an industry permit the efficient transfer of goods, equipment and men.

Section E—AERIAL CONDUITS

INTRODUCTION

Aerial conduits include at least two classes of structures. The first is exposed sewers, gravity water lines and service tunnels or "bridges". The second class includes ducts for air and various gases—for ventilation or circulation. Aerial access bridges for safe movement of humans or intra-plant materials handling also are described here. Fig. E-1.

SEWERS AND WATER LINES

Often the need arises to establish a satisfactory gradient above ground for sanitary outfall sewers, and irrigation and gravity water lines that cross depressions, streams, or channels. These exposed lines may be supported on bents, suitably spaced, without need for beams or rails between piers. See Figs. E-2 and E-3.

SERVICE TUNNELS

Rather than ground level crossings or subterranean passageways, aerial conduits can be a good choice in industry. Bridging between adjacent buildings of a manufacturing plant, Fig. E-5, may be desirable for more direct access for employees, materials, finished products, or utility lines. A variant is seen at mine tipples, quarries, or docks where the aerial lines may be quite lengthy.

VENTILATION DUCTS

Mining, industry and construction operations require various degrees of ventilation to protect against health hazards arising from toxic gases, excessive

Fig. E-2. An aerial corrugated steel pipe sewer with watertight seams and joints carries wastes across a lake.

Fig. E-3. Fastening rod-and-lug bands on a water-supply intake for a power station at a university.

heat, moisture, dust, and possible explosions. Ventilation codes and minimum standards are usually established and policed by state agencies and the U.S. Bureau of Mines.

The use of corrugated steel pipe and other steel products as important components of ventilating systems has been commonplace for many years. Fig. E-4.

Use of explosives in tunneling or mining makes resistance to concussion, and ease of coupling and uncoupling, desirable characteristics of the ventilation pipe. Helically corrugated steel pipe and various forms of smooth wall pipe meet these requirements.

Table E-1   Coefficients of Friction for Galvanized Helically Corrugated Steel Pipe for Air Conduction[1]

Diam. of Pipe in Inches	Coefficient of Friction $f*$	Diam. of Pipe in Inches	Coefficient of Friction $f*$
6	.029–.033	12	.023
8	.033–.038	15	.028
10	.036–.041	18	.032
		21	.035

*From Darcy-Weisbach formula: $h_f = f \dfrac{l}{d} \dfrac{V^2}{2g}$ . . . .(1)

where

h_f = loss in head of fluid under conditions of flow, in ft
f = a dimensionless friction coefficient
l = length of pipe, in ft
V = velocity in ft per sec
g = acceleration due to gravity = 32.174 ft per sec²
d = internal diameter of pipe, in ft

Fig. E-4. Providing fresh air for tunneling or mining is often done by means of corrugated steel pipe as shown here.

FAN DUCTS

Mine ventilation conduits or "fan ducts" extend from the ventilating fan to the portal of the fresh air tunnel or air shaft. Corrugated steel ducts find wide use, in part due to their high strength-weight ratio. Further, they are fully salvable if a change of operations is necessary. They resist destruction from explosions and are fire resistant, and contribute to mine safety through confining explosion and fire in event of disaster. They may range from 36 to 84-in. diameter, with 48, 60 and 72-in. being common.

The duct is normally fabricated so that the fan opening is offset from the centerline of the main conduit to prevent damage to the fan in case of explosion. Spring-loaded explosion doors installed on the outlet end of the main duct serve to relieve pressures and minimize damage to ventilating equipment.

Air lock chambers can be installed on the side of the main conduit for entry into the air tunnel if desired.

Fig. E-5. An 84-in. corrugated steel aerial bridge or "grade separation" for an industrial plant.

Fig. E-6. A corrugated steel tower serves to house some of the controlling equipment for an oil producing company.

HEAT MANIFOLDS AND STACKS

Concrete aggregates must, at times, be heated or cooled prior to mixing to obtain satisfactory working and setting properties of the concrete. Corrugated steel pipe inserted through aggregate piles have been commonly used as heat conduits. Heat transfer through pipe walls is rapid, and its adequate structural strength and complete salvability are advantageous.

Corrugated steel pipe is used for heat manifolds, ducts and stacks for smoke and fumes.

Galvanized steel is satisfactory except where the fumes are corrosive, in which case asbestos-protected steel can be specified.

Summary—Value Analysis

Corrugated steel products have been used for over 70 years for a wide range of important functions in every sector of construction. They are a material for which design parameters have been developed and correlated to decades of actual experience. Using proved techniques, the engineer can select with confidence the corrugated steel product and design that is right for his particular job.

The decision to specify any particular material or alternate should depend on careful analysis. It is a fundamental responsibility of the specifying engineer to make the right choice on the basis of the fact and not as a result of unfounded personal prejudices.

To objectively evaluate corrugated steel products for specific uses calls for a *value analysis* approach on the part of the engineer. When given this type of consideration, corrugated steel will justify its place in most plans and specifications in the best interests of the owner and builder. Table I-1.

A *value analysis* of competing materials or designs involving corrugated steel should include the following items:

1. Reserve strength for sudden overloads, unexpected conditions or future increased loads or conditional changes
2. Ability to accept differential settlements and dynamic shocks without failure
3. Resistance to disjointing, for assurance of continuity
4. Pre-engineered—requiring minimum design time
5. Minimum weight; minimum foundation requirements

Installation Features

1. Relatively light weight—minimum handling equipment
2. Unskilled or semi-skilled labor usually adequate
3. Maximum in-plant fabrication; less field labor required
4. Less construction engineering and field inspection
5. Readily available; immediate usability; fast placement
6. Minimum delay to earthmoving or other construction operations
7. Least affected by weather and temperature

Direct Costs and Advantages

1. Material can be installed on furnished-and-installed basis
2. Requires minimum excavation and bedding
3. Effect of alternate material competitive bidding

Table I-1 TYPICAL VALUE ANALYSIS (abbreviated)
Project: Storm Sewer Extension—3000' of x" Pipe

Principal Factors		Corrugated Steel Pipe	Reinforced Concrete Pipe
Material, f.o.b. plant (pipe, fittings, etc.)		$35,000	$34,000
Freight to Jobsite		1,000	2,500
Unloading and Handling		500	1,000
Excavation	10,000 cy	15,000	
	11,300 cy		17,000
Rock or Gravel Bedding	300 cy	600	
	1,000 cy		2,000
Backfill: Material, Handling and Compaction		3,000	3,500
Lay, Line and Join		6,000	9,000
Other Items*		1,000	1,500
	Total Cost	$62,100	$70,500
	Difference	$8,400 Less	

*Other items of consideration for Contractor, Engineer or Agency may include several of the following: prompt delivery as needed, minimum engineering and inspection costs, bad weather hazards, minimum interference with other phases of project, or business and residential areas, etc.

Fig. DM-1. Assembly of 21 plates is partially done on the bank, then lowered into place for joining onto the completed portion.

PART **II**

Design Methods

INTRODUCTION

Various drainage problems, and the application of steel pipe and other products to the solution of those problems, have been described and illustrated in the preceding Part I. These cover a wide segment of the construction field, including highways, railways, streets, urban areas, airports, industrial and commercial development, flood control and conservation.

These examples are not all-inclusive or complete solutions. They are intended only to show the adaptability and wide acceptance of one material—steel—for aiding in the solution of some of the problems facing the design engineer.

So vast are the annual expenditures for construction that the skills of resourceful qualified engineers are required to research (analyze), select, design and apply the available materials and products that most economically serve their purpose. For example, the cost of drainage facilities on the original interstate highway system was anticipated to be $4 billion, exclusive of bridges. Mass transportation, anti-pollution facilities, flood protection and other related construction can conceivably require drainage facilities in comparable measure. Hence the need for carefully considering the economics of providing and maintaining these facilities.

DESIGN FACTORS

Drainage design begins with reconnaissance and location surveys. The services of experienced soils and drainage engineers are the best assurance of economical construction and subsequent minimum maintenance.

The following design factors are applied:

1. Size, shape, alignment, grade and other configurations. These depend on hydrology and hydraulics, and on service requirements.

2. Structural adequacy to meet embankment and superimposed live loads, along with hydraulic forces.

3. Trouble-free service through selection of materials to resist wear, corrosion and disasters.

4. Economics—first cost of materials plus installation, maintenance cost, and cost per year.

In addition to these, the design engineer can make a "value-analysis" of such other factors as: suitable sources of supply, probable delivery schedule, influence of climate or season of year, coordination with other construction schedules, supplier's assistance, ease of repair or replacement in relation to the importance or service of the facility.

Alternate materials and designs should be considered so that the final selection will provide the most economical and satisfactory solution for the overall facility and its users.

Table 1-1 Shapes and Uses of Corrugated Conduits

Shape	Range of Sizes	Common Uses
Round	6 in. to 21 ft	Culverts, subdrains, sewers, service tunnels, etc. All plates same radius. For medium and high fills (or trenches).
Vertically-elongated (ellipse) 5% is common	4 ft to 21 ft nominal; before elongating	Culverts, sewers, service tunnels, recovery tunnels. Plates of varying radii; shop fabrication. For appearance and where backfill compaction is only moderate.
Pipe-arch	span x rise 18 in. x 11 in. to 20 ft 7 in. x 13 ft 2 in.	Where headroom is limited. Has hydraulic advantages at low flows. Corner plate radius, 18 inches or 31 inches for structural plate.
Underpass*	span x rise 5 ft 8 in. x 5 ft 9 in. to 20 ft 4 in. x 17 ft 10 in.	For pedestrians, livestock or vehicles (structural plate).
Arch	span x rise 6 ft x 1 ft 9½ in. to 25 ft x 12 ft 6 in.	For low clearance large waterway opening, and aesthetics (structural plate).
Specials	Various	For lining old structures or other special purposes. Special fabrication.

*For equal area or clearance, the round shape is generally more economical and simpler to assemble.

CHAPTER 1 Product Details and Fabrication

Section A—CONDUITS: Pipe, Pipe-Arches, Arches

BACKGROUND OF CORRUGATED STEEL CONDUITS

Corrugating a flat sheet has long been known to increase its stiffness and strength. Fig. 1-1. Corrugated steel sheets have been produced almost since the first rolling mill was built in England in 1784. But it was not until after 1890, when mass-produced steel sheets became abundant, that their use grew rapidly.

Corrugated metal pipe was first developed and used for culverts in 1896. As experience was gained in the use of this thin-wall, lightweight, *shop-fabricated* pipe, the diameters gradually increased to 96 in. and larger. Fill heights became greater, even exceeding 100 ft. A further development, in 1931, was structural plate pipe with larger corrugations, for *field assembly*. Diameters and arch spans beyond 25 ft. have been successfully installed.

SHAPES OF CONDUITS

The designer has a wide choice of standard cross-sectional shapes of corrugated steel and structural plate conduits as shown in Table 1-1. Size and service use may control the shape selected, with strength and economy as additional factors. For sectional properties of corrugated steel sheets and plates, see Tables 1-5 through 1-9. For sizes, weights and other details, use Tables 1-10 through 1-24.

Fig. 1-1. Demonstration of how corrugations increase the beam strength of a material.

PIPE AND PIPE-ARCHES   LINER PLATE

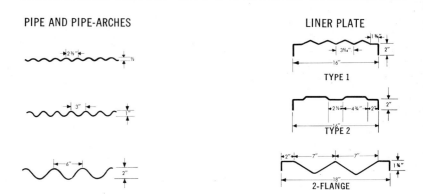

Fig. 1-2. Corrugation types commonly used for galvanized sheet and structural steel conduits and tunnel liner plate.

DESCRIPTION OF CORRUGATIONS

There are many kinds of corrugations, some of which are shown in Fig. 1-2. Corrugations commonly used for pipes or conduits are termed "circular arcs connected by tangents," and are described by pitch, depth and inside forming radius. Pitch is measured at right angles to the corrugations from crest to crest.

For riveted or resistance spot-welded pipe with circumferential (annular) seams, the corrugations are of 2⅔ in. pitch by ½ in. depth and 3-in. by 1-in.

For lock seam pipe, the seams and corrugations run helically (or spirally) around the pipe. For small diameters of subdrainage pipe (6, 8, 10 in., etc.) the pitch vs. depth dimension is 1½ x ¼ in. Larger sizes (with diameters to 120 in.) use 2 x ½ in., 2⅔ x ½ in. and 3 x 1 in. corrugations.

Structural plate pipe is a bolted structure. The 6 x 2 in. corrugation is the standard of the American Association of State Highway Officials.[13]

SECTIONAL PROPERTIES

Sectional properties of the arc-and-tangent type of corrugation are derived mathematically.[1] These include area, A, moment of inertia, I, section modulus, S, and radius of gyration, r. Research by American Iron and Steel Institute[2] has shown that failure loads in bending and deflection within the elastic range can be closely predicted by using computed sectional properties of the corrugated sheet. See Tables 1-5 through 1-9.[3,4]

(*Text continued, page 46*)

Table 1–2 Conversion of Nominal Gage to Thickness

Gage No.	22	20	18	16	14	12
Uncoated Thickness—In.	0.0299	0.0359	.0478	.0598	.0747	.1046
Galvanized Thickness*—In.	0.034	0.040	.052	.064	.079	.109
Galvanized Thickness—mm.	0.762	1.02	1.32	1.63	2.01	2.77

Gage No.	10	8	7	5	3	1
Uncoated Thickness—In.	.1345	.1644	.1838	.2145	.2451	.2758
Galvanized Thickness*—In.	.138	.168	.188	.218	.249	.280
Galvanized Thickness—mm.	3.51	4.27	4.78	5.54	6.32	7.11

*Also referred to as "specified thickness" for corrugated steel pipe products.
For tunnel liner plates, guardrail and other products, see chapters on those products.

Table 1-3 Cross-Sectional Area, A, of Corrugated Steel Sheets and Plates in Inches^2 per Foot of Width

Corrugation Pitch x Depth	Specified Thickness in Inches											
	.030	.040	.052	.064	.079	.109	.138	.168	.188	.218	.249	.280
1½ x ¼ in.	.380	0.456*	.608	.761	.950	1.331*	1.712*	2.093*				
2 x ½ in.	.409	0.489*	.652	.815	1.019	1.428	1.838*	2.249*				
2⅔ x ½ in.	.387	.465	.619	.775	.968	1.356	1.744	2.133				
3 x 1 in.	.445	0.534*	.711	.890	1.113	1.560	2.008	2.458	2.739	3.199	3.658	4.119
6 x 2 in.	.444					1.556	2.003	2.449	2.206	2.574	2.941	3.310
Flat Sheet	.360	0.431	.574	.718	.896	1.255	1.614	1.973				

*Non-standard. Information only. Corrugation dimensions are nominal, subject to manufacturing tolerances.

Table 1-4 Moment of Inertia, I, of Corrugated Steel Sheets and Plates in Inches to the Fourth Power, per Foot of Width
(also Radius of Gyration, r, in Inches)

Corrugation Pitch x Depth	Radius of Gyration r In.	Thickness in Inches											
		.034	.040	.052	.064	.079	.109	.138	.168	.188	.218	.249	.280
1½ x ¼ in.	0.080	0.00251	0.00304*	0.00412	0.00527	0.00679	0.01027*	0.01447*	0.01959*				
2 x ½ in.	0.170	0.01184	0.0137	0.0184	0.0233	0.0295	0.0425	0.0566*	0.0719*				
2⅔ x ½ in.	0.172	0.01119	0.0135*	0.0180	0.0227	0.0287	0.0411	0.0544	0.0687				
3 x 1 in.	0.344	0.05138	0.0618*	0.0827	0.1039	0.1306	0.1855	0.2421	0.3010				
6 x 2 in.	0.688						0.725	0.938	1.154	1.296	1.523	1.754	1.990
Flat Sheet	0.2887 × t	0.00003	0.00005	0.00011	0.00021	0.00042	0.00114	0.00243	0.0444	0.00621	0.0987	0.01472	0.02098

References 3 and 4.

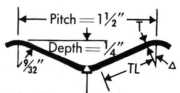

Table 1-5 Sectional Properties of Corrugated Steel Sheets[3]

Per Foot of Section Width for Corrugation: $1\frac{1}{2}$x$\frac{1}{4}$ in. (Helical)

Radius of Curvature: $\frac{9}{32}$ in.

Specified Thickness in.	Uncoated Thickness T In.	Area of Section A Sq. In./Ft.	Tangent Length TL In.	Tangent Angle △ Degrees	Moment of Inertia(a) I In.⁴/Ft.	Section Modulus(a) S In.³/Ft.	Radius of Gyration r In.	De- veloped Width Factor (b)
0.040	0.0359*	0.456	0.571	21.44	0.00304	0.0213	0.0816	1.060
0.052	0.0478	0.608	0.566	21.52	0.00412	0.0277	0.0824	1.060
0.064	0.0598	0.761	0.560	21.61	0.00527	0.0340	0.0832	1.060
0.079	0.0747	0.950	0.554	21.71	0.00679	0.0419	0.0846	1.060
0.109	0.1046*	1.331	0.540	21.94	0.01027	0.0580	0.0879	1.060
0.138	0.1345*	1.712	0.526	22.17	0.01447	0.0753	0.0919	1.061
0.168	0.1644*	2.093	0.511	22.42	0.01959	0.0945	0.0967	1.061

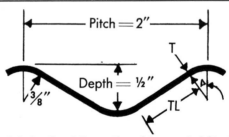

Table 1-6 Sectional Properties of Corrugated Steel Sheets[3]

Per Foot of Section Width for Corrugation: 2 x $\frac{1}{2}$ in. (Helical)

Radius of Curvature: $\frac{3}{8}$ in.

Specified Thickness In.	Uncoated Thickness T In.	Area of Section A Sq. In./Ft.	Tangent Length TL In.	Tangent Angle △ Degrees	Moment of Inertia(a) I In.⁴/Ft.	Section Modulus(a) S In.³/Ft.	Radius of Gyration r In.	De- veloped Width Factor (b)
0.040	0.0359*	0.489	0.681	33.12	0.0137	0.0513	0.1676	1.136
0.052	0.0478	0.652	0.672	33.29	0.0184	0.0673	0.1682	1.136
0.064	0.0598	0.815	0.663	33.46	0.0233	0.0832	0.1690	1.136
0.079	0.0747	1.019	0.625	33.68	0.0295	0.1025	0.1700	1.137
0.109	0.1046	1.428	0.629	34.13	0.0425	0.1406	0.1725	1.138
0.138	0.1345*	1.838	0.605	34.62	0.0566	0.1783	0.1754	1.139
0.168	0.1644*	2.249	0.579	35.13	0.0719	0.2166	0.1788	1.140

*Thicknesses not commonly available. Information only.
(a) Per foot of projection about the neutral axis.
    To obtain *A, I,* or *S* per *inch* of width, divide by 12.
(b) Developed width factor measures the increase in profile length due to corrugating.
                                Dimensions are subject to manufacturing tolerances.

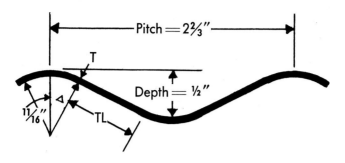

Table 1-7 Sectional Properties of Corrugated Steel Sheets[3,4]

Per Foot of Section Width for Corrugation: **$2\frac{2}{3}$ x $\frac{1}{2}$ in.** (Annular or Helical)

Radius of Curvature: $1\frac{1}{16}$ in.

Specified Thickness In.	Uncoated Thickness T In.	Area of Section A Sq. In./Ft.	Tangent Length TL In.	Gangent Angle △ Degrees	Moment of Inertia(a) I In.⁴/Ft.	Section Modulus(a) S In.³/Ft.	Radius of Gyration r In.	Developed Width Factor (b)
0.040	0.0359	0.465	0.785	26.56	0.0135	0.0503	0.1702	1.080
0.052	0.0478	0.619	0.778	26.65	0.0180	0.0659	0.1707	1.080
0.064	0.0598	0.775	0.770	26.74	0.0227	0.0812	0.1712	1.080
0.079	0.0747	0.968	0.760	26.86	0.0287	0.0998	0.1721	1.080
0.109	0.1046	1.356	0.740	27.11	0.0411	0.1360	0.1741	1.080
0.138	0.1345	1.744	0.720	27.37	0.0544	0.1714	0.1766	1.081
0.168	0.1644	2.133	0.699	27.65	0.0687	0.2069	0.1795	1.081

(a) Per foot of projection about the neutral axis.
To obtain **A, I,** or **S** per *inch* of width, divide the above values by 12.
(b) Developed width factor measures the increase in profile length due to corrugating.

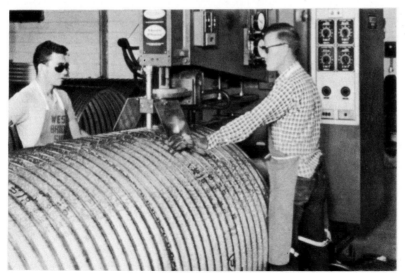

Fig. 1-3. Resistance spot welding is an alternate method of fabricating corrugated steel pipe.

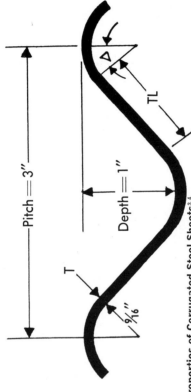

Table 1-8 Sectional Properties of Corrugated Steel Sheets[3,4]

Per Foot of Section Width for Corrugation: **3 x 1 in.** (Annular or Helical)

Radius of Curvature: 9/16 in.

Specified Thickness In.	Uncoated Thickness T In.	Area of Section A Sq. In./Ft.	Tangent Length TL In.	Tangent Angle Δ Degrees	Moment of Inertia(a) I In.⁴/Ft.	Section Modulus(a) S In.³/Ft.	Radius of Gyration r In.	Developed Width Factor(b)
0.040*	0.0359	0.534	0.963	44.19	0.0618	0.1194	0.3403	1.239
0.052	0.0478	0.711	0.951	44.39	0.0827	0.1578	0.3410	1.240
0.064	0.0598	0.890	0.938	44.60	0.1039	0.1961	0.3417	1.240
0.079	0.0747	1.113	0.922	44.87	0.1306	0.2431	0.3427	1.241
0.109	0.1046	1.560	0.889	45.42	0.1855	0.3358	0.3448	1.243
0.138	0.1345	2.008	0.855	46.02	0.2421	0.4269	0.3472	1.244
0.168	0.1644	2.458	0.819	46.65	0.3010	0.5170	0.3499	1.246

*Thickness not commonly available. Information only.
(a) Per foot of projection about the neutral axis.
To obtain A, I, or S per inch of width, divide by 12.
(b) Developed width factor measures the increase in profile length due to corrugating.
Dimensions are subject to manufacturing tolerances.

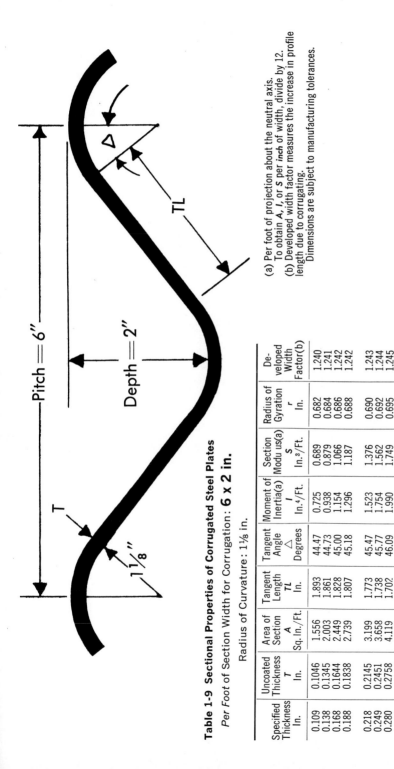

Table 1-9 Sectional Properties of Corrugated Steel Plates

Per Foot of Section Width for Corrugation: **6 x 2 in.**

Radius of Curvature: 1⅛ in.

Specified Thickness T In.	Uncoated Thickness T In.	Area of Section A Sq. In./Ft.	Tangent Length TL In.	Tangent Angle △ Degrees	Moment of Inertia(a) I In.⁴/Ft.	Section Modulus(a) S In.³/Ft.	Radius of Gyration r In.	Developed Width Factor(b)
0.109	0.1046	1.556	1.893	44.47	0.725	0.689	0.682	1.240
0.138	0.1345	2.003	1.861	44.73	0.938	0.879	0.684	1.241
0.168	0.1644	2.449	1.828	45.00	1.154	1.066	0.686	1.242
0.188	0.1838	2.739	1.807	45.18	1.296	1.187	0.688	1.242
0.218	0.2145	3.199	1.773	45.47	1.523	1.376	0.690	1.243
0.249	0.2451	3.658	1.738	45.77	1.754	1.562	0.692	1.244
0.280	0.2758	4.119	1.702	46.09	1.990	1.749	0.695	1.245

Pitch = 6″

Depth = 2″

TL

T

1⅛″

△

(a) Per foot of projection about the neutral axis.
To obtain A, I, or S per inch of width, divide by 12.
(b) Developed width factor measures the increase in profile length due to corrugating.
Dimensions are subject to manufacturing tolerances.

**Table 1-10   Ultimate Longitudinal Seam Strength
of Riveted Corrugated Steel Pipe**

Tested as Uncurved Short Columns
In Pounds Per Foot of Seam*

| Specified Thickness of Metal in Inches | 5⁄16" Rivets | | 3⁄8" Rivets | | | 7⁄16" Rivets |
| | 2⅔" x ½" | | 2⅔" x ½" | | 3" x 1" | 3" x 1" |
	Single	Double	Single	Double	Double	Double
.064	16,700	21,600			28,700	
.079	18,200	29,800			35,700	
.109			23,400	46,800		53,000
.138			24,500	49,000		63,700
.168			25,600	51,300		70,700

For pipe wall strengths of riveted, spot welded and helical pipe for use in design, see Chapter 3.
*Values in this table are based on tests conducted by Utah State Dept. of Highways, 1964, and by Pittsburgh Testing Laboratories, 1966.[6]

(*Text continued from page 40*)

PIPE SEAMS

Standard methods of shop-fabricating the seams of annularly corrugated steel pipe and pipe-arches are riveting or resistance spot welding; for helically corrugated, a lock seam or continuous welding.

Riveted Seams. Specifications for 2⅔ x ½ in. corrugation call for the use of 5⁄16-in., cold-driven rivets for material thicknesses of .064 and .079 in. and ⅜-in. rivets for thicknesses of .109, .138 and .168 in. Longitudinal seams are riveted with one rivet in each corrugation, but pipes 42 inches or larger diameter are double-riveted. Circumferential rivets for joining sections are spaced on 6-in. centers. The strength of such seams for steel sheets and rivets is shown in Table 1-10.

For the 3x1 in. corrugation, all longitudinal seams are double riveted with cold-driven rivets as shown in Table 1-10. Rivet diameters are ⅜ in. for sheets of .064 and .079 in. thickness, and 7⁄16 in. for sheets of .109, .138 and .168 in. thickness.

Spot Welded Seams. Resistance spot welding of lapped seams is a relatively new fabricating method resulting in strength equivalent to riveted seams. Elimination of rivet heads allows a smoother pipe interior and better seating of the connecting band on the exterior. Fig. 1-3.

Bolted Seams and Joints. For structural plate products, high strength carbonated bolts, ¾-in. diameter, hot-dip galvanized, meeting ASTM Specification A 449 are used. Table 1-11 shows strength of bolted longitudinal seams.

Table 1-11   Ultimate Strength of Bolted Structural Plate Longitudinal Seams[7]

In Pounds Per Foot of Seam

Specified Thickness of Plate in Inches	4 Bolts Per Foot	6 Bolts Per Foot	8 Bolts Per Foot
.109	42,000		
.138	62,000		
.168	81,000		
.188	93,000		
.218	112,000		
.249	132,000		
.280	144,000	180,000	194,000

Bolts used in tests were ¾-in. high strength bolts, meeting ASTM A 449.

Table 1-12 Handling Weight of Corrugated Steel Pipe (2⅔ x ½ in.)
Estimated Average Weights—Not for Specification Use*

Inside Diameter in Inches	Specified Thickness in In.	Approximate Pounds per Linear Foot**			
		Galva-nized	Full-Coated	Full-Coated and Invert Paved	Full-Coated and Full Paved
12†	.064	10	12	15	
	.079	12	14	17	
15	.064	12	15	18	
	.079	15	18	21	
18	.064	15	19	22	
	.079	18	22	25	
	.109	24	28	31	
21	.064	17	21	26	
	.079	21	25	30	
	.109	29	33	38	
24	.064	19	24	30	45
	.079	24	29	35	50
	.109	33	38	44	60
30	.064	24	30	36	55
	.079	30	36	42	60
	.109	41	47	53	75
36	.064	29	36	44	65
	.079	36	43	51	75
	.109	49	56	64	90
	.138	62	69	77	100
42	.064	34	42	51	
	.079	42	50	59	85
	.109	57	65	74	105
	.138	72	80	89	115
48	.064	38	48	57	
	.079	48	58	67	95
	.109	65	75	84	120
	.138	82	92	101	130
	.168	100	110	119	155
54	.079	54	65	76	105
	.109	73	84	95	130
	.138	92	103	114	155
	.168	112	123	134	175
60	.079	60	71	85	
	.109	81	92	106	140
	.138	103	114	128	180
	.168	124	135	149	190
66	.079	65	77	93	
	.109	89	101	117	160
	.138	113	125	141	180
	.168	137	149	165	210
72	.109	98	112	129	170
	.138	123	137	154	210
	.168	149	163	180	240
78	.109	105	121	138	200
	.138	133	149	166	230
	.168	161	177	194	260
84	.138	144	161	179	240
	.168	173	190	208	270
90	.138	154	172	192	
	.168	186	204	224	
96	.168	198	217	239	

*Lock seam construction only; weights will vary with other fabrication practices.
**For other coatings or linings the weights may be interpolated.
†For smaller diameters (6″, 8″, 10″) see Table 1-14.

Table 1-13 Handling Weight of Corrugated Steel Pipe* (3 x 1 in.)

Estimated Average Weights—Not for Specification Use

Inside Diameter, inches	Specified Thickness in In.	Approximate Pounds per Linear Foot **			
		Galvanized	Full-Coated	Full-Coated and Invert Paved	Full-Coated and Full Paved
36	.064	33	44	56	92
	.079	41	52	64	100
	.109	56	67	79	115
	.138	71	82	94	130
	.168	87	96*	110	146
42	.064	39	52	66	107
	.079	47	60	74	116
	.109	65	78	92	134
	.138	83	96	110	152
	.168	100	113	127	169
48	.064	44	59	75	123
	.079	54	69	85	132
	.109	74	89	105	152
	.138	95	110	126	174
	.168	115	130	146	194
54	.064	50	66	84	138
	.079	61	77	95	149
	.109	83	100	118	171
	.138	106	123	140	194
	.168	129	146	163	217
60	.064	55	73	93	153
	.079	67	86	105	165
	.109	92	110	130	190
	.138	118	136	156	216
	.168	143	161	181	241
66	.064	60	80	102	168
	.079	74	94	116	181
	.109	101	121	143	208
	.138	129	149	171	236
	.168	157	177	199	264
72	.064	66	88	111	183
	.079	81	102	126	197
	.109	110	132	156	227
	.138	140	162	186	257
	.168	171	193	217	288
78	.064	71	95	121	198
	.079	87	111	137	214
	.109	119	143	169	246
	.138	152	176	202	279
	.168	185	209	235	312
84	.064	77	102	130	213
	.079	94	119	147	230
	.109	128	154	182	264
	.138	164	189	217	300
	.168	199	224	253	335

(*Table continued on following page*)

Table 1-13 (Cont.) Handling Weight of Corrugated Steel Pipe* (3 x 1 in.)

Inside Diameter in Inches	Specified Thickness in In.	Approximate Pounds per Linear Foot**			
		Galvanized	Full-Coated	Full-Coated and Invert Paved	Full-Coated and Full Paved
90	.064	82	109	140	228
	.079	100	127	158	246
	.109	137	164	195	283
	.138	175	202	233	321
	.168	213	240	271	359
96	.064	87	116	149	242
	.079	107	136	169	262
	.109	147	176	209	302
	.138	188	217	250	343
	.168	228	257	290	383
102	.064	93	124	158	258
	.079	114	145	179	279
	.109	155	186	220	320
	.138	198	229	263	363
	.168	241	272	306	406
108	.079	120	153	188	295
	.109	165	198	233	340
	.138	211	244	279	386
	.168	256	289	324	431
114	.079	127	162	199	312
	.109	174	209	246	359
	.138	222	257	294	407
	.168	271	306	343	456
120	.109	183	220	259	378
	.138	234	271	310	429
	.168	284	321	360	479

*Weights vary slightly with method of fabrication; above table is based on lock seam fabrication.
**For other coatings or linings the weights may be interpolated.

Table 1-14 Perforated Galvanized Corrugated Pipe Data*
Dimensions, Weights, Perforations

Nominal Perforations		Minimum Width of Unperforated Bottom Segment in Inches	Specified Thickness			
			0.052 in.	0.064 in.	0.052 in.	0.064 in.
			Weight per Linear Foot of Pipe, Pounds			
Internal Diameter in Inches	Number of Rows		Helically Corrugated Pipe		Circumferentially Corrugated Pipe	
6	4	4.5	3.8 lb	4.7 lb	5.0 lb	5.6 lb
8	4	7.0	5.0	6.2	6.3	7.3
10	4	9.0	6.5	7.6	. . . .	9.0
12	6	9.5	. . . .	9.9	. . . .	10.5
15	6	13.0	. . . .	12.4	. . . .	12.9
18	6	16.5	. . . .	14.8	. . . .	15.3
21	6	20.0	. . . .	17.2	. . . .	17.7
24	8	22.0	. . . .	19.3	. . . .	20.0

*AASHO Spec. M 36

Table 1-15 Design Details of Corrugated Steel Pipe-Arches* (2⅔ x ½ in.)

Diam of Pipe of Equal Periphery, Inches	Span, Inches	Rise, Inches	Water-way Area, Sq Ft	Layout Dimensions			
				B, Inches	R_c, Inches	R_t, Inches	R_b, Inches
15	18	11	1.1	4½	3½	10 1/16	19⅛
18	22	13	1.6	4¾	4	11⅞	37 1/16
21	25	16	2.2	5¼	4	12¾	33½
24	29	18	2.8	5½	4½	14¾	55
30	36	22	4.4	6¼	5	18¼	73¼
36	43	27	6.4	7	5½	21 9/16	91 9/16
42	50	31	8.7	8	6	25⅛	97¼
48	58	36	11.4	9¼	7	29⅛	115 11/16
54	65	40	14.3	10½	8	32¾	129 5/16
60	72	44	17.6	11¾	9	36 5/16	142 15/16
66	79	49	21.3	13¼	10	39¾	145½
72	85	54	25.3	14½	11	42⅝	154½

*Data in this table is subject to manufacturing tolerances.

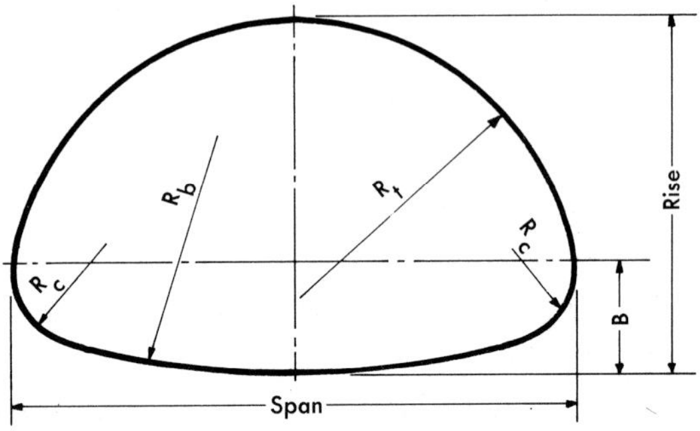

Table 1-16 Design Details of Corrugated Steel Pipe-Arches* (3 x 1 in.)

Diameter of Pipe of Equal Periphery, Inches	Span, Inches	Rise, Inches	Waterway Area, Sq Ft	Layout Dimensions			
				B, Inches	R_c, Inches	R_t, Inches	R_b, Inches
36	43	27	6.4	9¾	7¾	22½	54¾
42	50	31	8.7	11¼	9	26¼	67
48	58	36	11.4	13	10½	30½	82
54	65	40	14.3	14¾	12	34½	91¼
60	72	44	17.6	16¼	13¼	38½	98½
66	73	55	22	21	18	36¾	76¼
72	81	59	26	21½	18	40¾	92¾
78	87	63	31	22	18	43½	100½
84	95	67	35	22½	18	47¾	116
90	103	71	40	23	18	51¾	132½
96	112	75	46	23½	18	56¼	151¾
102	117	79	52	24	18	58¾	160½
108	128	83	58	24½	18	64½	185
114	137	87	64	25	18	69	201
120	142	91	71	25½	18	71¼	210

*Data in this table is subject to manufacturing tolerances.

CONVEYOR COVERS

Arch Sections. Perhaps the most commonly used cover is a half-circle steel arch section, 48 in. long, supported on band sheets 10 in. wide. These band sheets in turn are supported by bolting to the conveyor frame. See Fig. 1-4.

Diameters of support bands and cover sheets are optional, to meet the conveyor equipment manufacturer's designs, but usually range from 36 to 72 in., in suitable thicknesses of steel. Cover sheets are secured by one bolt at each corner and can be quickly removed when necessary. Corrugations should preferably run transverse to the conveyor for greater strength with minimum framing.

Where the arch covers not only the conveyor belt but also the walkway, sheets with larger corrugations (6 in. x 2 in.) can be provided.

Horseshoe or Full Round. The horseshoe shape finds use where weighing equipment or other facilities require a larger cover. A circular or elliptical shape can also serve as a beam to strengthen the span between bents.

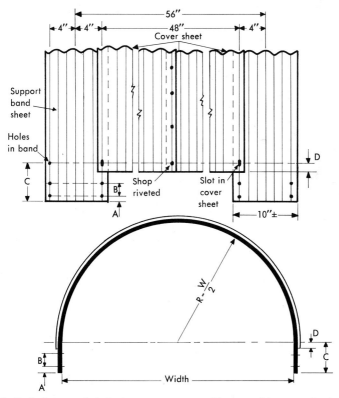

Fig. 1-4. Typical corrugated steel conveyor cover—with removable cover sheets supported by narrower band arches.

Table 1-17   Part Circle Corrugated Steel Culverts—Minimum Thickness, Weights and Dimensions

Weight Per Foot, in Pounds

Specified Thickness in inches																																
0.109	5.4	5.7	6.0	6.4	6.7	7.1	7.4	8.1	8.5	9.2	9.9	10.7	10.8	11.3	11.6	11.9	12.5	12.7	13.4	13.8	14.2	14.5	14.9	15.4	16.2	17.0	18.9	19.9	21.3	21.9	22.6	25.4
0.138	6.9	7.2	7.6	8.1	8.5	9.1	9.5	10.3	10.8	11.8	12.7	13.6	13.8	14.4	14.8	15.2	16.0	16.2	17.1	17.6	18.1	18.4	19.0	19.6	20.7	21.6	24.2	25.3	27.2	27.9	28.8	32.4
0.168	8.4	8.8	9.2	9.9	10.3	11.0	11.6	12.5	13.2	14.3	15.4	16.5	16.8	17.5	18.0	18.5	19.4	19.7	20.8	21.4	22.0	22.4	23.1	23.9	25.2	26.3	29.4	30.8	33.1	34.0	35.1	39.5

Rise, in Inches

Base in In.: 12, 14, 16, 18, 20, 22, 24, 26, 28, 30, 32, 34, 36, 42, 48

Annotations within grid:
- Nominal Thickness 0.109 in. Min.
- Nominal Thickness 0.168 in. Min.
- Nominal Thickness 0.138 in. Min.

Base in In.	Rise values (in inches)
12	2¾ 3½ 4⅛ 4⅝ 5⅛ 5⅝ 6¼ 6¾ 7¼ 7⅞ 8¼ 8¾ 9⅛ 9½ 10 10¼ 10¾ 11¼ 11⅝ 12⅜ 13⅜ 14⅝ 15¼ 15⅜ 15⅝ 16⅝ 17⅝
14	2¼ 3¼ 3¾ 4⅜ 4¾ 5⅜ 5¾ 6 6½ 7 7¾ 8 8½ 9 9¼ 9¾ 10⅛ 10½ 11⅛ 11¾ 12¾ 13⅜ 14⅜ 14⅞ 15 17½
16	2¾ 3⅜ 3¾ 4¼ 4¾ 5⅛ 5⅝ 6⅜ 6⅝ 7 7⅝ 8⅜ 9 9¼ 9⅝ 10 10¾ 11 11¼ 11⅞ 13⅜ 13⅜ 14⅜ 14½
18	2¼ 3¾ 4¾ 5⅛ 5½ 6 6⅜ 7 7⅝ 8 8⅜ 9 9¼ 9⅝ 10 10⅝ 11¼ 11⅜ 12¼ 13¼ 9⅝ 6⅝
20	2½ 3¾ 5⅛ 5⅝ 6 6⅜ 7 7⅞ 8¼ 8⅜ 9 9½ 9⅝ 10½ 10⅞ 11¼ 10⅞ 8½
22	3½ 4¾ 5½ 6½ 7 7⅞ 8¼ 8⅝ 9 9⅝ 10⅛ 10⅝ 11¼ 10⅞ 8¾ 5⅝
24	3¾ 5¼ 6¼ 7 7¾ 8¼ 8¾ 9¼ 9¾ 10¼ 10⅝ 11 10½ 7½ 5
26	5⅝ 6½ 7⅛ 7⅝ 8 8¾ 9⅜ 10⅛ 10½ 9⅝ 8¾ 7⅞ 7¼
28	6⅜ 7¼ 8 8½ 9 9¾ 10 9⅝ 8 5
30	5 7¾ 8¾ 9 9⅛ 8¾ 7½ 5
32	5 8¾ 7⅞ 6⅜ 5
34	4¼ 6 4½ 3½
36	3½ 3⅝
42	
48	

Diagram: Span (chord) and Rise shown on a part-circle culvert cross section.

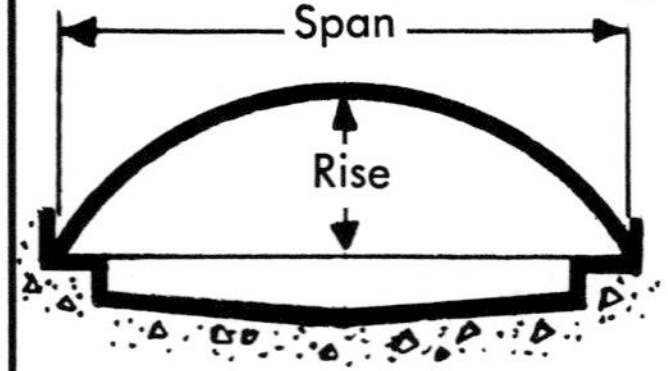

Note: Minimum gages shown on chart are for traffic conditions.
Thickness of 0.109 in. corrugated steel may be used under sidewalk areas for all sizes.
Part circles are made up in standard lengths of 25½ in., which, when lapped, make a length of 2 ft even.

PART CIRCLE CULVERTS

Storm water in larger towns and cities is controlled mostly by curbs and gutters, from which the water discharges into storm sewers. In the smaller towns and boroughs and in outlying districts of larger cities, street water is carried away in surface ditches and may not be connected to a sewer system.

A popular and economical solution to the problem, where excessive water is not a factor, consists of corrugated steel part circle culverts built within the depression and covered with pavement. Part circle edges rest on small steel angles set in a concrete or masonry base, or on a corrugated or flat metal base. The intake and outlet may be in the gutter, or the construction may be such that it does not restrict the width of the street.

With as little as 2 in. of cover over them, they develop strength sufficient to withstand traffic loads and impact quite well. With rigid type pavement, a thickness of 3 or 4 in. will minimize pavement cracking.

PART CIRCLE CULVERT SIZES

Part circles are made up in standard lengths of 25½ in., which, when lapped, make a length of 2 ft even. Lengths are not bolted; the pavement holds them in place. See Table 1-17 for sizes.

Fig. 1-5. Nestable half-circle sections, assembled into pipe, usually serve where transportation is a problem or where encasement of an existing sewer or pipe line is required. The twin 60-in. lines shown here were used for draining a highway interchange in a South American city.

Table 1-18 Details of Uncurved Structural Plate Steel Sections

Net Width in Inches				Over-all Width, Inches	Spaces (N) at 9.6 Inches	Number of Circumference Bolt Holes
Nominal		Detail				
3 N	9 Pi	28.8	28¹³⁄₁₆	33⁹⁄₁₆	3	4
5 N	15 Pi	48.0	48	52¾	5	6
6 N	18 Pi	57.6	57⅝	62⅜	6	7
7 N	21 Pi	67.2	67³⁄₁₆	71¹⁵⁄₁₆	7	8
8 N	24 Pi	76.8	76¹³⁄₁₆	81½	8	9

N = 3 Pi = 9.6 inches.   6″ x 2″ Corrugations.

DATA ON STRUCTURAL PLATE—FIELD ASSEMBLED

Description of Plates. Structural plates are field assembled into pipes, arches, pipe-arches, "underpasses" and other shapes. Corrugations of 6-in. pitch and 2-in. depth are at right angles to the length of each plate.

Thickness. Specified thickness of the plate varies from approximately .105 in. to 0.276 in. for uncoated plates. See table of sectional properties, Table 1-9.

Widths. Standard plates are fabricated in five net covering widths, 28.8 in., 48.0 in., 57.6 in., 67.2 in. and 76.8 in. Table 1-18. Fig. 1-6. These covering widths are listed by the manufacturers either in terms of *pi* or *N* (*N* = 3 *pi*).

The *pi* nomenclature translates circumference directly into nominal diameter, in inches. For example, four 15 *pi* plates gives a diameter of 60 in.; four 21 *pi* plates = 84 in., etc. Various widths may be used to obtain any standard diameters.

To obtain the number *N* in a pipe ring, the nominal diameter is divided by 3. With the number *N* determined, any combination of the five plate widths available in any gage can be used to form the specified pipe section. For example, a 60-in. diameter structural plate pipe contains 20 *N*.

This section is best provided through use of four *5N* plates.

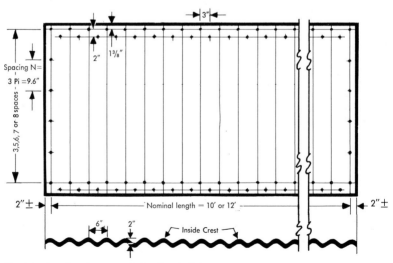

Fig. 1-6. Details of uncurved structural plate.

Table 1-19 Weight of Structural Plate Sections

Net Width		Net Length in Feet	Approximate Weight of Individual Plates Galvanized—in Pounds—without Bolts*							Short Bolts per plate**
			Specified Thickness in Inches							
No. of N	Inches		.109	.138	.168	.188	.218	.249	.280	
3 N	9 Pi	10	161	205	250	272	316	361	405	38
3 N	9 Pi	12	193	246	299	325	379	432	485	46
5 N	15 Pi	10	253	323	393	428	498	568	638	40
5 N	15 Pi	12	303	386	470	511	595	678	762	48
6 N	18 Pi	10	299	382	465	506	589	671	754	41
6 N	18 Pi	12	357	456	555	604	703	801	900	49
7 N	21 Pi	10	345	441	536	583	679	774	869	42
7 N	21 Pi	12	412	526	640	697	810	924	1038	50
8 N	24 Pi	10	396	504	613	667	775	878	986	43
8 N	24 Pi	12	473	603	732	797	927	1050	1176	51
Bolt lengths, in.			1¼ and 1½				1½ and 1¾		1½ and 2	Each plate also has 4 long bolts

*Weights are approximate; based on standard 4-hole punching in longitudinal seams. Plates are galvanized, 2 oz. per sq. ft. of double-exposed surface for 0.188 in. thickness and lighter and, 3 oz. per sq. ft. of double exposed surface for thickness 0.218 in. and heavier. AASHO Spec. 6″ x 2″ Corrugations.

**Weight of bolts only in lb per hundred:	1¼″ = 32	2″ = 39.5
	1½″ = 35	3″ = 52.5
	1¾″ = 37	Nuts = 20

Bolts are color coded for the different lengths.
To compute approximate weight of structures per foot of length: (1) multiply by "no. of plates in periphery"; (2) add weight of bolts and divide by plate length. N = 3 pi = 9.6 inches.

Lengths. Structural plates are furnished either in 10 or 12-ft nominal lengths. They are punched with ⅞-in. holes on 3-in. centers to provide the standard 4 bolts per ft of longitudinal seam, in two staggered rows on 2-in. centers. They may also be punched to provide either 6 or 8 bolts per ft of longitudinal seam on .276-in. specified thickness material, if required.

The inside crests of the end corrugations are punched for circumferential seams on centers of 9.6 in. or 9¹⁹⁄₃₂ in. (=3 *pi* or *N*).

Actual length of the square-end structure is about 4 in. longer than its nominal length because a 2-in. lip protrudes beyond each end of every plate for lapping purposes.

Curvature. Plates are furnished curved to various radii as indicated in Tables 1-20 through 1-24.

Weights of individual plate sections are shown in Table 1-19. Approximate weights of structural plate structures are readily computed.

Plate sections are clearly marked and delivered to the job site ready for field assembly into full-round pipe, elliptical pipe, arch, pipe-arch or any special shape. Detailed instructions for assembly accompany each structure.

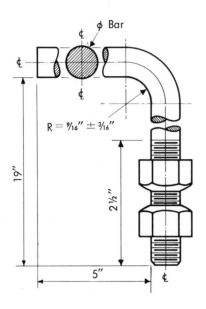

Fig. 1-7. Hook bolts and nuts
for imbedment in headwalls.

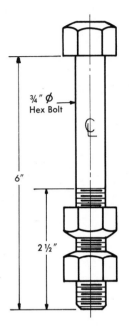

Fig. 1-8. Example of straight
anchor bolt.

Table 1-20 Sizes and End Areas of Structural Plate Steel Pipe[11]

Pipe Diameter in Feet	End Area in Sq Ft	Periphery No. of Plates	N	Total Pi	Pipe Diameter in Feet	End Area in Sq Ft	Periphery No. of Plates	N	Total Pi
5	19.6	4	20	60	14.5	165.1	10	58	174
5.5	23.8	4	22	66	15	176.7	10	60	180
6	28.3	4	24	72	15.5	188.7	10	62	186
6.5	33.2	4	26	78	16	201.1	10	64	192
7	38.5	4	28	84	16.5	213.8	10	66	198
					17	227.0	10	68	204
7.5	44.2	6	30	90	17.5	240.5	10	70	210
8	50.3	6	32	96					
8.5	56.7	6	34	102	18	254.5	12	72	216
9	63.6	6	36	108	18.5	268.8	12	74	222
9.5	70.9	6	38	114	19	283.5	12	76	228
10	78.5	6	40	120	19.5	298.6	12	78	234
10.5	86.6	6	42	126	20	314.2	12	80	240
					20.5	330.1	12	82	246
11	95.0	8	44	132	21	346.4	12	84	252
11.5	103.9	8	46	138					
12	113.1	8	48	144					
12.5	122.7	8	50	150					
13	132.7	8	52	156					
13.5	143.1	8	54	162					
14	153.9	8	56	168					

N = 3 Pi = 9.6 in.   6″ x 2″ Corrugations—Bolted Seams

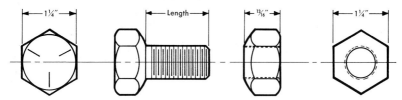

Fig. 1-9. Dimensions of bolts and nuts for structural plate. Lengths include: 1¼ in. 1½ in., 1¾ in., 2 in. and 3 in. The containers and bolt heads may come in individual color markings for ease in identification.

BOLTS AND NUTS

Galvanized ¾ in. diameter bolts and nuts, of special heat-treated steel meeting ASTM Specification A 449, are used to assemble structural plate sections. The galvanizing on bolts and nuts must meet ASTM Specification A 153. See Fig. 1-9 for dimensions of bolts and nuts. These are designed for fitting either the crest or valley of the corrugations, and to give maximum bearing area and tight seams without the use of washers.

Power wrenches are generally used, but simple hand wrenches are satisfactory for small structures.

Anchor Bolts are available for anchoring the ends of structural plate conduits into concrete headwalls or other end treatment (when required). Figs. 1-7 and 1-8. Material for these special ¾ in. bolts must conform to ASTM Specification A 307, and A 563 Grade C for the nuts. Galvanizing of bolts and nuts must conform to ASTM A 153.

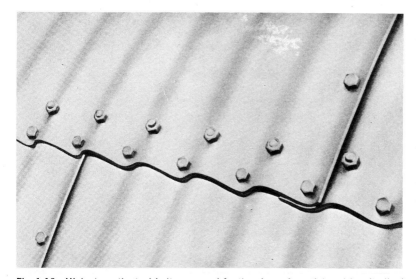

Fig. 1-10. High-strength steel bolts are used for the circumferential and longitudinal seams of structural plate pipe. Four, six or eight bolts per foot of longitudinal seam provide the strength required for the loading conditions.

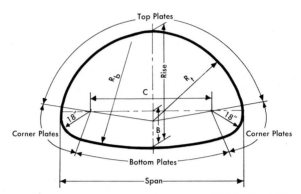

Table 1-21 Sizes and Layout Details—Structural Plate Steel Pipe-Arches

6 in. x 2 in. Corrugations—Bolted Seams

18-inch Corner Radius R_c

Dimensions			Layout Dimensions			Periphery		
Span Ft-In.	Rise Ft-In.	Waterway Area in Sq Ft	B in In.	R_t in Ft	R_b in Ft	No. of Plates	Total N	Pi
6-1	4-7	22	21.0	3.07	6.36	5	22	66
6-4	4-9	24	20.5	3.18	8.22	5	23	69
6-9	4-11	26	22.0	3.42	6.96	5	24	72
7-0	5-1	28	21.4	3.53	8.68	5	25	75
7-3	5-3	31	20.8	3.63	11.35	6	26	78
7-8	5-5	33	22.4	3.88	9.15	6	27	81
7-11	5-7	35	21.7	3.98	11.49	6	28	84
8-2	5-9	38	20.9	4.08	15.24	6	29	87
8-7	5-11	40	22.7	4.33	11.75	7	30	90
8-10	6-1	43	21.8	4.42	14.89	7	31	93
9-4	6-3	46	23.8	4.68	12.05	7	32	96
9-6	6-5	49	22.9	4.78	14.79	7	33	99
9-9	6-7	52	21.9	4.86	18.98	7	34	102
10-3	6-9	55	23.9	5.13	14.86	7	35	105
10-8	6-11	58	26.1	5.41	12.77	7	36	108
10-11	7-1	61	25.1	5.49	15.03	7	37	111
11-5	7-3	64	27.4	5.78	13.16	7	38	114
11-7	7-5	67	26.3	5.85	15.27	8	39	117
11-10	7-7	71	25.2	5.93	18.03	8	40	120
12-4	7-9	74	27.5	6.23	15.54	8	41	123
12-6	7-11	78	26.4	6.29	18.07	8	42	126
12-8	8-1	81	25.2	6.37	21.45	8	43	129
12-10	8-4	85	24.0	6.44	26.23	8	44	132
13-5	8-5	89	26.3	6.73	21.23	9	45	135
13-11	8-7	93	28.9	7.03	18.39	9	46	138
14-1	8-9	97	27.6	7.09	21.18	9	47	141
14-3	8-11	101	26.3	7.16	24.80	9	48	144
14-10	9-1	105	28.9	7.47	21.19	9	49	147
15-4	9-3	109	31.6	7.78	18.90	9	50	150
15-6	9-5	113	30.2	7.83	21.31	10	51	153
15-8	9-7	118	28.8	7.89	24.29	10	52	156
15-10	9-10	122	27.4	7.96	28.18	10	53	159
16-5	9-11	126	30.1	8.27	24.24	10	54	162
16-7	10-1	131	28.7	8.33	27.73	10	55	165

Dimensions are to inside crests and are subject to manufacturing tolerances.
N = 3 Pi = 9.6 in.

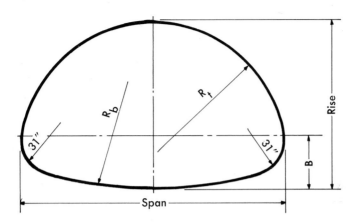

Table 1-22 Sizes and Layout Details—Structural Plate Steel Pipe-Arches[11]

6 in. x 2 in. Corrugations—Bolted Seams

31-inch Corner Radius, R_c

Dimensions			Layout Dimensions				Periphery	
Span Ft-In.	Rise Ft-In.	Waterway Area, in Sq Ft	B in In.	R_t in Ft	R_b in Ft	No. of Plates	Total N	Total Pi
13-3	9-4	97	38.5	6.68	16.05	8	46	138
13-6	9-6	102	37.7	6.78	18.33	8	47	141
14-0	9-8	105	39.6	7.03	16.49	8	48	144
14-2	9-10	109	38.8	7.13	18.55	8	49	147
14-5	10-0	114	37.9	7.22	21.38	8	50	150
14-11	10-2	118	39.8	7.48	18.98	9	51	153
15-4	10-4	123	41.8	7.76	17.38	9	52	156
15-7	10-6	127	40.9	7.84	19.34	10	53	159
15-10	10-8	132	40.0	7.93	21.72	10	54	162
16-3	10-10	137	42.1	8.21	19.67	10	55	165
16-6	11-0	142	41.1	8.29	21.93	10	56	168
17-0	11-2	146	43.3	8.58	20.08	10	57	171
17-2	11-4	151	42.3	8.65	22.23	10	58	174
17-5	11-6	157	41.3	8.73	24.83	10	59	177
17-11	11-8	161	43.5	9.02	22.55	10	60	180
18-1	11-10	167	42.4	9.09	24.98	10	61	183
18-7	12-0	172	44.7	9.38	22.88	10	62	186
18-9	12-2	177	43.6	9.46	25.19	10	63	189
19-3	12-4	182	45.9	9.75	23.22	10	64	192
19-6	12-6	188	44.8	9.83	25.43	11	65	195
19-8	12-8	194	43.7	9.90	28.04	11	66	198
19-11	12-10	200	42.5	9.98	31.19	11	67	201
20-5	13-0	205	44.9	10.27	28.18	11	68	204
20-7	13-2	211	43.7	10.33	31.13	12	69	207

Dimensions are to inside crests and are subject to manufacturing tolerances.
N = 3 Pi = 9.6 in.

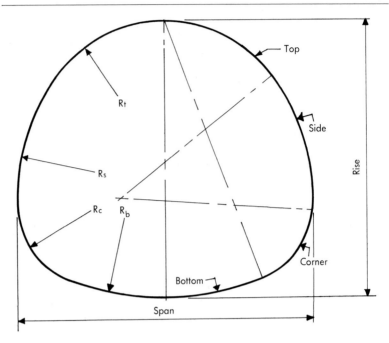

Table 1-23 Structural Plate Steel Underpasses[10]
Sizes and Layout Details

Span x Rise in Ft and In.		Periphery			Layout Dimensions in Inches			
		N	Pi	No. of Plates per Ring	R_t	R_s	R_c	R_b
5-8	5-9	24	72	6	27	53	18	Flat
5-8	6-6	26	78	6	29	75	18	Flat
5-9	7-4	28	84	6	28	95	18	Flat
5-10	7-8	29	87	7	30	112	18	Flat
5-10	8-2	30	90	6	28	116	18	Flat
12-2	11-0	47	141	8	68	93	38	136
12-11	11-2	49	147	9	74	92	38	148
13-2	11-10	51	153	11	73	102	38	161
13-10	12-2	53	159	11	77	106	38	168
14-1	12-10	55	165	11	77	115	38	183
14-6	13-5	57	171	11	78	131	38	174
14-10	14-0	59	177	11	79	136	38	193
15-6	14-4	61	183	12	83	139	38	201
15-8	15-0	63	189	12	82	151	38	212
16-4	15-5	65	195	12	86	156	38	217
16-5	16-0	67	201	12	88	159	38	271
16-9	16-3	68	204	12	89	168	38	246
17-3	17-0	70	210	12	90	174	47	214
18-4	16-11	72	216	12	99	157	47	248
19-1	17-2	74	222	13	105	156	47	262
19-6	17-7	76	228	13	107	158	47	295
20-4	17-9	78	234	13	114	155	47	316

All dimensions, to nearest whole number, are measured from inside crests.
Tolerances should be allowed for specification purposes.   6″ x 2″ Corrugations.

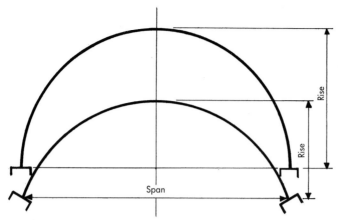

Table 1-24 Representative Sizes of Structural Plate Steel Arches

Span, in Feet	Rise, Ft-In.	Waterway Area, in Sq Ft	Rise over Span(2)	Radius, in In.	N(3)	Pi, In.
6.0	1-9½	7½	0.30	41	9	27
	2-3½	10	.38	37½	10	30
	3-2	15	.53	36	12	36
7.0	2-4	12	.34	45	11	33
	2-10	15	.40	43	12	36
	3-8	20	.52	42	14	42
8.0	2-11	17	.37	51	13	39
	3-4	20	.42	48½	14	42
	4-2	26	.52	48	16	48
9.0	2-11	18½	.32	59	14	42
	3-10½	26½	.43	55	16	48
	4-8½	33	.52	54	18	54
10.0	3-5½	25	.35	64	16	48
	4-5	34	.44	60½	18	54
	5-3	41	.52	60	20	60
11.0	3-6	27½	.32	73	17	51
	4-5½	37	.41	67½	19	57
	5-9	50	.52	66	22	66
12.0	4-0½	35	.34	77½	19	57
	5-0	45	.42	73	21	63
	6-3	59	.52	72	24	72
13.0	4-1	38	.32	86½	20	60
	5-1	49	.39	80½	22	66
	6-9	70	.52	78	26	78
14.0	4-7½	47	.33	91	22	66
	5-7	58	.40	86	24	72
	7-3	80	.52	84	28	84

(*Table continued on following page*)

(1)Dimensions are to inside crests and are subject to manufacturing tolerances.
(2)R/S ratio varies from 0.30 to 0.52. Intermediate spans and rises are available.
(3)N = 3 Pi = 9.6 in. 6″ x 2″ Corrugations—Bolted Seams.

Table 24 Continued. Representative Sizes of Structural Plate Steel Arches

Dimensions([1])		Waterway Area, in Sq Ft	Rise over Span([2])	Radius, in In.	Nominal Arc Length	
Span, in Ft	Rise, Ft-In.				N([3])	Pi, In.
15.0	4-7½	50	0.31	101	23	69
	5-8	62	.38	93	25	75
	6-7	75	.44	91	27	81
	7-9	92	.52	90	30	90
16.0	5-2	60	.32	105	25	75
	7-1	86	.45	97	29	87
	8-3	105	.52	96	32	96
17.0	5-2½	63	.31	115	26	78
	7-2	92	.42	103	30	90
	8-10	119	.52	102	34	102
18.0	5-9	75	.32	119	28	84
	7-8	104	.43	109	32	96
	8-11	126	.50	108	35	105
19.0	6-4	87	.33	123	30	90
	8-2	118	.43	115	34	102
	9-5½	140	.50	114	37	111
20.0	6-4	91	.32	133	31	93
	8-3½	124	.42	122	35	105
	10-0	157	.50	120	39	117
21.0	6-11	104	.33	137	33	99
	8-10	140	.42	128	37	111
	10-6	172	.50	126	41	123
22.0	6-11	109	.31	146	34	102
	8-11	146	.40	135	38	114
	11-0	190	.50	132	43	129
23.0	8-0	134	.35	147	37	111
	9-10	171	.43	140	41	123
	11-6	208	.50	138	45	135
24.0	8-6	150	.35	152	39	117
	10-4	188	.43	146	43	129
	12-0	226	.50	144	47	141
25.0	8-6½	155	.34	160	40	120
	10-10½	207	.43	152	45	135
	12-6	247	.50	150	49	147

See footnotes on preceding page.

ARCH CHANNELS

For arch seats, galvanized unbalanced channels with anchor lugs are available. Fig. 1-11.

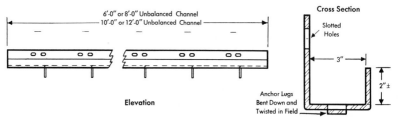

Fig. 1-11. General dimensions of unbalanced channels for structural plate arches.

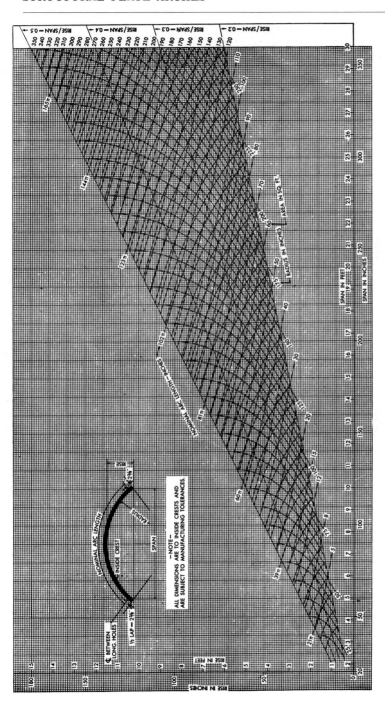

Fig. 1-12. Rise, span, radius and area of structural plate arches. (Reference No. 9)

Section A-2—SPECIFICATIONS

SPECIFICATIONS IN COMMON USE

Specifications are divided into two basic classes—those covering design and construction and those covering materials. Examples of *design and construction* specifications are the AASHO design specifications, Federal Highway Administration design criteria, and those of the Corps of Engineers, Forest Service, Soil Conservation Service and other agencies. Materials specifications are published by AASHO, ASTM, the Federal Government, AREA, NCSPA and others. Material specifications are listed in Table 1-25 for fabricated corrugated steel pipe, structural plate pipe and nestable pipe.

Design and construction specifications are based on half a century of experience and testing, first carried out by industry. In 1966 the Bureau of Public Roads published its first "structural design criteria and recommended installation practices",[14] aided by engineering data supplied by various steel company members of the American Iron and Steel Institute.

A key structural design specification was published in 1968 by the AASHO Committee on Bridges and Structures.[15] It covers design (Section 8) and construction and installation (Section 23). An industry task group cooperated with the AASHO committee in the preparation of this specification.

Design manuals published by industry * supplement the design specification with explanatory tables and charts for various loadings and for other than highway applications. These are provided to reduce the engineering time required to design a project. The construction and installation section spells out the conditions and installation practices to be used for a satisfactory job

MATERIAL SPECIFICATIONS

The AASHO M 218 specification covers the materials and inspection principles for materials to be used for fabricated corrugated steel pipe for all highway work. ASTM Specification A 444 (identical with wording of AASHO M 218) covers the steel sheets to be used for the manufacture of drainage pipe for Federal and other than highway work—including both fabricated pipe and structural plate.

These specifications include: type of material and tests required to insure compliance. They also include dimensions, tolerances, galvanized coatings and other applicable basic requirements. See Table 1-25.

*See references 10, 16, 17, 18, 19 page 65.

Table 1–25   Material Specifications for Corrugated Steel Drainage Structures

End Use	Fabricated Corrugated Steel Pipe		Structural Plate	Nestable Pipe
	Galvanized	Coated		
Highways**—Interstate, State, County, Local Municipal	AASHO M 36	AASHO M 190	AASHO M 167	
All Federal Agencies**	WW-P-405b	WW-P-405b	WW-P-405b	
Military—Dept/Defense				MIL-P-236E
Railroads	AREA 1-4-6	AREA 1-4-13	AREA 1-4-25	
Storm Sewers	AASHO M 36	AASHO M 190	AASHO M 167	

**Specification for culvert sheet material is AASHO M 218, identical with ASTM A-444.

REFERENCES AND BIBLIOGRAPHY

1. Wolford, D. S., *Sectional Properties of Corrugated Sheets Determined by Formula*, Civil Engineering, Vol. 24, No. 2, Feb. 1954, pp. 103–104.

2. American Iron and Steel Institute, *Sectional Properties of Corrugated Steel Sheets*, New York, N.Y., 1960, 17 pp.

3. Unpublished Investigation, *Computer-Calculated Sectional Properties of Arc and Tangent Corrugations as Applied to HEL-COR Pipe*, Macadam, J. N., Sept. 1964, Research and Technology, Armco Steel Corporation, Middletown, Ohio.

4. Unpublished Investigation, *Sectional Properties of Corrugations for Steel Culverts*, Feb. 1965, Macadam, J. N., 12 pp., Armco Steel Corp., Research and Technology, Middletown, Ohio.

5. Kay, B. J., *Culvert Design Based on Structural Strength*, Utah Dept. of Highways, Panel discussion at Annual Meeting of AASHO, Region IV, Phoenix, Ariz., Sept. 15, 1964.

6. Pittsburgh Testing Laboratories Report PG 12590, May 16, 1966.

7. Unpublished Investigation, *Testing of Multi-Plate Seam Strength*, Nov. 1951, Armco Steel Corporation, Research and Technology, Middletown, Ohio.

8. *Hel-Cor Pipe for Culverts and Storm Sewers*, Armco Metal Products Div., Middletown, Ohio, Catalog HC-4563, 1964, 12 pp.

9. *Handbook of Drainage and Construction Products*, Armco Drainage & Metal Products, Inc., Middletown, Ohio, 1955, 529 pp.

10. *Armco Multi-Plate Manual*, Armco Metal Products Div., Middletown, Ohio, 1969, 104 pp.

11. *Armco Multi-Plate Pipe*, Armco Metal Products Div., Middletown, Ohio, Catalog MP-1669, 1969, 16 pp.

12. Lane, W. W., *Comparative Studies on Corrugated Metal Culvert Pipes*, Ohio Dept. of Highways and U.S. BPR, Report No. EES-236, Ohio State Univ. Eng. Experiment Sta., Columbus, Ohio, 1965, 120 pp.

13. American Assn. of State Highway Officials, *Standard Specifications for Structural Plate for Pipe, Pipe-Arches and Arches*, AASHO M 167, 1969.

14. U. S. Federal Highway Administration. Structural Design Criteria and Recommended Installation Practices, 1970.

15. American Association of State Highway Officials, Committee on Bridges and Structures. Standard Specifications: Section 8—Design of CM and SPP and Pa; Section 23—Construction and Installation, Washington, D.C., 1969.

16. *Corrugated Steel Pipe Storm Sewers*, National Corrugated Steel Pipe Assn. Manual, 1968, 32 pp.

17. *Republic Steel Sectional Plate Handbook*, G-152. Republic Steel Corporation, Mfg. Div., Youngstown, Ohio.

18. *USS AmBridge Sectional Plate*, U S Steel Corporation, Pittsburgh, Pa. Manual ABD 168.

19. *Profile—USS 3″ x 1″ Corrugated Galvanized Steel Culvert Sheets*. U S Steel Corp., Pittsburgh. ADUSS 30-1423-03.

20. *End Sections and Culvert End Treatment Designs*, Armco Metal Products Div., Middletown, Ohio, Cat. ES-5070, 8 pp.

Section B—COUPLINGS AND FITTINGS

SIMPLICITY AND CONVENIENCE

Under ordinary or average conditions, the long lengths of shop-fabricated corrugated steel pipe are easily and quickly joined together. This is true for culverts, storm sewers and subdrains.

The basic coupling consists of a steel collar that overlaps the adjoining ends of pipe—keeping them in alignment and the backfill from entering the pipe. Under most installation conditions, there is but little tension or tendency for the pipe to pull apart or settle unevenly at the joints. Neither is there much tendency for storm or ground water to exfiltrate at the joints.

Where conditions are more severe, these can easily be overcome.

TYPES OF COUPLING BANDS[16]

A wide variety of couplings is available to meet the requirements and specifications for corrugated steel drainage pipe and pipe-arches.* The simplest type consists of a *smooth* steel collar of slightly larger diameter than the outside of the pipe sections. This is known as a stab-type and requires no bolting.

A second type consists of single-piece or two-piece *corrugated* band which meshes with the corrugations of the pipe ends. These bands are tightened by various methods such as: (1) bolting through steel angles, bars or integral lugs, or (2) the use of circumferential rods and silo-type lugs. See Fig. 1-16.

A third type is known as a "dimpled" band connection. It consists of a band smooth except for rows of dimpled depressions which mesh with and substantially fill the corrugations of the adjacent pipe ends. Bolts and angles or bars are ordinarily used to tighten the band around the pipes. This type of band is suitable for both types of corrugations—circumferential and helical. See Fig. 1-17.

Another type or variation consists of shop-attaching the bottom half of a two-piece band to simplify making connections in deep trenches or other inconvenient locations.

*See AASHO M 36

Fig. 1-13. Snug-fitting, rugged sleeve joint holds corrugated steel pipe together, resists shearing forces of soil settlement. No bolting is necessary.

"Inside" connecting bands are available where corrugated pipe is used to line failing culverts, drains or conduits.

Where pipes are jacked through an embankment, the pipe may be coupled by means of field bolting or riveting through pre-punched holes, or by welding.

GAIN IN LENGTH

The nominal length of corrugated pipe and pipe-arch is usually increased at each coupling (a maximum of 3 in.). Where exact lengths are required as between manholes or other fixed points, the designer should take this into account.

LEAKAGE

With the exception of aerial sewer or water lines, the exfiltration (or infiltration) of moderate amounts of water may not be important. Where more restricted leakage is required (or airtightness in the case of ventilation lines), the couplings can be supplemented with neoprene gaskets. See Fig. 1-17.

Fig. 1-14. Interior of a 36-in. and 42-in. short-sectional pipe sewer troubled with infiltration throughout much of its 3-mile length.

Fig. 1-15. Corrugated steel expanding bands placed in the same sewer. Sand and silt were removed before the sewer was restored to service.

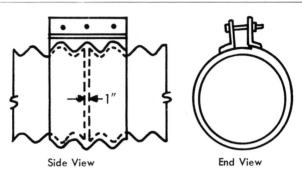

Side View   End View

STANDARD TYPE
Single piece band with angles.
Widths 7″, 12″ and 24″

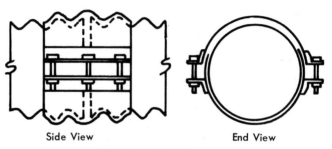

Side View   End View

TWO-PIECE TYPE
2 piece band with angles.
Lower half of band may be attached to one pipe section.

Widths 12″ and 24″

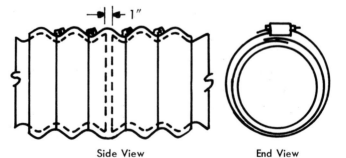

Side View   End View

ROD AND LUG TYPE
Single pre-curved corrugated sheet which laps itself.
4, 6, or 8 rods pass around it and are secured by
specially designed lugs.

Widths 12″ and 24″

Fig. 1-16. Types of connecting bands for corrugated steel pipe. For 3 x 1 in. corrugations the dimensions will vary.

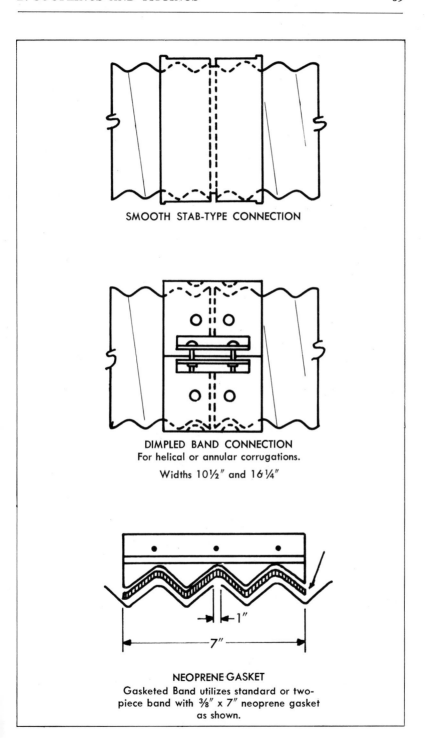

SMOOTH STAB-TYPE CONNECTION

DIMPLED BAND CONNECTION
For helical or annular corrugations.

Widths 10½″ and 16¼″

NEOPRENE GASKET
Gasketed Band utilizes standard or two-
piece band with ⅜″ x 7″ neoprene gasket
as shown.

Fig. 1-17. Additional types of connecting bands, and gasket.

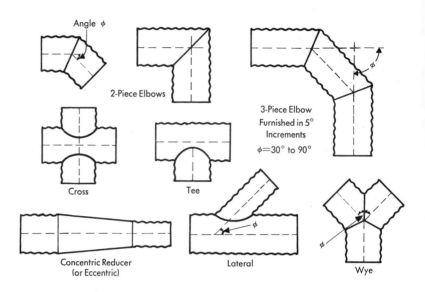

Fig. 1-18. Standard fittings for corrugated steel pipe and pipe-arches are available shop fabricated for a wide variety of conditions.

Fig. 1-19. Moderate horizontal curvature in a culvert or sewer line is possible with ordinary couplings. Greater changes in alignment will require fabricated fittings.

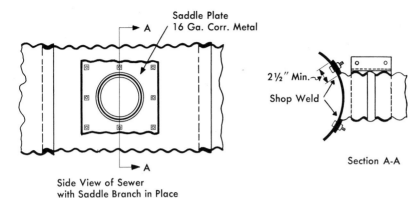

Side View of Sewer
with Saddle Branch in Place

Fig. 1-20. Saddle branch, bolted to main sewer on the job or at the plant, enables laterals and house connections to join the sewer.

FITTINGS: STANDARD AND SPECIAL

Flexibility exists in most metal conduits sufficient for several degrees of curvature to the pipe itself during installation. Camber in a pipe under a high fill is one example of such need. Field joints or couplings permit further curvature. Fig. 1-19.

More than these moderate changes in alignment, and where two or more pipes (or pipe-arches) are joined, will call for a junction made with a shop fabricated fitting or a manhole. Shop fabricated manholes are popular and economical. Fig. 1-24. Other shop fabricated fittings include "standard" elbows, tee or saddle branches, wyes, crosses, reducers, risers, and catchbasins. Standards usually include angles of 30°, 45°, 60° and 90°, and in some cases increments of 5°. See Figs. 1-18 through 1-26.

Fig. 1-21. Corrugated steel manhole, shop-fabricated, is quickly fitted into the line to expedite completion of the sewer.

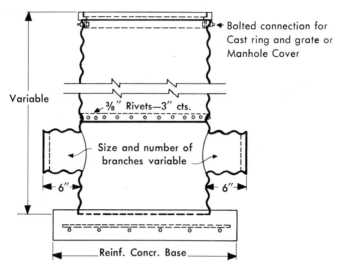

Fig. 1-22. Design of typical catchbasin of corrugated steel pipe.

FABRICATION NOTES

For small pipes (6, 8 and 10-in. diameter), standard fittings of smooth galvanized steel are available in many areas. These include 45° and 90° elbows, tees, 45° laterals or wyes, and reducers.

Larger fittings, up to 120-in. diameter, are shop-fabricated of corrugated sheets or pipe. All parts are shop welded. Welds are treated for corrosion protection equal to that of the pipe. All fittings are furnished in lengths as short as possible but sufficient to attach standard connecting bands.

Fig. 1-23. Corrugated steel sheets are used in building tanks for holding aggregates for trickling filters at sewage disposal plants. Cost here was 70 percent of alternate designs.

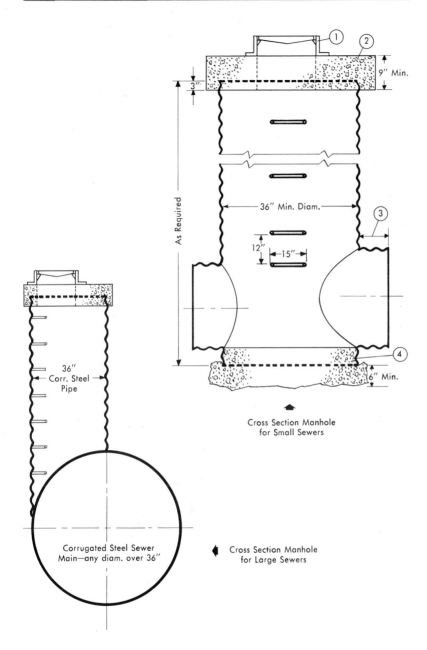

9" Min.

3"

As Required

36" Min. Diam.

12"

15"

①
②
③
④

36"
Corr. Steel
Pipe

6" Min.

Cross Section Manhole
for Small Sewers

Corrugated Steel Sewer
Main—any diam. over 36"

Cross Section Manhole
for Large Sewers

Fig. 1-24. Two designs for corrugated steel manholes.

Fig. 1-25. Special fitting of galvanized steel for lake water intake of power station. Sealant ribbons were used on all seams. Divers made underwater bolted connection between sections.

Structural Plate fittings are shop cut from curved corrugated plates and welded together. Such structures are usually assembled and bolted in the shop in a trial fit to assure that all parts mate properly, then are marked clearly for field assembly. Fig. 1-26.

Fig. 1-26. King-size wye or lateral for large storm sewer was shop-assembled, then dismantled and shipped to the job site for final erection.

Section C—END FINISH

PURPOSES

The principal purpose of end finish on corrugated steel pipe culverts or spillways is hydraulic efficiency—to prevent scour at the inlet and undermining at the outlet, and to increase capacity. Other purposes may be to retain the fill slope, discourage burrowing rodents or improve appearance. For information on hydraulic design, see Chapter 4 *Hydraulics*, page 176 and Chapter 3 *Structural Design*, page 129.

TYPES OF FINISH

Types of steel end finishes include (1) steel sheeting to serve as a low headwall and cutoff wall, (2) end sections, flared and prefabricated, and (3) skewed or beveled ends to fit the stream alignment or the embankment slopes.

1. *Steel Sheeting.* One practical form of end protection consists of driving corrugated steel sheeting as a cutoff wall and low height headwall or endwall. It is cut to receive the last section of the culvert barrel, and capped at about mid-diameter with an unbalanced steel channel, as shown in Fig. 1-27. This type of end finish is particularly appropriate for large culverts which may have the ends *beveled* or step beveled. Length of the sheeting below the flow line should be one-half to one diameter of the culvert, with a minimum of 3 ft.

2. *End Sections.* Steel end sections are shop fabricated for assembly in the field by attachment to corrugated metal culverts from 12 to 84 in. in diameter or pipe-arches from 18 by 11 in. to 85 by 54 in. Dimensions and other data are given in Tables 1-26 and 1-27 and in Figs. 1-28, 1-29 and 1-30.

These end sections are listed in standard specifications of state highway departments, county road departments, railroads and others. They meet the requirements for efficient and attractive end finish on culverts, conduits, spillways and sewer outfalls. They attach to the culvert ends by simple bolted connections of various designs, and so can be completely salvaged if lengthening or relocation is necessary.

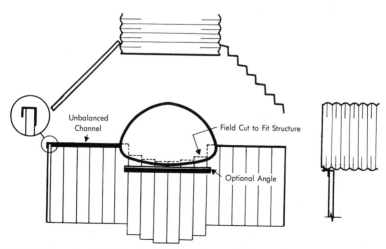

Fig. 1-27. How a steel sheeting headwall can be provided on a pipe-arch culvert.

Table 1-26 Dimensions of Galvanized Steel End Sections for Round Pipe

Pipe Diam. in Inches	Metal Thickness in Inches	Dimensions in Inches					Approximate Slope	Body
		A ± 1″	B (max.)	H ± 1″	L ±1½″	W ± 2″		
12	.064	6	6	6	21	24	2½	1 Pc.
15	.064	7	8	6	26	30	2½	1 Pc.
18	.064	8	10	6	31	36	2½	1 Pc.
21	.064	9	12	6	36	42	2½	1 Pc.
24	.064	10	13	6	41	48	2½	1 Pc.
30	.079	12	16	8	51	60	2½	1 Pc.
36	.079	14	19	9	60	72	2½	2 Pc.
42	.109	16	22	11	69	84	2½	2 Pc.
48	.109	18	27	12	78	90	2¼	2 Pc.
54	.109	18	30	12	84	102	2	2 Pc.
60	.109	18	33	12	87	114	1¾	3 Pc.
66	.109	18	36	12	87	120	1½	3 Pc.
72	.109	18	39	12	87	126	1⅓	3 Pc.
78	.109	18	42	12	87	132	1¼	3 Pc.
84	.109	18	45	12	87	138	1⅙	3 Pc.

1. All 3-piece bodies to have sides and center panels. Multiple panel bodies to have lap seams which are to be tightly joined by galvanized rivets or bolts.
2. For 60 in. thru 84 in. sizes, reinforced edges to be supplemented with galvanized stiffener angles. The angles to be attached by galvanized nuts and bolts. (Notes continued under Table 1-27 on facing page.)

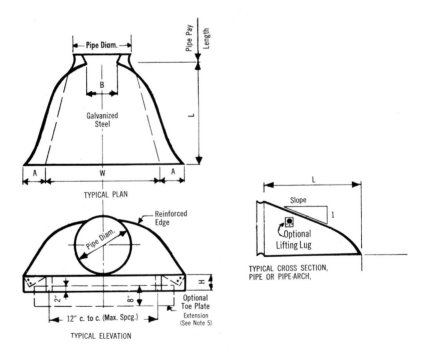

Fig. 1-28. Details of steel end sections for circular steel pipe.

Table 1-27 Dimensions of Galvanized Steel End Sections for Pipe-Arch

Pipe-Arch in Inches		Metal Thickness in Inches	Dimensions in Inches					Approxi-mate Slope	Body
Span	Rise		A ± 1″	B (max.)	H ± 1″	L ±1½″	W ± 2″		
18	11	.064	7	9	6	19	30	2½	1 Pc.
22	13	.064	7	10	6	23	36	2½	1 Pc.
25	16	.064	8	12	6	28	42	2½	1 Pc.
29	18	.064	9	14	6	32	48	2½	1 Pc.
36	22	.079	10	16	6	39	60	2½	1 Pc.
43	27	.079	12	18	8	46	75	2½	1 Pc.
50	31	.109	13	21	9	53	85	2½	2 Pc.
58	36	.109	18	26	12	63	90	2½	2 Pc.
65	40	.109	18	30	12	70	102	2¼	2 Pc.
72	44	.109	18	33	12	77	114	2¼	3 Pc.
79	49	.109	18	36	12	77	126	2	3 Pc.
85	54	.109	18	39	12	77	138	2	3 Pc.

3. For the 79 in. by 49 in. and 85 in. by 54 in. sizes, reinforced edge to be supplemented by galvanized angles. The angles to be attached by galvanized bolts and nuts.
4. Angle reinforcement will be placed under the center panel seams on the 79 in. by 49 in. and 85 in. by 54 in. sizes.
5. Galvanized toe plate to be available as an accessory, when specified on the order and will be the same thickness as the End Section. Same applies to toe plate extension.
6. Galvanized lifting lug available as an accessory when specified on the order.

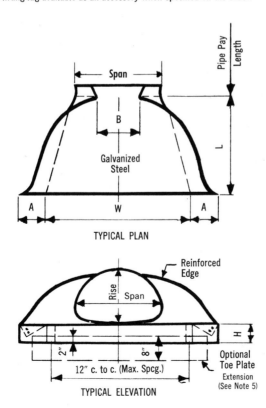

TYPICAL PLAN

TYPICAL ELEVATION

Fig. 1-29. Details of steel end sections for steel pipe-arches.

Fig. 1-30. Cost of headwalls or other end finish is properly a part of the total cost. Maintenance and ease of culvert extension are also factors.

3. *Riprap and Others.* The slope at the end of a culvert (mitered or square cut) can be economically protected against erosion by riprap. Stone riprap should preferably be sealed by portland cement grout or asphaltic concrete.

Sand bags filled with a dry sand-cement mixture (1 part cement to 4 parts sand) make a neat and satisfactory end treatment. These can be stacked vertically or sloped to fit the end of the culvert.

4. *Skews and Bevels.* Skew and bevel ends may be ordered to fit local conditions, or may consist of a standard design as shown in Fig. 1-31. Details and essential considerations are discussed in Chapter 3 *Structural Design*, pages 129-130.

Fig. 1-31. A standard "step-bevel" end finish on a structural plate pipe produces a neat appearance.

CHAPTER 2 **Culvert Location Factors**

PRINCIPLES OF CULVERT LOCATION

By culvert location is meant alignment and grade with respect to both roadway and stream. Proper location is important because it influences adequacy of the opening, maintenance of the culvert, and possible washout of the roadway. Although every culvert installation is a separate problem, the few principles set forth here apply in most cases.

A culvert is an enclosed channel serving as a continuation of and a substitute for an open stream where that stream meets an artificial barrier such as a roadway, embankment, or levee. It is necessary to consider abutting property, both as to ponding upstream and as to safe exit velocities in order to avoid undue scour or silting downstream.

An open stream is not always stable. It may be changing its channel—straightening itself in some places, and becoming more sinuous in others. It may be scouring itself deeper in some places, silting in others. Change of land use upstream by clearing, deforestation or real estate development can change both stability and flood flow of a stream.

Because a culvert is a *fixed* line in a stream, engineering judgment is necessary in properly locating the structure.

ALIGNMENT

The *first* principle of culvert location is to provide the stream with a direct entrance and a direct exit. Any abrupt change in direction at either end will retard the flow and make necessary a larger structure.

A direct inlet and outlet, if not already existing, can be secured in one of three ways—by means of a channel change, a skewed alignment, or both. The cost of a channel change may be partly offset by a saving in culvert length or decrease in size. A skewed alignment requires a greater length of culvert, but is usually justified by improving the hydraulic condition and the safety of the roadbed. See *skew angles*, page 83, and method of specifying same.

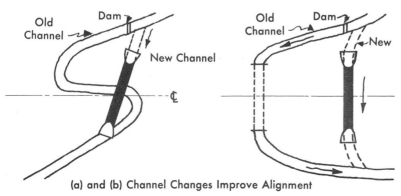

(a) and (b) Channel Changes Improve Alignment

Fig. 2-1. A channel change can provide more-direct flow.

The *second* principle of culvert location is to use reasonable precautions to prevent the stream from changing its course near the ends of the culvert. Otherwise the culvert may become inadequate, cause excessive ponding, and possibly wash out,—any one of which can lead to expensive maintenance of the roadway. Steel end sections, riprap, sod, or paving will help protect the banks from eroding and changing the channel.

Culvert alignment may also be influenced by choice of a grade line. Methods of selecting proper alignment are illustrated in Figs. 2-1 and 2-2.

At roadway intersections and private entrances, culverts should be placed in the direct line of the roadway ditch, especially where ditches are required to carry any considerable amount of storm water.

Culverts for drainage of cut-and-fill sections on long descending grades should be placed on a skew of about 45 degrees across the roadway. Thus the flow of water will not be retarded at the inlet.

Broken alignment under a roadway may be advisable on long culverts. Consideration should be given to entrance and exit conditions, and to increasing the size of the structure to handle or to cleaning out debris the stream may carry during flood periods.

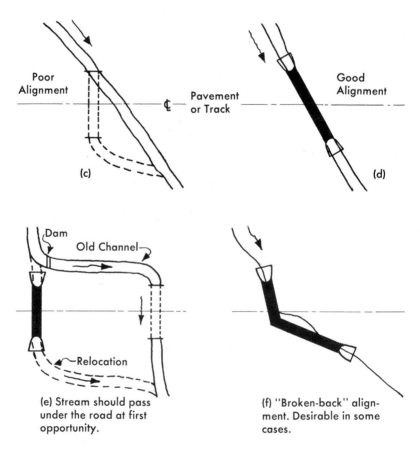

Fig. 2-2. Various methods of securing correct culvert alignment.

CULVERT GRADES

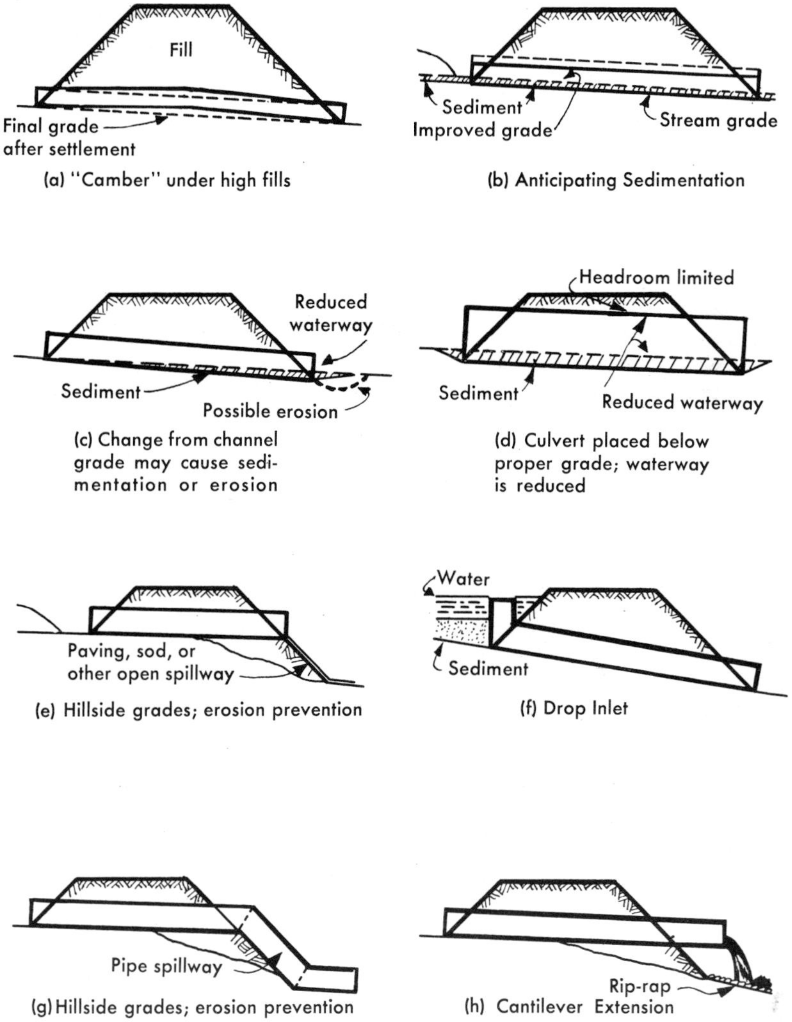
Fill
Final grade after settlement
(a) "Camber" under high fills
Sediment
Improved grade
Stream grade
(b) Anticipating Sedimentation
Reduced waterway
Sediment
Possible erosion
(c) Change from channel grade may cause sedimentation or erosion
Headroom limited
Sediment
Reduced waterway
(d) Culvert placed below proper grade; waterway is reduced
Paving, sod, or other open spillway
(e) Hillside grades; erosion prevention
Water
Sediment
(f) Drop Inlet
Pipe spillway
(g) Hillside grades; erosion prevention
Rip-rap
(h) Cantilever Extension

Fig. 2-3. Proper culvert grades are essential to safe functioning of the structure.

GRADE

The ideal grade line for a culvert is one that produces neither silting nor excessive velocities and scour, one that gives the shortest length, and one that makes replacement simplest.

Velocities as great as 10 ft per second cause destructive scour downstream and to the culvert structure itself unless protected. Safe streambed velocities are given in Table 4–7, page 150. The silt carrying capacity of a stream varies as the square of the velocity.

Capacity of a culvert with a free outlet (not submerged) is not increased by

placing on a slope steeper than its "critical slope." (About 1 percent for a
96-in. pipe.) The capacity is controlled by the amount of water that can get
through the inlet.

On the other hand, the capacity of a pipe on a very slight gradient and
with a *submerged* outlet is influenced by the head (difference in elevation of
water surface at both ends). In this case, the roughness of the culvert interior,
in addition to the velocity head and entrance loss, is a factor.

A slope of 1 to 2 percent is advisable to give a gradient equal to or greater
than the critical slope, provided the velocity falls within permissible limits.
In general, a minimum slope of 0.5 ft in 100 ft will avoid sedimentation.

In ordinary practice the grade line coincides with the average streambed
above and below the culvert. However, deviation for a good purpose is
permissible.

CULVERT LENGTH

The required length of a culvert depends on the width of the roadway or
roadbed, the height of fill, the slope of the embankment, the slope and skew of
the culvert, and the type of end finish such as end section, headwall, beveled
end, drop inlet or spillway.

A culvert should be amply long so that its ends do not clog with sediment
or become covered with a settling, spreading embankment.

A cross-sectional sketch of the embankment and a profile of the streambed
will perhaps best determine the length of culvert needed. Lacking such a
sketch, the length of a simple culvert under an embankment can be determined as follows:

To the width of the roadway (and shoulders), add twice the slope ratio times
the height of fill at the center of the road. The height of fill should be
measured to the flow line if headwalls are not to be used, and to the top
of the culvert if headwalls or end sections are to be installed.

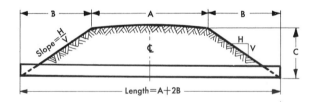

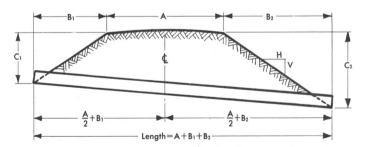

Fig. 2-4. Top: Computation of culvert length when flow line is on a flat grade.

Fig. 2-5. Bottom: Determining culvert length on a steep grade.

Example: A roadway is 40 ft wide on top, two to one side slopes, and at the center of the road the height of fill to flow line is 7 ft: 40 + (4 x 7) = 68 ft length at flow line. See example in Fig. 2-4.

If the culvert is on a slope of 5 percent or more, it may be advisable to compute the sloped length in the manner shown in Fig. 2-5, bottom drawing. However, as fill slopes usually vary from the established grade stakes, any refinement in computing culvert length may not be necessary.

PIPE LENGTH FOR SKEW ANGLES

Where a culvert crosses the roadway at other than a right angle, the increased bottom center line length should be computed as follows:

First determine the length at right angles to the roadway, as in Fig. 2-4. Then divide by the cosine of the angle between the normal and skewed direction.

Correction for pipe diameter on a skew may be made by multiplying diameter by tangent of angle between normal and skew.

If the roadway is on a horizontal or vertical curve or on a steep gradient, the additional length may be estimated.

Example: Assume a normal length of 62 ft and an angle of 14 degrees skewed from the normal.

$$\text{Skew length} = \frac{62}{.970} = 63.8 \text{ ft}$$

The bottom center line length is specified to the nearest 2-ft length.

The ends of the structure may be cut to make them parallel to the center line of the road. For correct fabrication of corrugated steel culverts it is essential to specify the *direction of flow* as well as the *skew angle* or skew number.

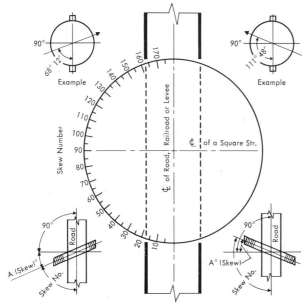

Fig. 2-6. Diagram for method of properly specifying skewed culverts. The direction of flow should also be indicated for fabrication as a left or right.

Fig. 3-1. Mainline railroad crosses over twin 20-ft structural plate highway underpasses.

CHAPTER 3 Structural Design

INTRODUCTION

Corrugated steel conduits, long recognized for outstanding structural strength under the heaviest of underground loadings, are now understood to be a complex composite—the result of soil and steel interaction.

Soil-steel interaction means that a flexible steel conduit acts with the surrounding soil fill to support the loads. Modern research has shown that the ideal underground structure would function so as to place *all* of the load on the soil around and over it. Corrugated steel structures approach this ideal condition.

Design methods for buried corrugated steel pipe are turning more toward the all-important soil component of the composite soil-steel system. While still conservative in reference to the soil structure, the present design procedures do formally recognize it and open the way to future developments.

RESEARCH AND DEVELOPMENT OF BURIED STRUCTURES

Earliest "strength tests" on corrugated steel pipe were quite crude. The tests included circus elephants balanced on unburied pipe and threshing rigs placed over shallow buried pipe.

Laboratory "sand box" and hydraulic tests followed later, by Talbot, Fowler and others. Fill loads were measured on buried pipe and on their foundations at Iowa State College (Marston, Spangler and others, 1913)[1] and at the University of North Carolina (Braune, Cain, Janda)[2] in cooperation with the U. S. Bureau of Public Roads.

Large-scale field tests measuring dead loads were run in 1923 on the Illinois Central Railroad at Farina, Ill.[3] by American Railway Engineering Association (AREA). Measurements with earth pressure cells showed that flexible corrugated pipes carried only 60 percent of the 35-ft column or prism of fill above it while adjacent soil carried the remaining 40 percent of the load. These tests demonstrated for the first time that flexible conduit and compacted earth embankment can combine to act as a composite structure. See Fig. 3-2.

Early efforts to rationalize the load-carrying performance of flexible conduits led to the concept of *passive side pressures* and the *Iowa Formula* for predicting deflection[4].

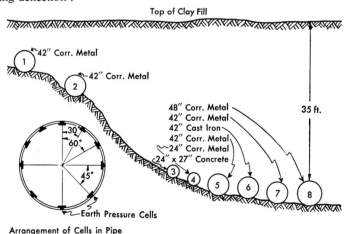

Fig. 3-2. American Railway Engineering Association tests on culvert pipe at Farina, Illinois. Readings were taken on earth pressure cells.

After World War II the concept of a thin compression ring supported by soil pressures was introduced.[5,6] This fundamental concept proved compatible with experience and provided a path to rational design criteria.[7] The national interest in blast effects from nuclear devices supplied a wealth of research and development on buried flexible structures[8,9]. This work clearly showed the potential for more efficient designs of buried corrugated steel structures. Further extensive research was sponsored by American Iron and Steel Institute, 1967 to 1970, at Utah State University under the direction of Dr. Reynold K. Watkins.[10] Procedures, results and conclusions are described in condensed form at the end of this chapter.

Research and continued practical experience on the higher fills and larger corrugated pipes has made possible a more refined design approach with greater accuracy. Design factors for estimating the actual load on the pipe are now available; ultimate compressive stress in a pipe wall is known over the useful range of soil density; and allowable compressive stress in the steel can now be established without excessive safety factors. (Fig. 3-6).

Section A— LOADS ON BURIED STRUCTURES

First consideration in design is the evaluation of the loads on the conduit. Underground conduits are subject to two principal kinds of loads:
    (1) dead loads developed by the embankment or trench backfill, plus stationary superimposed surface loads, uniform or concentrated; and
    (2) live loads—moving loads, including impact.

LIVE LOADS

In practice, live loads on the conduit due to highway and railway traffic are related to the design of underground conduits through charts prepared by the corrugated steel pipe industry. (Figs. 3-3 and 3-4.) These charts modify the theoretical distribution of live loads to values compatible with observed performance of structures under relatively light covers. Minimum cover recommendations are given in this chapter under Section G *Minimum Cover.*

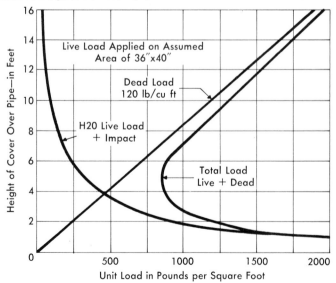

Fig. 3-3. Combined H 20 highway live load and dead load is a minimum at about 5 ft. of cover, applied through a pavement 1 ft thick.

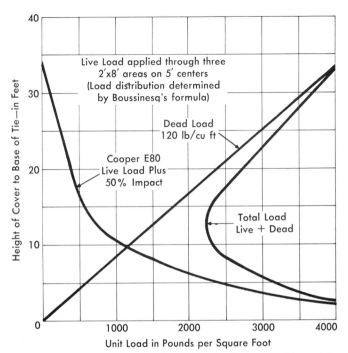

Fig. 3-4. Railroad live load, Cooper E 80, combined with dead load is a minimum at about 12 ft. Load is applied through three 2 ft x 8 ft areas on 5 ft centers.

Table 3-1   Highway and Railway Live Loads

Highway H 20 Loading[11]   Railway E 80 Loading[12]

Height of Cover (Ft)	Load, psf	Height of Cover (Ft)	Load, psf
1	1800	2	3800
2	800	5	2400
3	600	8	1600
4	400	10	1100
5	250	12	800
6	200	15	600
7	175	20	300
8	100	30	100

*Neglect live load when less than 100 psf; use dead load only.

AIRPORT LOADS

The significance of aircraft loads is principally in the area of required minimum cover. Some modern airport design involves very heavy wheel loads of planes not yet designed. Projected wheel configurations and weights for airplanes weighing up to 1½ to 2 million pounds have been used to develop minimum cover tables for the Federal Aviation Agency. See Tables HC-19, -20, -21 and 22, pages 122–124.

DEAD LOADS

Two basic types of installation are common. The "projecting" or embankment condition represented by a culvert, and the trench condition typical of a sewer. The true trench condition results in significant load reductions on the conduit. However, the practical restriction on trench depths limits the load so that this is not significant to the design of ordinary corrugated steel sewers. The minimum wall thickness of most corrugated steel pipe sizes is adequate for fill heights equal to or greater than ordinary trench depths. There are therefore, no criteria given herein for computing trench loads. (Methods of computing trench loads are published in the ASCE Sewer Design Manual.)[13]

The dead load is considered to be the soil prism over the pipe. The unit pressure of this prism acting on the horizontal plane at the top of pipe is equal to:

$$DL = w \times h \dots\dots\dots\dots\dots\dots\dots (1)$$

where w = Unit weight of soil, in lb per cu ft

h = Height of fill over pipe

DL = Dead load pressure, in lb per sq ft

Section B—STRUCTURAL DESIGN OF BURIED STRUCTURES

The structural design process consists of the following:

1. Select the backfill soil density to be required or expected
2. Apply the corresponding load factor to the total load to establish the pressure acting on the steel
3. Select the allowable compressive stress for the pipe size, corrugation and soil density
4. Compute the compression in the pipe wall
5. Determine the thickness required
6. Check minimum handling stiffness
7. Check bolted seam requirements (when applicable).

1. Backfill Density

Select a percent compaction of pipe backfill for *design*. The value chosen should reflect the importance and size of the structure and the quality that can reasonably be expected. The recommended value for routine use is 85%. This value will easily apply to ordinary installations in which most specifications will call for compaction to 90%. However, for more important structures in higher fill situations, consideration must be given to selecting higher quality backfill and requiring same in construction.

2. Design Pressure

When the height of cover is equal to or greater than the span or diameter of the structure, enter the load factor chart, Fig. 3-5, to determine the percentage of the total load acting on the steel. For routine-use the 85% soil value will provide a factor of 0.86. The load factor, K, is applied to the total load to obtain the design pressure, P_v, acting on the steel. If the height of

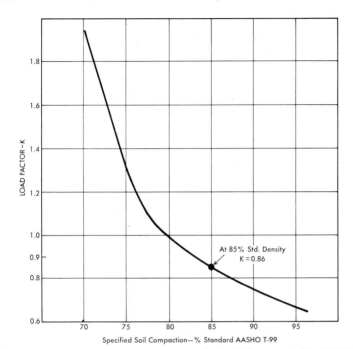

Fig. 3-5. Load factors for corrugated steel pipe for backfill compacted to AASHO stan dard density. For example, at 85% the load factor K is 0.86. This factor is applied to the total load to obtain the design pressure.

cover is less than one pipe diameter, the total load is assumed to act on the pipe, and TL = P_v.

$$P_v = K \times (DL + LL), \text{ when } H \geq S \ldots \ldots \ldots (2)$$
$$P_v = (DL + LL), \text{ when } H < S$$

where: P_v = Design pressure, in psf
$\quad\quad K$ = Load factor
$\quad\quad DL$ = Dead load, in psf
$\quad\quad LL$ = Live load, in psf
$\quad\quad H$ = Height of cover
$\quad\quad S$ = Span

3. Ring Compression[5]

The compressive thrust in the conduit wall is equal to the radial pressure acting on the wall multiplied by the wall radius or: $C = P \times R$. This thrust, called the "ring compression", is the force carried by the steel. The ring compression is an axial load acting tangentially to the conduit wall. For conventional structures in which the top arc approaches a semicircle, it is convenient to substitute half the span for the wall radius.

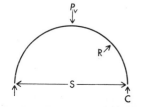

Then: $C = P_v \times \dfrac{S}{2} \ldots \ldots \ldots \ldots \ldots (3)$

where: C = Ring compression, lb per ft
$\quad\quad P_v$ = Design pressure, lb per ft²
$\quad\quad S$ = Span, in ft

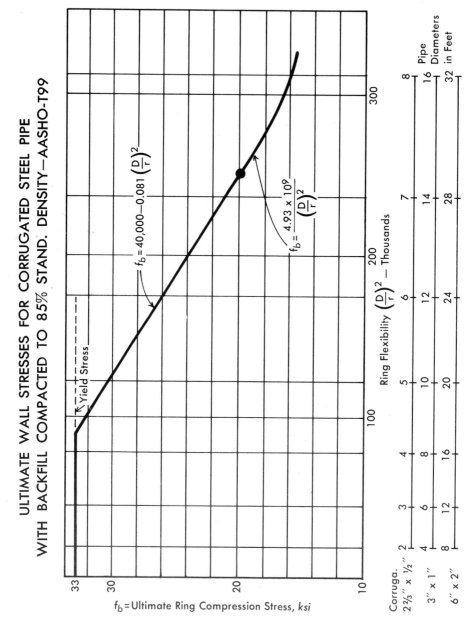

Fig. 3-6. Ultimate wall or buckling stresses for corrugated steel pipe of various diameters and corrugations. The allowable stress is taken as one-half the ultimate.

4. Allowable Wall Stress

The ultimate compressive stresses, f_b, for corrugated steel structures with backfill compacted to 85% Standard AASHO density and a minimum yield point of 33,000 psi, are shown in Fig. 3-6. The ultimate compression in the pipe wall is expressed by the following equations: (4), (5), (6). The first is the, specified minimum yield point of the steel which represents the *zone of wall crushing* or yielding. The second represents the *interaction zone of yielding* and ring buckling. And third, the *ring buckling zone*.

$$1.\ f_b = f_y = 33,000 \text{ psi, when } \frac{D}{r} < 294 \dots\dots\dots\dots\dots (4)$$

$$2.\ f_b = 40,000 - .081 \left(\frac{D}{r}\right)^2, \text{ when } \frac{D}{r} > 294 \text{ and } < 500 \dots (5)$$

$$3.\ f_b = \frac{4.93 \times 10^9}{\left(\dfrac{D}{r}\right)^2}, \text{ when } \frac{D}{r} > 500 \dots\dots\dots\dots\dots (6)$$

$$\text{where: } D = \text{Diam. or span, in in.}$$
$$r = \text{Radius of gyration}$$

A factor of safety of 2 is applied to the ultimate wall stress to obtain the design stress, f_c.

$$f_c = \frac{f_b}{2} \dots\dots\dots\dots\dots (7)$$

5. Wall Thickness

Required wall area, A, is computed from calculated compression in the pipe wall, C, and the allowable stress, f_c.

$$A = \frac{C}{f_c} \dots\dots\dots\dots\dots (8)$$

From Table 3-2 select the wall thickness providing the required area in the same corrugation used to select the allowable stress. See page 92.

6. Check Handling Stiffness

Minimum pipe stiffness requirements for practical handling and installation, without undue care or bracing have been established through experience and formulated. The resultant flexibility factor, FF, limits the size of each combination of corrugation and metal thickness.

$$FF = \frac{D^2}{EI} \dots\dots\dots\dots\dots\dots\dots\dots\dots (9)$$

$$\text{where: } E = \text{Mod. of elasticity} = 30 \times 10^6 \text{ psi}$$
$$D = \text{Diam. or span, in inches}$$
$$I = \text{Moment of inertia of wall, in in.}^4 \text{ per in.}$$

Recommended maximum values of FF for ordinary installations:

$$FF = 0.0433 \text{ for factory-made pipe with riveted,}$$
$$\text{welded, or helical seams 120-in. diam. or less}$$

$$FF = 0.0200 \text{ for field-assembled pipe with}$$
$$\text{bolted seams and all sizes over 120-in. diam.}$$

Higher values can be used with special care or where experience has so proved. Trench condition, as in sewer design, is one example. Aluminum pipe experiences are another. For example, the flexibility factor permitted for aluminum pipe in some national specifications is more than twice that recommended above for steel. This has come about because aluminum has only one-third the stiffness of steel, the modulus for aluminum being approximately 10×10^6

Table 3-2 Moment of Inertia and Cross-Sectional Area of Corrugated Steel Sheets and Plates for Underground Conduits

Corruga. Pitch x Depth	Specified Thickness in Inches											
	.034	.040	.052	.064	.079	.109	.138	.168	.188	.218	.249	.280
	Moment of Inertia, I, in Inches⁴ per Foot of Width*											
1½ x ¼"	.0025	.0030	.0041	.0053	.0068	.0103	.0145	0.0196				
2 x ½"	.0118	.0137	.0184	.0233	.0295	.0425	.0566	0.0719				
2⅔ x ½"	.0112	.0135	.0180	.0227	.0287	.0411	.0544	0.0687				
3 x 1"	.0514	.0618	.0827	.1039	.1306	.1855	.2421	0.3010				
6 x 2"						.725	.938	1.154	1.296	1.523	1.754	1.990

In the first set of columns header the label is I in Inches^4 per Foot of Width.

Corruga. Pitch x Depth	Cross-Sectional Wall Area, in Inches² per Foot of Width*											
1½ x ¼"	.3801	0.456	.608	.761	.950	1.331	1.712	2.093				
2 x ½"	.4086	0.489	.652	.815	1.019	1.428	1.838	2.249				
2⅔ x ½"	.3873	0.465	.619	.775	.968	1.356	1.744	2.133				
3 x 1"	.4445	0.534	.711	.890	1.113	1.560	2.008	2.458				
6 x 2"						1.556	2.003	2.449	2.739	3.199	3.658	4.119

Corrugation dimensions are nominal, subject to manufacturing tolerances.
*Note that values are per *foot* of width.

psi vs 30 x 10⁶ for steel. Where this degree of flexibility is acceptable in aluminum, it will be equally acceptable in steel.

7. Check Bolted Seams

Standard factory-made pipe seams as shown in *Product Details*, page 46, are satisfactory for all designs within the maximum allowable wall stress of 16,500 psi. However, seams bolted either in the shop or field will continue to be evaluated on the basis of test values for uncurved, unsupported columns. A bolted seam (standard for structural plate) must have a test strength of twice the design load in the pipe wall.

Table 3-3 lists the allowable design values (one-half the ultimate) of bolted joints for 6x2-in. and 3x1-in. corrugations tested as unsupported short columns. For convenience, the wall stress which corresponds to the allowable joint strength is also shown.

Table 3-3 Bolted Seam Design Data

Thickness in Inches	Structural Plate Pipe 6-in. x 2-in. Corruga. (Four ¾-in. Bolts per Ft)		Corrugated Steel Pipe 3-in. x 1-in. Corruga. (Eight ½-in. Bolts per Ft)	
	Allowable Strength (½ Ultimate) in Lb per Ft	Corresponding Wall Stress psi	Allowable Strength (½ Ultimate) in Lb per Ft	Corresponding Wall Stress psi
.064			14,400	16,200
.079			17,900	15,800
.109	21,000	13,500	26,500	17,000
.138	31,000	15,500	31,900	15,900
.168	40,500	16,500	35,400	14,400
.188	46,500	17,000		
.218	56,000	17,500		
.249	66,000	18,100		
.280	72,000	17,500		

DEFLECTION

Deflection of the conduit is not ordinarily the criterion for design of the conduit wall, i.e., metal thickness and corrugation size. It has been shown that backfill soil compacted to normal minimum practice ($\geq 85\%$ standard AASHO density) is more than enough to allow the conduit to carry load in ring compression up to its full strength in crushing or buckling without deflection distress. See Fig. 3-6.

However, flexible conduit deflection is still an important consideration in buried conduits. In some cases clearance dimensions or shape is important. When improper backfill does permit significant deflection, it is important to evaluate the situation structurally.

The importance of deflection to the structural integrity of the conduit is a function of the magnitude and character of the movement. If the deflection is smooth, symmetrical distortion of the conduit wall, a movement of 5% below round is considered structurally sound. A movement of approximately 20% below round will ordinarily result in reversal of curvature.

Deflection of a buried corrugated steel structure is most likely of interest in high fill situations. In such cases, the ring stiffness of the pipe is quite small in relation to the load and it is practical to assume the vertical deflection of the pipe to be equal to the vertical strain of the soil.

The vertical soil strain under a given height of fill can only be determined with a knowledge of the stress-strain relationship of the soil in question. In short, it is necessary to know the modulus of elasticity of the soil in the state of compaction to be expected in the installation and under the amount of pressure that the particular fill height will impose.

Figure 3-7 is a plot of stress-strain for cohesionless soil from actual field tests. It can be seen from these curves that several things must be pinned down for a specific installation if deflection is to be accurately estimated. The curves do illustrate what has been stated here before, that is that deflection will be less than critical for pipe performance when compaction is to 85% standard AASHO density. But, assuming that it is desired to estimate whether deflection will be 1%, 2% or 3% in a given case, it is essential to know the stress-strain property of the soil for the conditions in question.

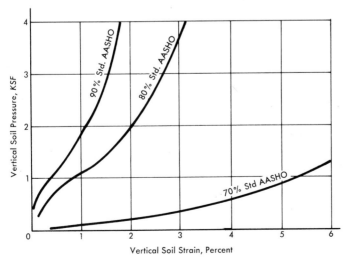

Vertical Soil Strain, Percent

Fig. 3-7. Vertical stress-strain curves for cohesionless soil compacted to AASHO standard densities of 70, 80 and 90%-

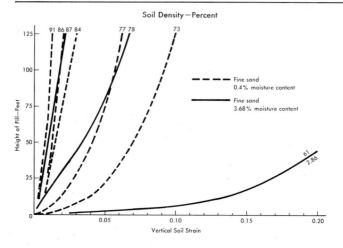

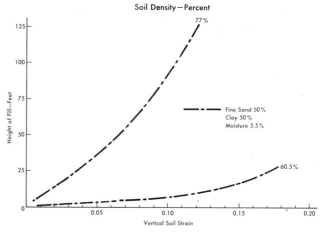

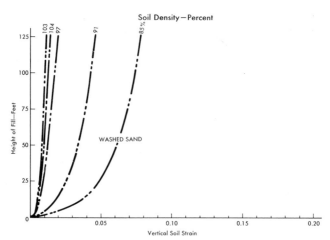

Figs. 3-8, -9, -10. Stress-strain curves for various types of soils at different densities and moisture content.

For important installations, where this information is significant, samples of the soil can be laboratory tested to determine the soil modulus at the required percent standard AASHO density desired. Various methods for determining this modulus have been proposed. References (14) and (15) are recommended to the designer. For the less sophisticated situation, Figs. 3-8, 3-9, 3-10, are typical stress-strain curves for various soil types, which can provide guidelines for deflection estimating.

Fig. 3-11. Twin structural plate pipe-arch stream enclosure provides valuable land for shopping area.

PIPE-ARCHES

The pipe-arch shape poses special design problems not found in round or vertically-elongated pipe. Pipe-arches generate corner pressures greater than the pressure in the fill. This becomes the practical limiting design factor rather than stress in the pipe wall.

To calculate the corner pressure, ignore the bending strength of the corrugated steel and establish allowable loads based on the allowable pressure on the soil at the corners. Assuming zero moment strength of the pipe wall, ring compression, C, is the same at any point around the pipe-arch. And $C = P \times R$ at any point on the periphery. This means the normal pressure to the pipe-arch wall is inversely proportional to the wall radius.

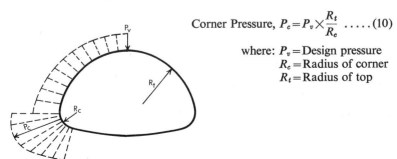

Corner Pressure, $P_c = P_v \times \dfrac{R_t}{R_c}$ .....(10)

where: P_v = Design pressure
R_c = Radius of corner
R_t = Radius of top

Fig. 3-12. The pressures on a pipe-arch vary with location and radius, being greatest at the corners.

Proper installation of pipe-arches is essential. Refer to Fig. 3-18 page 126, for guidance.

Limiting design pressure is established by the allowable soil pressure at the corners. Special backfill such as crushed stone or soil cement at the corners can extend these limitations. A maximum value of 3 tons per ft² for corner pressure is suggested for routine use.

Table for E 80 Live Loads

For pipe-arches made from standard sizes of corrugated pipe (2⅔x½-in. corr.), ignoring the bending strength in the pipe-arch wall does not produce usable results for heavy loads such as Cooper E 80 or similar loadings. The combination of the bending strength of the small-radius corners and the longitudinal distribution of live load through the pipe crown allows acceptable performance where zero moment analysis would preclude the product. The basis for such designs is strictly empirical "gage tables". Table HC-9 for railroad loadings on standard corrugated pipe-arch sizes continues the experience gage table that has been in use for the past 25 years.

Fig. 3-12a. Structural plate pipe-arch being installed under relatively shallow cover under railroad tracks.

ARCHES

Another "special case" is involved in the structural design of arches of corrugated steel on unyielding foundations. Because the steel ring is restrained at the base of the arch and cannot move into the backfill at this point, the influence of column type buckling must be considered.

Design criteria for arches are divided into two classes: (1) arches semicircular or less than semicircular in shape; (2) arches of horseshoe shape with the reentrant angle of the arch at the base 20 degrees or more to the vertical. This latter configuration allows the arch ring to "sit down" into the soil at the base and prevent local buckling at that point.

The most restrictive case is that of the arch that is semicircular (or less than semicircular) in shape. The ultimate compressive strength of such shapes has been shown to be significantly less than equivalent full-round pipe. Only the use of very high safety factors has made this common arch shape practical. It is evident then that the allowable compressive stresses in such shapes must continue to be of the order of magnitude established by the "seam strength" divided by 4.

ARCH CRITERIA

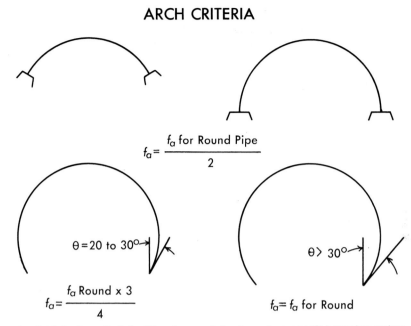

$$f_a = \frac{f_a \text{ for Round Pipe}}{2}$$

$\theta = 20$ to $30°$

$$f_a = \frac{f_a \text{ Round} \times 3}{4}$$

$\theta > 30°$

$$f_a = f_a \text{ for Round}$$

Fig. 3-13. Design criteria for (1) arches semi-circular or less, and (2) horseshoe arches with various degrees of reentrant angle at base.

A better situation exists when the arch is of the horseshoe type with a reentrant angle of the arch at its base of 20 degrees of more.

ARCHES ON UNYIELDING FOUNDATIONS

1. **Arches Semicircular or Less, and Horseshoe Arches where $\theta < 20°$**

   Use one-half the allowable wall stress computed for round pipe of equivalent span.

2. **Horseshoe Arches**

   a. Reentrant angle at base 20 degrees to 30 degrees. Use an allowable stress of 75% of that computed for round pipe of equivalent span.
   b. Reentrant angle at base greater than 30 degrees. Use full design stress for equivalent round pipe.

For further design practices, including foundation preparation, backfill, minimum cover, and end treatment, see pages 126–131.

EXAMPLES

The following examples illustrate the application of design procedures developed in the preceding pages. They include: (1) 48-in. diameter pipe under a 60-ft fill; (2) 120-in. diameter pipe under a 65-ft fill; (3) a 20-ft × 13-ft pipe-arch under 6 ft of cover; (4) a 23-ft arch; and (5) a large vehicular underpass under 32 ft of fill.

Example 1

Given: Pipe diameter required = 48-in.

Height of cover, $H = 60$ ft

Live load, $LL = H\ 20$

Weight of soil, (unit) $w = 120$ lb/cu ft

Find: Wall thickness and type of corrugation

SOLUTION: (See Section B—*STRUCTURAL DESIGN*, pp 88–97)

1.   Backfill Soil Density (compaction) Required:

90% Std. AASHO specified. Assume a minimum of 85% for design.

2.   Design Pressure:

$$P_v = K(DL + LL) \dotfill \text{Equa. (2)}$$

where: $DL = H \times w = 60 \times 120 = 7200$ lb/sq ft

From Table 3-1, LL = negligible for cover greater than 8 ft ....

From Fig. 3-5, $K = 0.86$

Then $P_v = 0.86(7200 + 0) = 6192$ lb/sq ft = load on pipe

3.   Ring Compression:

$$C = P_v \times \frac{S}{2} \dotfill (3)$$

where: S = span, in ft

Then $C = 6192 \times \dfrac{4}{2} = 12,384$ lb/ft

4.   Allowable Wall Stress:

$$f_c = \frac{f_b}{2}$$

where: f_b = ultimate wall stress

From Fig. 3-6, $f_b = 33,000$ psi for 2⅔" × ½" corruga.............(4)

Then $f_c = \dfrac{33,000}{2} = 16,500$ lb/sq in...........................(7)

5. Wall Cross-Sectional Area:

$$A = \frac{C}{f_c} = \frac{12,384}{16,500} = 0.750 \text{ sq in./ft required} \dots\dots\dots\dots\dots\dots (8)$$

From Table 3-2, a specified *thickness* of 0.064 in. provides an uncoated wall *area* of 0.775 sq in./ft

6. Handling Stiffness:

$$FF = \frac{D^2}{EI} = \text{flexibility factor} = 0.0433 \text{ max.}$$

where: D = diameter, in in. = 48

E = modulus of elasticity = 30×10^6 psi

I = moment of inertia, in.^{4}/in.

From Table 3-2, for .064 in. specified thickness,

I = .00189 in.^{4}/in.*

Then $FF = \dfrac{48^2}{30 \times 10^6 \times .00189} = 0.0406$

.0406 < .0433; therefore 2⅔″ × ½″ corruga. is OK.

*Values in Table 3-2 are "per foot". Divide by 12.

ALTERNATE SOLUTION—Using 3″ × 1″ Corrugated Pipe

4A. *Allowable Wall Stress:*

f_c = 16,500 psi (using same computations)

5A. *Wall Cross-Sectional Area:*

From Table 3-2, a specified *thickness* of 0.064 in. provides an uncoated wall *area* of 0.890 sq. in./ft

6A. *Handling Stiffness:*

From Table 3-2, for .064-in. specified thickness, I = .00866 in.^{4}/in.

Then $FF = \dfrac{48^2}{30 \times 10^6 \times .00866} = 0.0088$

.0088 < .0433; therefore, 3″ × 1″ corruga. is OK.

ANSWER: A specified wall thickness of 0.064 in. is adequate for corrugated steel pipe of **either 2⅔″ × ½″ or 3″ × 1″** corrugations.

Note: See Page 218, Chapter 5, for Corrosion-Abrasion Requirements for this structure.

Example 2

Given: Pipe diameter required = 120-in.

Height of cover, $H = 65$ ft

Live load, $LL = E$ 80

Weight of soil (unit), $w = 120$ lb/cu ft

Find: Wall thickness and type of corrugation (Try $3'' \times 1''$ corr. and $6'' \times 2''$)

SOLUTION: See Section B—STRUCTURAL DESIGN, pp 88–97 (or follow same procedure as preceding Example 1)

1. **Backfill Soil Density Required:**

    90% Std. AASHO specified. Assume a minimum of 85% for design.

2. **Design Pressure:**

    $DL = H \times w = 65 \times 120 = 7800$ psf (LL, negligible)

    From Fig. 3-5, $K = 0.86$

    $P_v = 0.86 \times (7800 + 0) = 6708$ lb/sq ft......................Equa. (2)

3. **Ring Compression:**

    $$C = P_v \times \frac{S}{2} = 6708 \times \frac{10'}{2} = 33{,}540 \text{ lb/ft} \dots\dots\dots\dots\dots\dots\dots\dots\dots\dots, \dots (3)$$

4. **Allowable Wall Stress:**

    $$f_c = \frac{f_b}{2}$$

    where: f_b = ultimate wall stress

    From Fig. 3-6, $f_b = 30{,}500$ psi for $3'' \times 1''$ corruga................(4)

    Then $f_c = \dfrac{30{,}500}{2} = 15{,}250$ lb/sq in ....(7)

5. **Wall Cross-Sectional Area:**

    $$A = \frac{C}{f_c} = \frac{33{,}540}{15{,}250} = 2.199 \text{ sq in./ft required}$$

    From Table 3-2, a specified *thickness* of 0.168 in. provides an uncoated wall *area* of 2.458 sq. in.

6. **Handling Stiffness:**

    $$FF = \frac{D^2}{EI} = \text{flexibility factor} = 0.0433 \text{ max.}$$

    From Table 3-2, for 0.168 in. specified thickness, $I = 0.0251$ in.⁴/in.

    $$FF = \frac{120^2}{30 \times 10^6 \times 0.0251} = 0.0191$$

    $0.0191 < 0.0433$; therefore $3'' \times 1''$ **corruga.** is OK.

ALTERNATE SOLUTION—Using **6″ × 2″** Corr. Structural Plate Pipe

4A. *Allowable Wall Stress:*

$f_c = 16,500$ psi

5A. *Wall Cross-Sectional Area:*

From Table 3-2, a specified *thickness* of 0.168 in. provides an uncoated wall *area* of 2.449 sq in./ft

6A. *Handling Stiffness:*

From Table 3-2, for 0.168 specified thickness, $I = 0.0961$ in.⁴/in.

$$FF = \frac{120^2}{30 \times 10^6 \times 0.0961} = 0.005 < 0.020$$

therefore **6″ × 2″ corruga.** is also OK.

7. Bolted Seam Strength:

From Table 3-3, the allowable seam strength for 0.168-in. plates is 40,500 lb/ft which is > design load 33,540 lb/ft (Item 3)

ANSWER: A specified wall thickness of 0.168 in. is adequate for 3″ × 1″ or 6″ × 2″ corrugation.

Note: See Page 219, Chapter 5, for Corrosion-Abrasion Requirements for this structure.

Example 3

Given: Pipe-arch; Span 20 ft 5 in., Rise 13 ft 0 in.,
Corrugations 6″ × 2″ 31-in. corner radius
Height of cover, $H = 6$ ft
Live load, $LL = H$ 20
Weight of soil, $w = 120$ lb/cu ft

Find: (a) Wall thickness and bolting requirements
(b) Corner plate pressure

SOLUTION: See Section B—STRUCTURAL DESIGN, pp 88–97

1. Backfill Soil Density Required:

90% Std. AASHO specified. Assume a minimum of 85% for design.

2. Design Pressure:

$P_v = K(DL + LL)$.....................................Equa. (2)
where: $DL = H \times w = 6 \times 120 = 720$ lb/sq ft
From Table 3-1, $LL = 200$ psf
$K = 1.0$ when height of cover < span
$P_v = 1.0(720 + 200) = 920$ psf

3. Ring Compression:

$$C = P_v \times \frac{S}{2} \dots \dots \dots \dots \dots (3)$$

where: S = span, in ft = 20.42

Then $C = 920 \times \dfrac{20.42}{2} = 9393$ lb/ft

4. Allowable Wall Stress:

$$f_c = \frac{f_b}{2}$$

where: f_b = ultimate wall stress
From Fig. 3-6, f_b = 29,700 psi for $6'' \times 2''$ corruga. . . . . (4)

Then $f_c = \dfrac{29,700}{2} = 14,850$ psi. . . . . (7)

5. Wall Cross-Sectional Area:

$$A = \frac{C}{f_c} = \frac{9393}{14,850} = 0.6325 \text{ sq in./ft required} \dots \dots \dots (8)$$

From Table 3-2, a specified *thickness* of 0.109 in. provides an uncoated wall *area* of 1.556 sq in./ft.

6. Handling Stiffness:

$$FF = \frac{D^2}{EI} = \text{flexibility factor} = 0.020 \text{ max.}$$

where: D = diam. or span in in. = 245
E = modulus of elasticity = 30×10^6 psi
I = moment of inertia, in.^{4}/in.
From Table 3-2, for 0.109 in. specified thickness, I = 0.0604 in.^{4}/in.

Then $FF = \dfrac{245^2}{30 \times 10^6 \times 0.0604} = 0.033$ which is > 0.020 max.

From Table 3-2, try 0.188 in. specified thickness. I = 0.108 in.^{4}/in.

Then $FF = \dfrac{245^2}{30 \times 10^6 \times 0.108} = 0.0185; < 0.020;$ therefore OK.

7. Bolted Seam Strength:
From Table 3-3, the allowable seam strength for 0.188-in. thickness, is 46,500 lb/ft. This is greater than the design load of 9393 lb/ft (Item 3); therefore OK.

b. Corner Bearing Pressure on Soil:

$$P_c = P_v \frac{R_t}{R_c} = \text{corner pressure in psf}$$

where: R_t = top radius (use half span) = 122.5 in.
R_c = 31 in.

Then $P_c = 920 \times \dfrac{122.5}{31} = 3640$ lb/sq ft

It is imperative that the allowable corner bearing pressure be at least 2 tons per sq ft.

ANSWER: (a) A specified wall thickness of 0.188 in. with standard seam bolting is adequate.

(b) The corner bearing pressure for this installation would be 3640 psf.

Example 4

Given: Structural plate **arch;** Span = 23 ft 0 in., Rise = 10 ft 3 in.,
Corrugations 6″ × 2″
Height of cover, $H = 19$ ft
Live load, $LL = H$ 20
Weight of soil, $w = 120$ lb /cu ft

Find: Wall thickness and seam bolting requirements

SOLUTION: (See Section B—*STRUCTURAL DESIGN*, pp 88–97)

1. Backfill Soil Density Required:

90% Std. AASHO specified. Assume a minimum of 85% for design.

2. Design Pressure:

$P_v = K(DL + LL)$
where: $DL = H \times w = 19 \times 120 = 2280$ lb /sq ft
From Table 3-1, LL = negligible
$K = 1.0$ (height of cover is less than span)
Then $P_v = 1.0(2280 + 0) = 2280$ lb /sq ft

3. Ring Compression:

$$C = P_v \times \frac{S}{2} \dots\dots\dots\text{Equa. (3)}$$

where: S = span in feet = 23.0

then $C = 2280 \times \dfrac{23}{2} = 26,220$ lb /ft of arch

4. Allowable Wall Stress:

$f_c = \dfrac{f_b}{2}$ for round pipe

$f_c = \dfrac{f_b}{4}$ for arches half circle or less in shape

where: f_b = ultimate wall stress
From Fig. 3-6, $f_b = 26,945$ lb /sq in. for 6″ × 2″ corruga$\dots\dots$(4)

Then $f_c = \dfrac{26,945}{4} = 6736$ lb /sq in$\dots\dots\dots$(7)

5. Wall Cross-Sectional Area:

$$A = \frac{C}{f_c} = \frac{26,220}{6736} = 3.892 \text{ sq in.}/\text{ft required} \dots\dots\dots\dots\dots\dots\dots\dots (8)$$

From Table 3-2, a specified *thickness* of 0.280 in. provides an uncoated wall *area* of 4.119 in.

6. Handling Stiffness:

$$FF = \frac{D^2}{EI} = \text{flexibility factor} = 0.020 \text{ max.}$$

where: D = diam. or span, in. = 276
E = modulus of elasticity = 30×10^6 psi
I = moment of inertia, in.^{4}/in.
From Table 3-2, for 0.280 specified thickness, $I = 0.1659$ in.^{4}/in.

$$\text{Then } FF = \frac{276^2}{30 \times 10^6 \times 0.1659} = 0.015 < 0.020 \quad \text{OK.}$$

ANSWER: A specified wall thickness of 0.280 in. with standard bolting is required.

Example 5

Given: Vehicular Underpass; Span 19 ft 6 in., Rise 17 ft 7 in.,
Corrugations 6" × 2"
Height of cover, $HC = 32$ ft
Live load, $LL = H$ 20
Weight of soil, $w = 120$ lb/cu ft

Find: (a) Wall thickness and bolting requirements
(b) Corner bearing pressure

SOLUTION: (See Section B—STRUCTURAL DESIGN, pp 88–97)

1. Backfill Soil Density Required:

90% Std. AASHO specified. Assume a minimum of 85% for design.

2. Design Pressure:

$P_v = K(DL + LL)$
where: $DL = H \times w = 32 \times 120 = 3840$ psf
From Table 3-1, LL = negligible
From Fig. 3-5, $K = 0.86$
Then $P_v = 0.86(3840 + 0) = 3300$ psf

3. Ring Compression:

$$C = P_v \times \frac{S}{2} \dots\dots\dots\dots\dots\dots\dots\dots\dots\dots\dots\dots\dots\dots\dots \text{Equa. (3)}$$

where: S = span, in ft = 19.5

Then $C = 3300 \times \dfrac{19.5}{2} = 32{,}175$ lb/ft

4. **Allowable Wall Stress:**

$$f_c = \frac{f_b}{2}$$

where: f_b = ultimate wall stress

From Fig. 3-6, $f_b = 30{,}630$ psi for 6″ ×2″ corruga................(4)

Then $f_c = \dfrac{30{,}630}{2} = 15{,}315$ psi.................................(7)

5. **Wall Cross-Sectional Area:**

$$A = \frac{C}{f_c} = \frac{32{,}175}{15{,}315} = 2.10 \text{ sq in./ft required}........................(8)$$

From Table 3-2, a specified *thickness* of 0.168 in. provides an uncoated wall *area* of 2.449 sq in.

6. **Handling Stiffness:**

$$FF = \frac{D^2}{EI} = \text{flexibility factor} = 0.020 \text{ max.}$$

where: D = diam. or span in inches = 234
  E = modulus of elasticity = 30×10^6 psi
  I = moment of inertia, in.⁴/in.

From Table 3-2, for 0.168 in. specified thickness, $I = 0.0961$ in.⁴/in.

Then $FF = \dfrac{234^2}{30 \times 10^6 \times 0.0961} = 0.0190 < 0.020$ max. OK.

7. **Bolted Seam Strength:**

From Table 3-3, the allowable seam strength for the 0.168 in. thickness is 40,500 lb/ft, which is greater than the design load of 32,175 lb/ft.

(b) **Corner Plate Bearing Pressure on Soil:**

$$P_c = P_v \frac{R_t}{R_c} \text{ in psf}$$

where: R_t = top radius (use half span) = 117 in.
  R_c = corner radius = 47 in.

Then $P_c = 3300 \times \dfrac{117}{47} = 8215$ psf

The foundation and backfill at the corner plates should have a bearing power of 4 tons/sq ft. Crushed stone or bank-run gravel placed in an excavated space under the corner plates may be required.

ANSWER: (a) A specified wall thickness of 0.168 in. with standard seam bolting will be adequate.

  (b) The corner pressure for this structure will be 8215 psf, which may require special measures.

Fig. 3-14. Twin 15-foot diameter structural plate pipes under an Interstate highway.

Fig. 3-15. Roomy two-lane underpass under an important highway.

Height-of-Cover Tables for Corrugated Steel Conduits

The following height-of-cover tables are presented for the designer's convenience for use in routine applications.

They are based on the design procedure presented in this chapter, pages 88–97, using the following values for the soil and steel parameters:

Unit Weight of Soil—120 lb per cu ft
Relative Density of Compacted Backfill—Minimum 85% Std AASHO
Yield Point of Steel—33,000 psi

Where large or important projects can justify individual structure design, or when the quality of regular installations is known to be above that used here, the design procedure illustrated in the Examples, pages 98–105, should be used with the appropriate values of the soil and steel parameters.

LIST OF TABLES

Table No.	Shapes				Loading		Size of Corrugations			Corner Radius in In.
	Pipe	Pipe-Arch	Arch	Under-pass	H 20	E 80	2⅔" x ½"	3" x 1"	6" x 2"	
HC- 1	X				X		X			
HC- 2	X				X			X		
HC- 3	X					X	X			
HC- 4	X					X		X		
HC- 5	X				X				X	
HC- 6	X					X			X	
HC- 7		X			X		X			
HC- 8		X			X			X		
HC- 9		X				X	X			
HC-10		X				X		X		
HC-11		X			X				X	18
HC-12		X			X				X	31
HC-13		X				X			X	18
HC-14		X				X			X	31
HC-15			X		X				X	Vari.
HC-16			X			X			X	Vari.
HC-17				X	X				X	
HC-18				X		X			X	
HC-19	X	X	X	X	Airport		X			
HC-20	X	X	X	X	"			X		
HC-21	X	X	X	X	"				X	
HC-22	X	X	X	X	"		X	X	X	

Table HC-1   Height-of-Cover Limits for Corrugated Steel Pipe
H 20 LIVE LOAD   2⅔″ x ½″ Corrugations

Diameter or Span in Inches	Min.* Cover	Maximum Cover in Feet					
		Specified Thickness in Inches					
		0.052	.064	.079	.109	.138	.168
12		199	248	310			
15		159	199	248			
18		132	166	207			
21		113	142	178	249		
24		99	124	155	218		
27			111	138	193		
30	12-in. Minimum Cover		99	124	174		
36			83	103	145	186	
42			71	88	124	160	195
48			62	77	109	140	171
54				66	93	120	147
60					79	102	125
66					68	87	107
72						73	89
78							74
84							61
90							50
96							41

*From top of pipe to top of subgrade.

Table HC-2   Height-of-Cover Limits for Corrugated Steel Pipe
H 20 LIVE LOAD   3″ x 1″ Corrugations

Diameter or Span in Inches	Min.* Cover	Maximum Cover in Feet					
		Specified Thickness in Inches					
		0.052	.064	.079	.109	.138	.168
36		76	95	121	167	214	263
42		65	81	102	143	185	225
48		57	71	91	125	161	197
54			63	80	111	143	175
60	12 inches		57	72	100	129	156
66			52	66	91	117	143
72			47	60	83	107	131
78			44	55	76	99	121
84			40	53	71	92	112
90			38	48	66	85	105
96			35	45	62	80	98
102			33	42	58	75	92
108	18 inches			39	54	69	84
114				35	49	63	77
120					45	58	72

*From top of pipe to top of subgrade.

Table HC-3   **Height-of-Cover Limits for Corrugated Steel Pipe**

E 80 LIVE LOAD   **2⅔″ x ½″** Corrugations

Diameter or Span in Inches	Min. Cover	Maximum Cover in Feet					
		Specified Thickness in Inches					
		0.052	.064	.079	.109	.138	.168
12	12 inches	199	248	310			
15		159	199	248			
18		132	166	207			
21		113	142	178	249		
24		99	124	155	218		
27			111	138	193		
30			99	124	174		
36			83	103	145	186	
42			71	88	124	160	195
48			62	77	109	140	171
54	18 inches			66	93	120	147
60					79	102	125
66					68	87	107
72						73	89
78	24 inches						74
84							61
90							50
96							41

Table HC-4   **Height-of-Cover Limits for Corrugated Steel Pipe**

E 80 LIVE LOAD   **3″ x 1″** Corrugations

Diameter or Span in Inches	Min. Cover	Maximum Cover in Feet					
		Specified Thickness in Inches					
		0.052	.064	.079	.109	.138	.168
36	12 in.	76	95	121	167	205	263
42	12 in.	65	81	102	143	185	225
48	12 in.	57	71	91	125	161	197
54	18 in.		63	80	111	143	175
60	18 in.		57	72	100	129	156
66	18 in.		52	66	91	117	143
72	18 in.		47	60	83	107	131
78	24 in.		44	55	76	99	121
84	24 in.		40	53	71	92	112
90	24 in.		38	48	66	85	105
96	24 in.		35	45	62	80	98
102	30 in.		33	42	58	75	92
108	30 in.			39	54	69	84
114	30 in.			35	49	63	77
120	30 in.				45	58	72

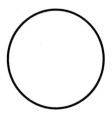

Table HC-5   Height-of-Cover Limits for Structural Plate Pipe

H 20 LIVE LOAD   6″ x 2″ Corrugations

Diameter or Span		Min. Cover	Maximum Cover in Feet						
			Specified Thickness in Inches						
in Ft	in In.		0.109	.138	.168	.188	.218	.249	.280
5	60	12 inches	81	120	157	176	205	234	264
5.5	66		74	110	143	159	186	213	240
6	72		68	101	131	146	171	195	220
6.5	78		62	92	121	135	157	180	203
7	84		58	86	112	125	146	168	188
7.5	90		54	80	105	117	137	156	176
8	96		51	75	98	111	128	146	165
8.5	102	18 inches	48	71	92	103	120	137	155
9	108		45	67	87	97	114	130	146
9.5	114		43	63	82	92	108	123	139
10	120		40	60	78	87	102	117	132
10.5	126		39	57	74	83	97	112	126
11	132		37	54	71	79	93	106	120
11.5	138		35	52	68	76	89	102	114
12	144		34	50	65	73	85	97	110
12.5	150	24 inches	32	48	63	70	82	93	106
13	156		31	46	60	67	79	90	101
13.5	162		30	44	58	65	76	87	98
14	168		29	43	56	62	73	83	94
14.5	174		28	41	54	60	70	80	91
15	180		27	40	52	58	68	78	88
15.5	186		26	39	50	56	66	75	85
16	192		25	37	49	54	64	73	82
16.5	198	30 inches		36	47	53	62	71	80
17	204			35	45	51	60	68	77
17.5	210			34	43	49	57	65	74
18	216			33	42	47	55	63	71
18.5	222				40	45	52	60	68
19	228				38	43	50	58	65
19.5	234				37	41	48	55	62
20	240				35	40	47	53	60
20.5	246	36 inches				38	45	51	57
21	252					36	43	49	56
21.5	258					35	41	47	53
22	264						39	45	51
22.5	270						38	43	49
23	276						36	41	46
23.5	282							40	45
24	288	42 inches						38	43
24.5	294							36	41
25	300							35	39
25.5	306								37
26	312								35

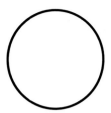

Table HC-6   Height-of-Cover Limits for Structural Plate Pipe

E 80 LIVE LOAD   6″ x 2″ Corrugations

Diameter or Span in Ft.	Diameter or Span in In.	Min. Cover	Maximum Cover in Feet — Specified Thickness in Inches						
			0.109	.138	.168	.188	.218	.249	.280
5.0	60	24 inches	81	120	157	176	205	234	264
5.5	66		74	110	143	159	186	213	240
6.0	72		68	101	131	146	171	195	220
6.5	78		62	92	121	135	157	180	203
7.0	84		58	86	112	125	146	168	188
7.5	90		54	80	105	117	137	156	176
8.0	96		51	75	98	111	128	146	165
8.5	102		48	71	92	103	120	137	155
9.0	108		45	67	87	97	114	130	146
9.5	114		43	63	82	92	108	123	139
10.0	120		40	60	78	87	102	117	132
10.5	126	30 in.	39	57	74	83	97	112	126
11.0	132		37	54	71	79	93	106	120
11.5	138		35	52	68	76	89	102	114
12.0	144		34	50	65	73	85	97	110
12.5	150		32	48	63	70	82	93	106
13.0	156	36 in.	31	46	60	67	79	90	101
13.5	162		29	44	58	65	76	87	98
14.0	168		28	43	56	62	73	83	94
14.5	174		26	41	54	60	70	80	91
15.0	180		25	40	52	58	68	78	88
15.5	186	42 in.	24	39	50	56	66	75	85
16.0	192		23	37	49	54	64	73	82
16.5	198			36	47	53	62	71	80
17.0	204			35	45	51	60	68	77
17.5	210			34	43	49	57	65	74
18.0	216	48 in.		33	42	47	55	63	71
18.5	222				40	45	52	60	68
19.0	228				38	43	50	58	65
19.5	234				37	41	48	55	62
20.0	240				35	40	47	53	60
20.5	246	54 in.				38	45	51	57
21.0	252					36	43	49	56
21.5	258					35	41	47	53
22.0	264						39	45	51
22.5	270	60 inches					38	43	49
23.0	276						36	41	46
23.5	282							40	45
24.0	288							38	43
24.5	294							36	41
25.0	300							35	39
25.5	306								37
26.0	312								35

Table HC-7 Height-of-Cover Limits for Corrugated Steel Pipe-Arch

H 20 LIVE LOAD   2⅔″ X ½″ Corrugations

Size in Inches	Minimum Specified Thickness Required in In.	Maximum Height-of-Fill Over Pipe-Arch for the Following Corner Bearing Pressures in Tons per Sq Ft		
Span x Rise		2 Tons	3 Tons	4 Tons
18 x 11	0.064	15	22	30
22 x 13	0.064	14	21	28
25 x 16	0.064	12	19	25
29 x 18	0.064	12	18	24
36 x 22	0.064	12	18	24
43 x 27	0.064	10	15	20
50 x 31	0.079	9	14	19
58 x 36	0.109	9	14	19
65 x 40	0.109	9	14	19
72 x 44	0.138	9	14	19
79 x 49	0.168	9	14	19
85 x 54	0.168	10	15	20

Minimum cover from top of pipe-arch to top of subgrade = 1 ft

Table HC-8   Height-of-Cover Limits for Corrugated Steel Pipe-Arch

H 20 LIVE LOAD   3″ x 1″ Corrugations

Size in Inches		Minimum Specified Thickness Required in Inches	Minimum Cover	Maximum Height-of-Fill Over Pipe-Arch for the Following Corner Bearing Pressures in Tons per Sq Ft		
Equiv. Pipe Diam.	Span x Rise			2 Tons	3 Tons	4 Tons
36	43 x 27	0.064	12 inches	14	21	28
42	50 x 31			14	21	28
48	58 x 36			14	21	28
54	65 x 40			14	21	28
60	72 x 44			14	21	28
66	73 x 55			19	28	38
72	81 x 59			17	26	34
78	87 x 63			16	24	32
84	95 x 67		12 inches	15	22	29
90	103 x 71	0.064	18 inches	13	20	27
96	112 x 75	0.079	18 inches	13	18	25
102	117 x 79	0.109	18 inches	12	18	24
108	128 x 83	0.109	24 inches	11	16	22
114	137 x 87	0.109	24 inches	10	15	20
120	142 x 91	0.138	24 inches	10	15	20

Table HC-9   Thicknesses of Corrugated Steel Pipe-Arches

   E 80 LIVE LOAD   2⅔" x ½" Corrugations

Size	Height of Cover in Feet			
	2	3–4	5–7	8–15
Span x Rise, in In.	Specified Thickness in Inches			
18 x 11	.079	.079	.079	.079
22 x 13	.079	.079	.079	.079
25 x 16	.109	.079	.079	.079
29 x 18	.109	.109	.079	.079
36 x 22	.138	.109	.109	.109
43 x 27	.168	.138	.138	.109
50 x 31		.168	.138	.138
58 x 36			.168	.168
65 x 40				.168
72 x 44				.168

The above table is an empirical "gage" table based on experience. See Page 96.

Table HC-10   Height-of-Cover Limits for Corrugated Steel Pipe-Arch

   E 80 LIVE LOAD   3" x 1" Corrugations

Size in Inches	Minimum Specified Thickness Required in Inches	Minimum Cover	Maximum Height of Fill Over Pipe-Arch for the Following Corner Bearing Pressures in Tons per Sq Ft	
Span x Rise			3 Tons	4 Tons
43 x 27	0.064	24 inches	17	26
50 x 31	0.064	30 inches	17	26
58 x 36	0.064	36 inches	17	26
65 x 40	0.064	36 inches	18	27
72 x 44	0.064	36 inches	18	27
73 x 55	0.064	36 inches	27	38
81 x 59	0.064	42 inches	24	34
87 x 63	0.079	48 inches	21	32
95 x 67	0.079	48 inches	18	28
103 x 71	0.079	54 inches	16	25
112 x 75	0.109	60 inches	12	22
117 x 79	0.109	60 inches		21
128 x 83	0.109	72 inches		18
137 x 87	0.109	72 inches		16
142 x 91	0.138	72 inches		15

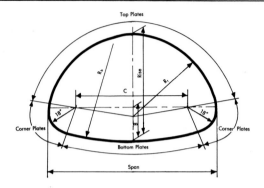

Table HC-11   Height-of-Cover Limits for Structural Plate Pipe-Arch
18″ R_c Corner Radius

H 20 LIVE LOAD   6″ x 2″ Corrugations

Size		Minimum Specified Thickness Required in In.	Minimum Cover	Maximum Height-of-Fill Over Pipe-Arch for the Following Corner Bearing Pressures in Tons per Sq Ft		
Span Ft-In.	Rise Ft-In.			2 Tons	3 Tons	4 Tons
6-1	4-7	0.109		19	28	38
6-4	4-9			18	27	36
6-9	4-11		12 inches	17	26	34
7-0	5-1			16	25	33
7-3	5-3			16	24	32
7-8	5-5			15	23	30
7-11	5-7			14	22	29
8-2	5-9			14	22	28
8-7	5-11			13	21	27
8-10	6-1			13	20	26
9-4	6-3			12	18	25
9-6	6-5			12	18	24
9-9	6-7		18 inches	10	17	24
10-3	6-9			9	16	22
10-8	6-11			9	16	21
10-11	7-1			9	16	21
11-5	7-3			8	15	20
11-7	7-5			7	15	20
11-10	7-7			7	14	19
12-4	7-9			6	12	19
12-6	7-11			6	12	18
12-8	8-1			6	11	18
12-10	8-4			6	11	18
13-5	8-5			5	11	17
13-11	8-7		24 inches	5	10	16
14-1	8-9			5	10	16
14-3	8-11				10	14
14-10	9-1				10	13
15-4	9-3				9	13
15-6	9-5				9	12
15-8	9-7				9	12
15-10	9-10	0.109			9	12
16-5	9-11	0.138	30 in.		9	12
16-7	10-1	0.138			9	12

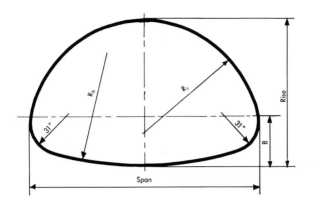

Table HC-12   Height-of-Cover Limits for Structural Plate Pipe-Arch
31" R_c Corner Radius

H 20 LIVE LOAD   **6" x 2"** Corrugations

Size		Minimum Specified Thickness Required in In.	Minimum Cover	Maximum Height-of-Fill Over Pipe-Arch for the Following Corner Bearing Pressures in Tons per Sq Ft		
Span Ft-In.	Rise Ft-In.			2 Tons	3 Tons	4 Tons
13-3	9-4	0.109		15	22	30
13-6	9-6			14	22	29
14-0	9-8			12	21	28
14-2	9-10			12	21	28
14-5	10-0			11	20	28
14-11	10-2			11	20	27
15-4	10-4			11	19	26
15-7	10-6			11	19	25
15-10	10-8	0.109		10	19	25
16-3	10-10	0.138		10	18	24
16-6	11-0		30 inches	10	18	24
17-0	11-2			10	17	23
17-2	11-4			10	17	23
17-5	11-6			9	17	22
17-11	11-8	0.138		9	16	22
18-1	11-10	0.168		9	16	22
18-7	12-0			9	16	21
18-9	12-2			9	16	21
19-3	12-4			8	15	20
19-6	12-6			8	15	20
19-8	12-8			7	15	20
19-11	12-10	0.168		7	15	20
20-5	13-0	0.188	36 in.	7	14	19
20-7	13-2	0.188		6	14	19

Table HC-13   Height-of-Cover Limits for Structural Plate Pipe-Arch
18″ Rc Corner Radius
E 80 LIVE LOAD   **6″ x 2″** Corrugations

Span Ft-In.	Rise Ft-In.	Minimum Specified Thickness Required in In.	Minimum Cover	Maximum Height-of-Fill Over Pipe-Arch for the Following Corner Bearing Pressures in Tons per Sq Ft		
				2 Tons	3 Tons	4 Tons
6-1	4-7	0.109	24 inches	13	27	38
6-4	4-9				25	37
6-9	4-11				23	34
7-0	5-1				22	33
7-3	5-3				21	32
7-8	5-5				19	30
7-11	5-7				18	28
8-2	5-9				17	27
8-7	5-11				16	25
8-10	6-1				15	24
9-4	6-3				13	22
9-6	6-5					22
9-9	6-7		24 inches			21
10-3	6-9		30 inches			19
10-8	6-11					18
10-11	7-1			13		17
11-5	7-3					16
11-7	7-5					15
11-10	7-7					15
12-4	7-9					13
12-6	7-11		30 inches			12
12-8	8-1		36 inches			
12-10	8-4					
13-5	8-5					
13-11	8-7					
14-1	8-9					
14-3	8-11					
14-10	9-1		36 inches			
15-4	9-3		42 inches		13	
15-6	9-5					
15-8	9-7					
15-10	9-10	0.109				
16-5	9-11	0.138				
16-7	10-1	0.138	42 inches			12

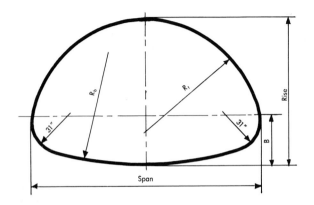

Table HC-14 Height-of-Cover Limits for Structural Plate Pipe-Arch
31" R_c Corner Radius

E 80 LIVE LOAD   6" x 2" Corrugations

Size		Minimum Specified Thickness Required in In.	Minimum Cover	Maximum Height-of-Fill Over Pipe-Arch for the Following Corner Bearing Pressures in Tons per Sq Ft		
Span Ft—In.	Rise Ft—In.			2 Tons	3 Tons	4 Tons
13-3	9-4	0.109	36 inches	12	19	29
13-6	9-6				19	28
14-0	9-8				18	27
14-2	9-10				17	26
14-5	10-0				17	26
14-11	10-2				16	25
15-4	10-4		42 inches		15	24
15-7	10-6				14	23
15-10	10-8	0.109		12	12	23
16-3	10-10	0.138				22
16-6	11-0					21
17-0	11-2					16
17-2	11-4					15
17-5	11-6					15
17-11	11-8	0.138	48 inches			14
18-1	11-10	0.168			12	13
18-7	12-0					12
18-9	12-2					
19-3	12-4					
19-6	12-6					
19-8	12-8					
19-11	12-10	0.168				
20-5	13-0	0.188				
20-7	13-2	0.188				12

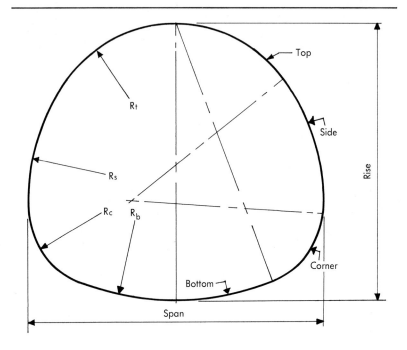

Table HC-15   Height-of-Cover Limits for Structural Plate Underpass

H 20 LIVE LOAD   6″ x 2″ Corrugations

Span Ft—In.	Rise Ft—In.	Corner Radius Inches	Minimum Specified Thickness Required in In.	Minimum Cover	Maximum Height-of-Fill Over Pipe-Arch for the Following Corner Bearing Pressures in Tons per Sq Ft		
					2 Tons	3 Tons	4 Tons
5-8	5-9	18	0.109	12 inches	20	30	40
5-8	6-6	18			20	30	40
5-9	7-4	18			20	30	40
5-10	7-8	18			20	30	40
5-10	8-2	18		12 inches	20	30	40
12-2	11-0	38		24 inches	20	30	33
12-11	11-2	38			19	28	31
13-2	11-10	38			18	28	30
13-10	12-2	38			17	26	30
14-1	12-10	38			17	26	29
14-6	13-5	38			17	25	28
14-10	14-0	38			16	24	27
15-6	14-4	38			15	23	26
15-8	15-0	38	0.109	24 inches	15	23	25
16-4	15-5	38	0.138	36 inches	15	22	30
16-5	16-0	38	0.138		14	22	30
16-9	16-3	38	0.138		14	22	29
17-3	17-0	47	0.138		17	26	35
18-4	16-11	47	0.168		16	25	33
19-1	17-2	47	0.168		16	24	32
19-6	17-7	47	0.168		15	23	31
20-4	17-9	47	0.188	36 inches	15	22	30

Table HC-16   **Height-of-Cover Limits for Structural Plate Underpass**

E 80 LIVE LOAD   **6″ x 2″** Corrugations

Size		Corner Radius Inches	Minimum Specified Thickness Required in In.	Minimum Cover	Maximum Height-of-Fill Over Pipe-Arch for the Following Corner Bearing Pressures in Tons per Sq Ft		
Span Ft—In.	Rise Ft—In.				2 Tons	3 Tons	4 Tons
5-8	5-9	18	0.109	24 inches	17	29	40
5-8	6-6	18			17	29	40
5-9	7-4	18			17	29	40
5-10	7-8	18			17	29	40
5-10	8-2	18		24 inches	17	29	40
12-2	11-0	38		36 inches		29	33
12-11	11-2	38				27	31
13-2	11-10	38				26	30
13-10	12-2	38				25	30
14-1	12-10	38				24	29
14-6	13-5	38				23	26
14-10	14-0	38		36 inches		22	25
15-6	14-4	38		48 inches		21	24
15-8	15-0	38	0.109			21	23
16-4	15-5	38	0.138			19	29
16-5	16-0	38	0.138			19	29
16-9	16-3	38	0.138			19	28
17-3	17-0	47	0.138			24	35
18-4	16-11	47	0.168			22	33
19-1	17-2	47	0.168			21	32
19-6	17-7	47	0.168			20	31
20-4	17-9	47	0.188	48 inches		19	29

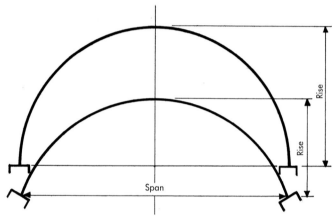

Table HC-17   Height-of-Cover Limits for Structural Plate Arches

H 20 LIVE LOAD   6″ x 2″ Corrugations

$$.30 \lessgtr \frac{\text{Rise}}{\text{Span}} \lessgtr .50$$

Span in Feet	Minimum Cover	Maximum Cover in Feet						
		Specified Thickness in Inches						
		0.109	.138	.168	.188	.218	.249	.280
5	12 inches	40	60	78	87	102	117	132
6	12 inches	34	50	65	73	97	104	110
7	12 inches	29	43	56	62	73	84	94
8	12 inches	25	37	49	55	64	73	82
9	24 inches	22	33	43	48	57	65	73
10		20	30	39	44	51	58	66
11		18	27	35	40	46	53	60
12		17	25	32	36	42	48	55
13		15	23	30	33	39	45	51
14		14	21	28	31	36	42	47
15		13	20	26	29	34	39	44
16	24 inches	12	18	24	27	32	36	41
17	36 inches		17	23	25	30	34	38
18			16	21	23	27	31	35
19				19	21	25	29	32
20				18	20	23	27	30
21					18	21	24	28
22						20	22	25
23						18	20	23
24	36 inches						19	21
25	48 inches						17	19
26	48 inches							18

For structural plate arches of horseshoe shape with reentrant angle at the base of 30° or more, the above fill heights may be doubled.

Table HC-18   Height-of-Cover Limits for Structural Plate Arches

E 80 LIVE LOAD   6″ X 2″ Corrugations

$$.30 \lesseqgtr \frac{Rise}{Span} \lesseqgtr .50$$

Span in Feet	Minimum Cover	Maximum Cover in Feet						
		Specified Thickness in Inches						
		0.109	.138	.168	.188	.218	.249	.280
5	24 inches	40	60	78	87	102	117	132
6		34	50	65	73	97	104	110
7		28	43	56	62	73	84	94
8		23	37	49	55	64	73	82
9		20	33	43	48	57	65	73
10	24 inches	16	29	39	44	51	58	66
11	36 inches	12	25	35	40	46	53	60
12			22	32	36	42	48	55
13			20	29	33	39	45	51
14			18	26	31	36	42	47
15	36 inches		15	24	28	34	39	44
16	48 inches			22	25	32	36	41
17				20	23	29	34	38
18					21	26	31	35
19					18	23	28	32
20	48 inches					21	25	29
21	60 inches					18	22	26
22							20	23
23								20
24								18
25								
26	60 inches							

SPECIAL NOTE ON ARCHES

For structural requirements of the various types of arches, see pages 96-97.

Tables HC-17 and HC-18 are applicable to semi-circular arches and those less than semi-circular. However, these tables may be used for the other types of arches by simply multiplying the above fill heights by the applicable factor. For horseshoe arches with reentrant angle of 20°, multiply by 1.5. For reentrant angle of 30°, multiply by 2.

Table HC-19   Minimum Cover From Top Surface of Flexible Pavement[21]* To Corrugated Steel Pipe—Corrugations 2⅔" x ½"

For Airplane Wheel Loads

Minimum Depths of Cover D, in Feet

Case 1. Loads to 40,000 Lb—Dual Wheels

Wall Thickness in Inches	Pipe Diameter in Inches								
	12	18	24	36	48	60	72	84	96
.052	1.0'	1.0'	1.5'	1.5'					
.064	1.0'	1.0'	1.0'	1.5'	1.5'				
.079	1.0'	1.0'	1.0'	1.5'	1.5'	1.5'			
.109			1.0'	1.0'	1.0'	1.0'	1.5'		
.138				1.0'	1.0'	1.0'	1.0'	1.5'	
.168				1.0'	1.0'	1.0'	1.0'	1.5'	1.5'

Case 2. Loads to 110,000 Lb—Dual Wheels

.052	1.5	2.0	2.0	2.5					
.064	1.5	1.5	2.0	2.5	2.5				
.079	1.5	1.5	2.0	2.5	2.5	2.5			
.109			1.5	2.0	2.0	2.0	2.5		
.138				2.0	2.0	2.0	2.0	2.5	
.168				2.0	1.5	2.0	2.0	2.0	2.5

Case 3. Loads to 750,000 Lb—Dual-Dual

.052	2.0	2.5	3.0	3.0					
.064	2.0	2.5	2.5	3.0	3.0				
.079	2.0	2.0	2.5	2.5	2.5	3.0			
.109			2.0	2.5	2.5	2.5	3.0		
.138				2.0	2.0	2.5	3.0	3.0	
.168				2.0	2.0	2.5	3.0	3.0	3.0

Case 4. Loads to 1.5 Million Lb

.052	2.5	2.5	3.0	3.0					
.064	2.5	2.5	2.5	3.0	3.0				
.079	2.5	2.5	2.5	2.5	2.5	3.0			
.109			2.5	2.5	2.5	3.0	3.0		
.138				2.5	2.5	2.5	3.0	3.0	
.168				2.5	2.5	3.0	3.0	3.0	3.0
Diam.	12"	18"	24"	36"	48"	60"	72"	84"	96"

*From **Airport Drainage**, U.S. Dept. of Transportation, F.A.A., July 1970.

Table HC-20   Minimum Cover From Top Surface of Flexible Pavement*
To Corrugated Steel Pipe—Corrugations 3″ x 1″

For Airplane Wheel Loads

Minimum Depths of Cover D, in Feet

Case 1. Loads to 40,000 Lb—Dual Wheels

Wall Thickness in Inches	Pipe Diameter in Inches							
	36″	48″	60″	72″	84″	96″	108″	120″
.052	1.5	2.0	2.0	2.0				
.064	1.0	1.5	1.5	2.0	2.0	2.0		
.079	1.0	1.0	1.5	1.5	2.0	2.0	2.0	
.109	1.0	1.0	1.0	1.0	1.5	1.5	2.0	2.0
.138	1.0	1.0	1.0	1.0	1.0	1.5	2.0	2.0
.168	1.0	1.0	1.0	1.0	1.0	1.5	2.0	2.0

Case 2. Loads to 110,000 Lb—Dual Wheels

Wall Thickness	36″	48″	60″	72″	84″	96″	108″	120″
.052	2.5	3.0	3.0	3.0				
.064	2.0	2.5	2.5	3.0	3.0	3.0		
.079	1.5	2.0	2.5	2.5	3.0	3.0	3.0	
.109	1.5	1.5	2.0	2.0	2.0	2.5	3.0	3.0
.138	1.5	1.5	1.5	2.0	2.0	2.0	2.5	2.5
.168	1.5	1.5	1.5	1.5	2.0	2.0	2.0	2.5

Case 3. Loads to 750,000 Lb—Dual-Dual

Wall Thickness	36″	48″	60″	72″	84″	96″	108″	120″
.052	3.0	3.5	3.5					
.064	2.5	3.0	3.5	3.5	3.5			
.079	2.0	2.5	3.0	3.0	3.5	3.5		
.109	2.0	2.0	2.5	2.5	3.0	3.5	3.5	3.5
.138	2.0	2.0	2.0	2.5	3.0	3.0	3.5	3.5
.168	2.0	2.0	2.0	2.0	2.5	2.5	3.0	3.0

Case 4. Loads to 1.5 Million Lb

Wall Thickness	36″	48″	60″	72″	84″	96″	108″	120″
.052	3.0	3.5	3.5					
.064	2.5	3.0	3.5	3.5	3.5			
.079	2.5	2.5	3.0	3.0	3.5	3.5		
.109	2.5	2.5	2.5	2.5	3.0	3.5	3.5	3.5
.138	2.5	2.5	2.5	2.5	3.0	3.0	3.5	3.5
.168	2.5	2.5	2.5	2.5	2.5	2.5	3.0	3.0
Diam.	36″	48″	60″	72″	84″	96″	108″	120″

*From **Airport Drainage**, U.S. Dept. of Transportation, F.A.A., July 1970.

**Table HC-21   Minimum Cover From Top Surface of Flexible Pavement
to STRUCTURAL PLATE PIPE—Corrugations 6″ x 2″***

Airport Wheel Loads			
40,000 lb	110,000 lb	750,000 lb	1.5 Million lb
D/8 but not less than 1.0 ft	D/6 but not less than 1.5 ft	D/5 but not less than 2.0 ft	D/4 but not less than 2.5 ft

Note: For maximum permissible fill heights for Railroad E 80 loads, see Table HC-6.
*From **Airport Drainage**, U.S. Dept. of Transportation, F.A.A., July 1970.

Table HC-22   Minimum Cover for Pipe Under RIGID PAVEMENT*
For All Loadings and All Types of Pipe

H-1.5 ft From Top of Pipe to Bottom of Slab

*From **Airport Drainage**, U.S. Dept. of Transportation, F.A.A., July 1970.

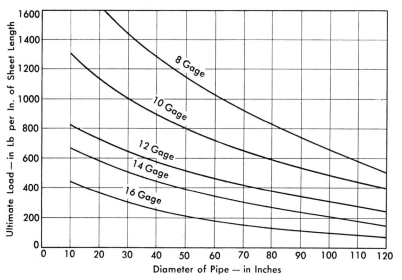

Fig. 3-16. Ultimate unit compressive strength of short standard corrugated metal pipe columns as determined at University of Illinois.[16]

Section C—COLUMN OR END LOADS

Tests were conducted on riveted corrugated pipe at the University of North Carolina in 1927 and the following was determined:

1. Proper size and spacing of circumferential rivets in corrugated metal pipe used as columns.
2. Supporting strength of corrugated pipe for bridge piers and caissons and for columns in general construction.
3. Maximum pressure that can safely be exerted on the end of corrugated pipe in jacking it through an embankment without buckling the corrugations.

Further tests were made at the University of Illinois in 1936.[16] The results of these and the earlier tests are shown in Fig. 3-16.

Section D — EXTERNAL HYDROSTATIC PRESSURE

Conduits not buried in compacted soil and subjected to external hydrostatic pressure must be designed for buckling as circular tubes under uniform external pressure. No variable passive soil pressure is available in this condition and the pipe ring itself must resist the bending moments resulting from out-of-roundness.

The "Theory of Elastic Stability" by Timoshenko details methods of analysis for such thin tubes.[17] No extensive correlation has been made with these formulae and corrugated pipe. However, a few tests have been run which suggest the following buckling formula of Timoshenko, modified as shown, provide the approximate collapse pressure of corrugated steel pipe.

$$\text{Timoshenko buckling formula: } Pcr = \frac{3\,EI}{(1-\gamma^2)\,R^3} \dots \dots \dots \dots \dots (11)$$

where $E =$ Modulus of elasticity of pipe wall
        $I =$ Moment of inertia of pipe wall, inches^4 per inch
        $\gamma =$ Poisson's ratio $= .3$ for steel
        $R =$ Radius of pipe, in inches
        $Pcr =$ Critical pressure, in psi

To provide for out-of-roundness and material variations, divide critical pressure by 2. Result is estimated collapse pressure: PE.

$$\text{Collapse pressure: } PE = \frac{Pcr}{2} \dots\, PE = \frac{3\,EI}{2(1-\gamma^2)\,R^3} \dots \dots \dots \dots (12)\ (13)$$

$$\text{For corrugated steel pipe,} \qquad PE = \frac{49.5 \times 10^6 \times I}{R^3}$$

This theory with suitable safety factors is useful as a design guide. Any critical application should be tested to collapse as this is the only positive design verification.

Fig. 3-17. A comparatively shallow fill will cover this 18-ft diameter steel culvert under a mainline railroad. The backfill was well compacted.

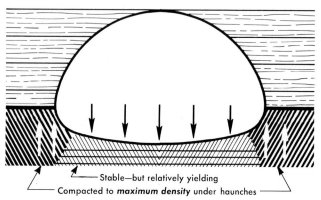

Stable—but relatively yielding

Compacted to *maximum density* under haunches

Fig. 3-18. Pipe-arch loads are carried at the corners. Arrows show the direction of favorable relative motion for all pipe-arches.

Section E—EARTH BACKFILL DESIGN

For the roadway conduit to support the pavement or track above it adequately and uniformly, a stable composite structure is vital. Stability in a soil-structure interaction system requires not only adequate design of the structure barrel, it also presumes a well engineered backfill. Performance of the flexible conduit in retaining its shape and structural integrity depends greatly on selection, placement and compaction of the envelope of earth surrounding the structure and distributing its pressures to the abutting soil masses.

Requirements for selecting and placing backfill material around or near the conduit are similar to those for a roadway embankment. The main difference in requirements is due to the fact that the conduit generates more lateral pressure than would the earth within the embankment if no structure existed. This important phase is described under *Research and Development* at the beginning of Chapter 3.

CHOICE OF MATERIAL

All highway and railroad engineering departments have adequately detailed specifications for selecting and placing material in embankments. These specifications provide for wide variations in terrain and for available local materials, and so can generally apply to backfill material around conduits for normal installations. If abnormal conditions exist at a specific site or if unusual performance is expected of a conduit and embankment, a competent soils engineer should be consulted for designing the backfill.

Backfill material should preferably be granular to provide good structural performance. Cohesive type material can also be used if careful attention is given to compaction at optimum moisture content. Very fine granular material may infiltrate into the structure and should be avoided when high ground water table is anticipated. Bank run gravel or similar material compacted to 90 to 95% standard density is ideal.

The "critical density" of the backfill has been shown to be between 70 and 80% standard AASHO density. Backfill must be compacted to a greater density than "critical" to assure good performance. Compaction to 85% is recommended as a *minimum* allowable under any circumstances.

For Complete Data on Installation See Chapter 7

FILL TECHNIQUE

Backfill should cover the conduit at least one foot* and extend along both sides at least one diameter away from the conduit surface at mid-height where (1) for construction reasons, backfill is placed before building the embankment, or (2) backfill around the conduit is stiffer than the rest of the embankment. This material should be placed and compacted in simultaneous layers on each side of the conduit.

Conduits of pipe-arch or underpass shape exert greater pressures against the soil at the corner plates than elsewhere around the conduit. Excessive pressures at the corners will require material of better bearing capacity which should extend far enough to transfer distributed pressures to the abutting embankment at acceptably low intensities.

It is very important in pipe-arch installation to insure that relative movement of the corners to the bottom is favorable. A softer or yielding foundation under the bottom as compared to the corners is essential. See Fig. 3-18.

Section F—FOUNDATION PREPARATION

Purpose. A good foundation for an underground conduit will maintain the elevation and grade of the invert to a planned position (1) with the conduit in the desired cross-sectional shape, (2) without concentration of foundation pressures that tend to produce excessive stresses in the conduit.

Buried conduit must always be relatively yielding compared to the side fill. Never create a "hard bed" for the pipe which would be equivalent to placing the conduit on an anvil for the load to "strike". If the foundation cushions the conduit, it creates earth arching and reduces load on the conduit.

FOUNDATION SOILS

Evaluation of the conduit site may require subsurface exploration to detect undesirable foundation material, such as muck or rock ledges. Either of these gives uneven support, and in muck the conduit can shift after the embankment is constructed. Any large structure, and any size structure under high fill, is especially sensitive to inferior foundation material. Materials of poor or non-uniform bearing capacity should be removed and replaced with suitable fill to provide uniform and relatively yielding support. Large rocks or ledge rock should be replaced with suitable material, such as sand. See Chapter 7, Fig. 7-5.

WIDTH OF FOUNDATION

Where foundation soils must be replaced, excavation should extend along the entire length of the conduit to a width at least one diameter on both sides of the conduit's greatest width. Soft materials must be removed and replaced across the entire foundation width, but ledge rock or rocks beyond the bedding may be left. Foundation preparation in a trench bottom, while based on these principles, should be confined to practical widths.

BEDDING

Bedding is that portion of the foundation which is shaped to contact the bottom of the conduit. The flat surface makes compaction difficult at the very

*For completed height of minimum cover, see Section G Minimum Cover.

bottom of large structures. Foundation shaping to fit the entire bottom interferes with assembly of field-bolted structures and is costly as well as unnecessary. Bedding or shaping should therefore be wide enough to permit efficiently compacting the remainder of the backfill under the haunches of the structure, but not so wide as to interfere with bolting procedures.

A uniform blanket of loose material should cover the shaped bedding to a depth sufficient to allow the corrugations to become filled with the material.

CAMBER

An embankment exerts more load on the foundation at the center of the embankment than at the toe of slope, so more settlement will occur in the center area. A corresponding settlement of the conduit will occur. Hence, the bedding profile should be cambered longitudinally. The upstream half of the pipe may be laid on almost a flat grade and the downstream half on a steeper grade. Fig. 3-19. The mid-ordinate of the curve should be determined by the soils engineer. For further details on foundation preparation see Chapter 7 *Installation*.

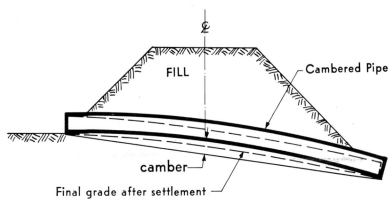

Fig. 3-19. Camber allows for settlement of a culvert under a high fill. Most of the fall is in the outlet half. Diameters 10 ft and smaller are easier to camber, as are the lighter wall thicknesses.

Section G—MINIMUM COVER

Section A of this chapter, *Loads on Buried Structures*, implies sizable fills and dead loads. However, with decreasing fill height, live loads assume increasing importance. Strength design that involves the minimum cover possible with a specific conduit and known live load requires further research to define completely.

Nonetheless, satisfactory minimum cover requirements have been formulated. These are based on long-time observations by the corrugated steel pipe industry of structure performance under live loads. See Figs. 3-3 and 3-4. From these field observations, a minimum cover requirement has been tentatively established of one eighth of the barrel diameter (or span) for highway conduits and one-quarter and one-fifth of the diameter for railway conduits, with a minimum of 1 ft.

Note that this minimum cover requirement is not always adequate during construction. When construction equipment—frequently heavier than traffic loads for which the conduit has been designed—is to be driven over or close to the buried structure, it is the responsibility of the contractor to provide the additional cover required to avoid damage to the conduit.

Section H—END TREATMENT

Designing the ends of a flexible culvert differs in analysis from designing the barrel of that structure. Cutting the ends of a corrugated drainage structure to a skew or bevel, to conform with the embankment slopes, destroys the ability of the end portion of the structure to resist ring compression. Headwalls, rip-rap slopes or slope pavements may in some cases be required to serve as flanges on the ends of the structure to stiffen them against asymmetric loading from the embankment and the dynamic forces of the water. Such "flanges," when needed, can vary from half-headwalls with cutoff walls (on the inlet end particularly), to elaborate headwalls which not only stiffen the structure end against damage from water energy, but also improve the hydraulic efficiency of the inlet.

Structures designed to flow under pressure head are more vulnerable to end problems than those designed to flow less than full. Also, large diameter structures, and those structures where there is a combination of skew and bevel offer problems of end distortion. In general, a skew of 20 degrees with a 2:1 bevel should not be exceeded.

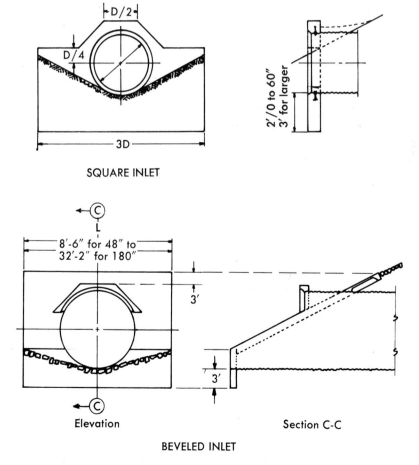

SQUARE INLET

BEVELED INLET

Fig. 3-20. Treatment of *inlet end* of large corrugated steel structures as recommended by the Federal Highway Administration.[22]

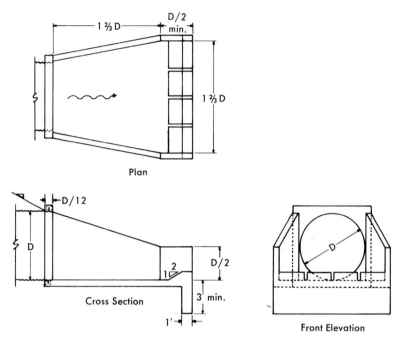

Fig. 3-21. Treatment of *outlet end* of large corrugated steel structures.[22]

Cut ends should be anchor-bolted to headwalls or slope pavements at approximately 18-in. intervals. Uncut, square-end structures may be anchored to a headwall with bolts in alternate standard circumferential holes.

TEMPORARY BRACING

During backfill and the construction of headwalls, the ends of structures may require temporary bracing, generally horizontal, to prevent unsightly distortion. The overhang of a conduit cut on an extreme skew and bevel may require support by shoring until the slope pavement is completed.

STANDARD DESIGNS

Most highway and railway design offices have adequate design standards suitable to their terrain. Reference to these is valuable for design of headwalls, riprap protection and slope pavements. For typical end treatment recommended by Federal Highway Administration, see Figs. 3-20 and 3-21.[22]

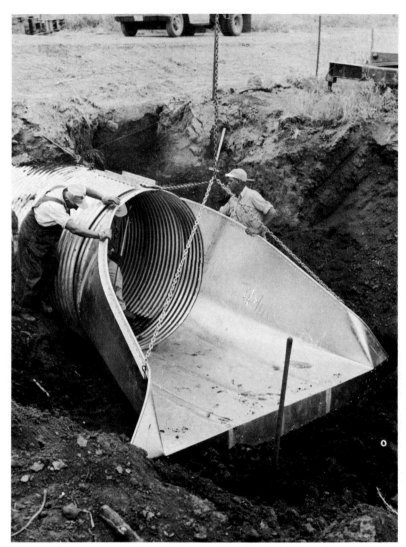

Fig. 3-22. Steel end sections in sizes 12 to 84 in. diameter, and for pipe-arches, are a very satisfactory end treatment. Maintenance and ease of culvert extension are also favorable factors. For details of design, see pages 75–77.

Appendix A

UTAH TEST PROGRAM 1967-1970

Extensive research on buried corrugated steel structures was sponsored by American Iron and Steel Institute and carried on at Utah State University, Logan, Utah, under the direction of Dr. Reynold K. Watkins. The methods, results and conclusions are summarized here.[10]

SCOPE

Approximately 130 pipes, 20 ft long, in sizes from 24-in. to 60-in. diameter were loaded to performance limit in low grade soil backfills compacted from 70% to 99% standard AASHO density. Riveted, spot welded and helical pipe fabrications were included in both 2⅔x½-in. and 3x1-in. corrugations. Confined compression tests were made on six different soils to correlate results to commonly used backfill materials.

PROCEDURE

The test cell was constructed of ⅝-in. steel plate of elliptic cross-section. See Figs. 3-23 and 3-24. The cell was 24 ft long, 15 ft wide and 18 ft high. Steel trusses pinned to the top of the cell walls supported hydraulic cylinders which

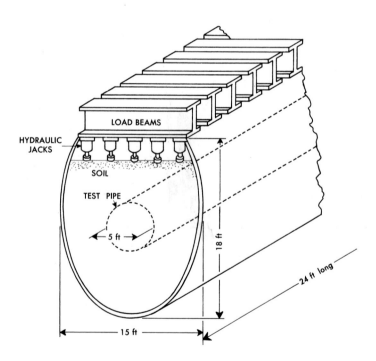

Fig. 3-23. Diagramatic sketch of test cell showing method of applying load with hydraulic jacks. The cell was buttressed with reinforced concrete retaining walls and wing walls. Tests were performed by Engineering Experiment Station of Utah State University for American Iron and Steel Institute.

Fig. 3-24. Test cell loaded and ready to commence a test.

applied a uniform pressure up to 20,000 pounds per square foot on the upper surface of the soil.

Backfill material used was a silty sand installed in lifts and compacted with normally used contractor's equipment. Pipes were instrumented with several pressure gages around the circumference to measure soil pressures on the pipe. Compactive effort and moisture contents were varied to obtain densities from 70% to 99% standard AASHO.

After backfill, steel plates were placed on top of the soil to improve the bearing of the hydraulic rams. Load was applied in planned increments with readings being taken of: loading force, soil pressure on pipe, vertical deflection, ring profile. Testing was terminated when the hydraulic ram pressure could no longer be increased. In this condition the pipe could continue to deform in the test cell and soil arching made the structure stable under field loads much higher than those recorded in the test.

RESULTS

Results of the tests plotted for five degrees of standard AASHO density for the backfill are shown in Fig. 3-25. Assuming the load applied by the hydraulic rams as the pressure acting on the pipe, the ultimate steel stresses are plotted on the previously used buckling chart.* It is immediately apparent that most of the steel stresses, calculated by this criteria, are fictitious because they greatly exceed the yield point. This is explained by Fig. 3-26 which illustrates how the applied load is actually carried in part by the *soil arch* formed in the compacted backfill as load is applied thereto and pipe and soil strains occur. Because the stresses on the ordinate are calculated from the total load, with no reduction therein for the load carried by the soil in arching action, they are designated "apparent stress".

DISCUSSION AND CONCLUSIONS

A prime objective of the Utah program was to establish a practical correlation between backfill density and pipe-behavior. The then-current design criteria of AISI, AASHO, and FHwA set ultimate buckling stresses below yield for common combinations of standard corrugations, diameters, and backfill density.

---

*1967 edition of this Handbook, Fig. 2-13, page 48.

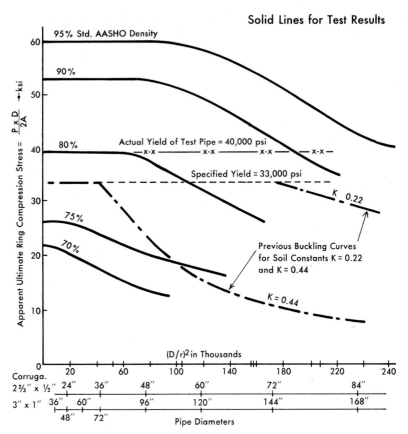

Fig. 3-25. Results of Utah loading tests on corrugated steel pipe, showing apparent *ultimate ring compression stress* as a function of diameter and corrugations for various values of soil density determined by AASHO standards.

These criteria, however, were based on hydrostatic theory modified by model studies. The Utah program provided, for the first time, ultimate performance data of soil-steel installations to full scale, utilizing a low-grade backfill soil and normal field methods and equipment. The Utah research confirmed what has been observed in field installations for decades: The quality and density of backfill required to permit the pipe to carry high stress levels, to or near the yield point, is of ordinary magnitude, comparable to current common practices for most highway embankments. The soil moduli previously used for wall buckling and deflection criteria were correlated to an unrealistically high level of soil compaction. The test results (Fig. 3-25) are plotted on the old buckling stress graph.* The wide disparity between the K = 0.44 curve for 85% compaction and the actual performance results at 85% is readily apparent.

---

*1967 edition of this Handbook, Fig. 2-13, page 48.

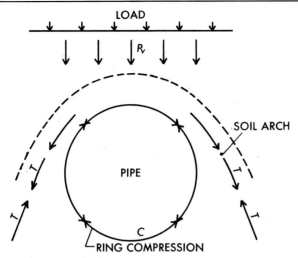

Fig. 3-26. Diagram showing how load Pᵥ is partly carried by means of a "soil arch" over the pipe.

CRITICAL DENSITY

The existence of a "critical density" for flexible pipes had been observed before. This current research established the zone of "critical density" between 70% and 80% standard AASHO density. Critical density is a narrow zone separating the levels of backfill compaction which will and will not prevent deflection failure of the pipe. At 70% standard AASHO density the pipe will not carry stresses anywhere near the yield point and the ultimate failure mode is a collapse or excessive deflection beyond 20 or 25%. At 80% standard AASHO there is enough soil support to preclude the deflection collapse and the pipe carries stress near the yield point.

The test soil used in the Utah research was referred to as "low grade" for pipe backfill. Specifically it was a silty sand which bulked very easily and could be placed to a wide range of standard AASHO densities, something very necessary to a good test program. This soil was quite purposely far from an "ideal" material and is representative of what would be obtained in a normal installation.

A number of laboratory tests and field observations were made of a full range of constructional soils. These soils showed the same relationships of soil modulus to AASHO density exhibited by the test soil.

The relationship between pipe performance and backfill properties is simplified to standard AASHO density. It has been shown that various other moduli such as confined compression modulus and secant modulus can be used for more accurate results. However, these criteria are not in a state of practical usefulness for the pipe designer. The backfill can be readily and easily designed, specified or evaluated on the basis of percent standard AASHO density, regardless of soil type. The only exceptions are unstable soils, such as those which turn plastic with moisture, even though they have been well compacted to 85% or more standard AASHO and confined in the fill. Such soils would, of course, not be suitable for a high embankment base, much less for pipe backfill.

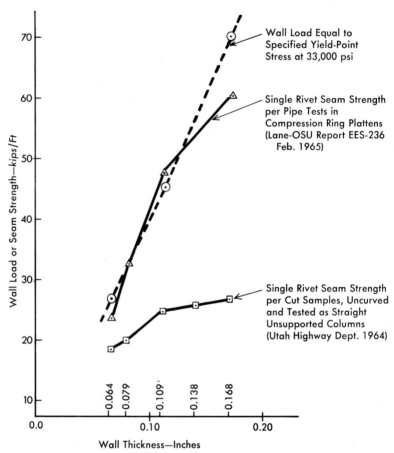

Fig. 3-27. Comparison of single-riveted seams tested as straight, unsupported columns by Utah and those tested in compression ring plattens (comparable to actual service) by Ohio. Pipe seams have no apparent effect on the strength of the pipe.

SEAM STRENGTH

The Utah research included all standard pipe seam types. See *Product Details*, page 46. Pipe seam construction had no apparent effect on the strength of the pipe. Pipe seams failed only after the pipe reached ultimate load and other modes of failure were developing.

The magnitude of compressive load on the pipe wall was from 25% to over 100% greater than the ultimate strength values previously used. However, these values were from tests on uncurved and unsupported columns of corrugated sheets with a seam in the middle—a convenient method of testing, but not representative of installed characteristics. When the Ohio State tests, made on full-scale pipe rings, confined in plattens, are examined, it is readily seen that the results are compatible with the Utah results. See Fig. 3-27. It is reasonably concluded that the standard pipe seams tested in this program are satisfactory for ultimate performance of the pipe itself.

REFERENCES AND BIBLIOGRAPHY

1. Marston, Anson, *The Theory of External Loads on Closed Conduits,* Bulletin No. 96, Iowa Eng. Experiment Sta., Ames, Iowa, 1930, pp. 5–8.

2. Braune, G. M., Cain, William, and Janda, H. F., *Earth Pressure Experiments on Culvert Pipe,* Public Roads, Nov. 1929, p. 157.

3. American Railway Engineering Association, *Culvert Load Determination,* Bulletin 284, Vol. 27, Chicago, Ill., 1926.

4. Spangler, M. G., *Underground Conduits—An Appraisal of Modern Research,* ASCE Transactions, (Discussion), Vol. 113, p. 346, 1948.

5. White, H. L., and Layer, J. P., *The Corrugated Metal Conduit as a Compression Ring,* Highway Research Board Proceedings, Vol. 39, 1960, pp. 389–397.

6. Meyerhof, G. G., and Fisher, C. L., *Composite Design of Underground Steel Structures.* Engineering Journal of the Engineering Institute of Canada, Montreal, Que., Sept. 1963.

7. Watkins, R. K., and Smith, A. B., *Ring Deflection of Buried Pipes,* Utah State University, Engineering Experiment Station, Logan, Utah, May 1966.

8. Burns, J. A., and Richard, R. H., *Attenuation of Stresses for Buried Cylinders,* Proc. of Symposium on Soil-Structure Interaction, Univ. of Arizona, pp. 378–392, Sept. 1964.

9. Hoeg, K., *Stresses Against Underground Structural Cylinders,* Jnl. of Soil Mech. & Founda. Div., Proc. ASCE, Vol. 94, SM4, pp. 833–858, July 1968.

10. Watkins, R. K., and Moser, A. P., *The Structural Performance of Buried Corrugated Steel Pipes,* Utah State University, Logan, Utah. Sponsored by AISI. Sept. 1969, 56 pp.

11. American Association of State Highway Officials, *Standard Specifications for Highway Bridges,* Washington, D. C., 1969.

12. American Railway Engineering Assn., *Manual of Recommended Practice,* Chicago, Illinois. (AREA Spec. 1-4-28).

13. ASCE and Water Pollution Control Federation, New York, N. Y., *Design and Construction of Sanitary and Storm Sewers,* 1969, 332 pp.

14. Allgood, J. R., *Structures in Soils Under High Loads,* a paper presented at ASCE National Structural Engineering Meeting, Portland, Oregon, April 1970.

15. Nielsen, F. D., and Bhandhausavee, C., and Yeh, K., *Determination of Modulus of Soil Reaction from Standard Soil Tests.* Highway Research Board Record No. 284. HRB, Washington, D. C. 1969, pp. 1–12.

16. Univ. of Illinois, Engineering Experiment Station Bulletin No. 22, 1936.

17. Timoshenko, S. P., and Gere, J. M., *Theory of Elastic Stability,* 2nd Ed., McGraw-Hill Book Co., 1961.

18. *The Influence of Wall Stiffness on the Design of Corrugated Metal Culverts.* Technical Report 57.12-400 (3). U.S. Steel Corp., Pittsburgh, Pa.

19. *The Structural Design of Pipe-Arch Culverts with 1 by 3 inch Corrugation.* Technical Report 57.019-400 (5). U.S. Steel Corp. Pittsburgh, Pa.

20. *Republic Steel Sectional Plate Handbook,* Republic Steel Corp., Mfg. Div., Youngstown, Ohio, Catalog G-152.

21. Airport Runway Depth of Cover Tables, National Corrugated Steel Pipe Assn., Schiller Park, Illinois, 60176.

22. Williams, G. M., *Plans for Pipe Culvert Inlet and Outlet Structures.* Circular memo plus Sheets No. G-39-66 to G-44-66, FHwA, 1966.

Fig. 4-1a. Vortex at submerged upstream end of culvert.

Fig. 4-1b. Vigorous discharge at outlet end of same culvert. Courtesy: Federal Highway Administration.

CHAPTER 4 Hydraulics

INTRODUCTION

Many millions of dollars are spent annually on culverts, storm sewers and subdrains, all vital to the protection of streets, highways and railroads. If inadequate, they can jeopardize the roadway and bring excessive property damage and loss of life. Overdesign means extravagance. Good engineering can find an economic solution.

Because topography, soil and climate combine in infinite variety, drainage sites should be designed individually from reasonably adequate data for each particular site. In addition, the designer is advised to consult with those of long experience in maintaining drainage structures in the area. One state highway engineer comments:

> "With the exception of the riding qualities of the traveled way, no other single item requires as much attention on the part of the maintenance man as highway culverts. Many of the problems of culvert maintenance stem from the fact that designers in all too many instances consider that culverts will be required to transport only clear water. This is a condition hardly ever realized in practice,

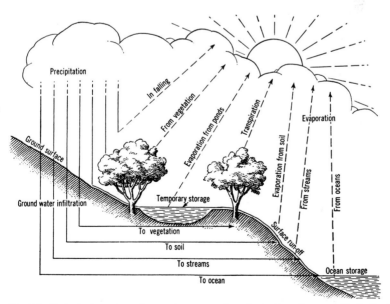

Fig. 4-2. Hydrologic cycle—where water comes from and where it goes.—From M. G. Spangler's "Soil Engineering."

and in many instances storm waters may be carrying as much as 50 percent
detrital material which, due to a rapid change in grade line at the culvert entrance, causes complete blockage of the culvert, with resulting overflow across
the highway and in some cases, especially where high fills are involved, the
intense static pressure results in loss of the embankment."

Section A—ESTIMATING RUNOFF FROM SMALL AREAS

The design procedures described in this chapter include determining the peak
storm runoff for a chosen frequency at any point in a waterway channel and
then selecting the proper size and shape of structure and appurtenances to
best handle that amount of runoff.

RAINFALL INTENSITY—FREQUENCY ANALYSIS

"The expected frequency of occurrence of the design discharge is of concern
... Overdesign and underdesign both involve excessive costs on a long-time
basis," says the Federal Highway Administration.[1]

Memorandum PPM 20-4 of the Bureau of Public Roads requires that on
Interstate System projects, all drainage facilities other than culverts and bridges
be designed to keep the traveled way usable during storms at least as great as
that for a 10-year frequency, except that a 50-year frequency shall be used
for underpasses or other depressed roadways where ponded water can be removed only through the storm drain system.

Rainfall intensity data are taken from the U.S. Weather Bureau Atlas[3], or
from Weather Bureau Technical Paper 25[4].

Approximate rainfall intensity—duration—frequency data can also be
obtained from Fig. 4-3 by the use of coefficients. The 2-year rainfall intensity for other durations is obtained by multiplying the 30-minute intensity
for the project location from Fig. 4-3 by the factors listed in Table 4-1.

To convert 2-year recurrence interval rainfall for a given duration to other
frequencies (recurrence intervals) multiply by the factors in Table 4-2 to
obtain acceptable results.

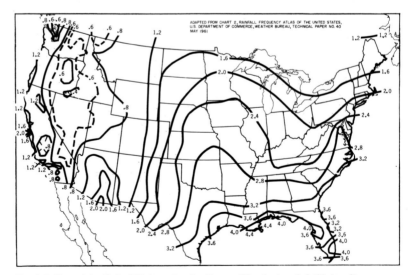

Fig. 4-3. Map of the United States, showing 2-year, 30-minute rainfall intensity.

Table 4-1 Rainfall Intensity Conversion Factors[1]

Duration in Minutes	Factor	Duration in Minutes	Factor
5	2.22	40	0.8
10	1.71	50	0.7
15	1.44	60	0.6
20	1.25	90	0.5
30	1.00	120	0.4

Note: U.S. Weather Bureau says "Rainfall amounts for the 5-, 10-, and 15-minute durations may be obtained by multiplying the 30-minute values by 0.37, 0.57 and 0.72 respectively.[3]

Table 4-2 Recurrence Interval Factors[1]

Recurrence Interval in Years	Factor
2	1.0
5	1.3
10	1.6
25	1.9
50	2.2

Table 4-3 Storm Rating Based on 50-Year Maximum Rainfall

Storm Rating	One-Hour Maximum Rainfall
1 year	0.428
5 years	0.659
10 years	0.762
25 years	0.898
50 years	1.000
100 years	1.108

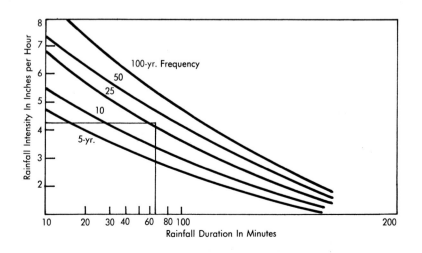

Fig. 4-4. Rainfall intensities for various storm frequencies vs. rainfall duration.

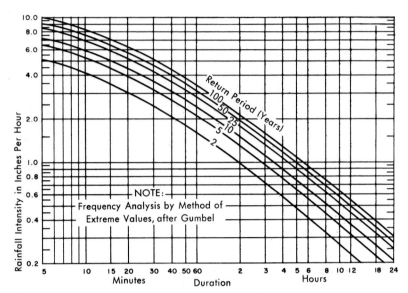

Fig. 4-5. Rainfall intensity for various durations and return periods.

Another chart, Fig. 4-4, applying only to conditions east of the Rocky Mountains shows the relationship between intensity of storms and their frequency of recurrence.

RUNOFF: THE RATIONAL METHOD

Total or peak rainfall can be converted into estimated storm runoff or design discharge by the rational method or formula.

For **storm sewers,** most engineering offices in the United States use the *rational method* of design which has been in use since 1889. This method, recommended by the Federal Highway Administration for roadside channels draining less than about 200 acres, uses the equation:

$$Q = CiA \dots\dots\dots\dots\dots\dots\dots\dots\dots\dots\dots\dots\dots\dots\dots\dots\dots\text{Equation (1)}$$

where Q = peak rate of runoff, in cfs

C = weighted runoff coefficient, expressing the ratio of rate of runoff to rate of rainfall (Table 4-4)

i = average intensity of rainfall, in inches per hour (for the selected frequency and for duration equal to the time of concentration)

A = drainage area, in acres, tributary to the point under design

This formula although not dimensionally correct, gives numerically correct results, since 1 cfs runoff equals 1.008 in. per hour per acre.

Table 4-4   Values of Relative Imperviousness[1]

Type of Surface	Factor C
For all watertight roof surfaces...............................	.75 to .95
For asphalt runway pavements..............................	.80 to .95
For concrete runway pavements............................	.70 to .90
For gravel or macadam pavements..........................	.35 to .70
*For impervious soils (heavy)................................	.40 to .65
*For impervious soils, with turf.............................	.30 to .55
*For slightly pervious soils................................	.15 to .40
*For slightly pervious soils, with turf.......................	.10 to .30
*For moderately pervious soils.............................	.05 to .20
*For moderately pervious soils, with turf....................	.00 to .10

*For slopes from 1% to 2%

WATERSHED CHARACTERISTICS

Some of the watershed characteristics that influence the amount and rate of runoff are:

1. Area and shape

2. Steepness and length of slopes

3. Kind and extent of vegetation or cultivation

4. Condition of surface—dry, saturated, frozen—pervious or impervious soil

5. Number, arrangement and condition of drainage channels on the watershed

The changes of land use during the lifetime of a drainage structure should be considered in evaluating runoff characteristics. Where the drainage area is composed of several types of ground cover, the runoff should be weighted according to the area of each type of cover present.

TIME OF CONCENTRATION

An important factor is the time required for runoff from the remotest part of a drainage area to reach the point under design. This is known as the time of concentration. It is used in the rational design method but must be clearly understood to avoid misapplication of the method and its proposed refinements.[1]

A minimum time of 5 minutes is recommended by the Federal Highway Administration. See Fig. 4-6.

DRAINAGE AREA

The drainage area can be measured on a topographic map or determined in the field by estimation, pacing, aerial photos, or a survey comparable in accuracy to a stadia-compass traverse.

Example

Find the discharge for a 10-year frequency rainfall at the outlet of a grassed roadside channel 400 ft from the crest of a hill with the contributing area 238 ft wide, consisting of 12 ft of concrete pavement, 26 ft of gravel shoul-

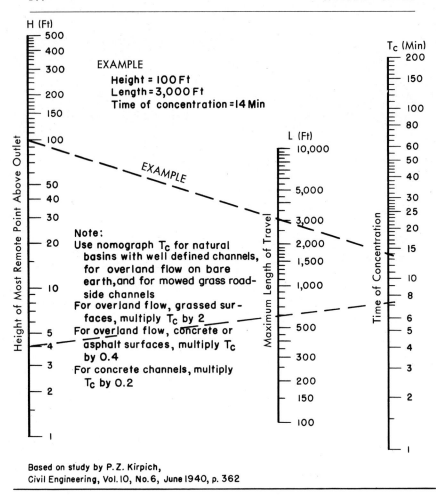

Based on study by P. Z. Kirpich,
Civil Engineering, Vol. 10, No. 6, June 1940, p. 362

Fig. 4-6. Time of concentration of rainfall on small drainage basins.

der, channel, and 200 ft backslope of grassed pasture—giving a weighted $C = 0.35$. The channel grade is 0.5 per cent; and the outer edge of the contributing area is 4 ft above the channel. Location is near Washington, D.C.

The distance from the channel to the ridge of the area is 210 ft and that of the channel is 400 ft making $L = 610$ ft. The height of the most remote point above the outlet $= 4$ ft $+ (0.005 \times 400) = 6$ ft. From Fig. 4-6, the time of concentration, $Tc = 6.5$ min.

The rainfall intensity for a 6.5-minute duration and 10-year return period is 6.9 in. per hr. (Fig. 4-5).

The drainage area $= 238 \times 400 = 95,200$ sq ft or

$$\frac{95,200}{43,560} = 2.2 \text{ acres}$$

Then $Q = 0.35 \times 6.9 \times 2.2 = 5.3$ cfs.

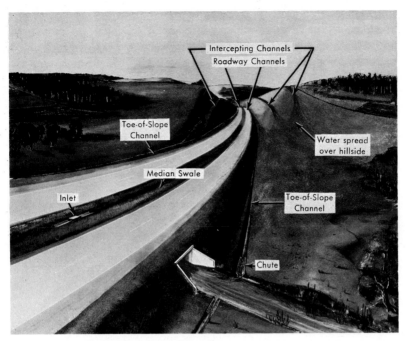

Fig. 4-7. Types of roadside drainage channels.

Section B—HYDRAULICS OF
OPEN DRAINAGE CHANNELS

GENERAL

Before designing culverts, storm sewers and other drainage structures, it is well to consider the design of ditches, gutters, chutes, median swales, and other channels leading to these structures. Fig. 4-7.

The design engineer with needs beyond the scope of this handbook will wish to refer to the publication, *Design of Roadside Drainage Channels*,[1] which includes numerous examples of calculations and a list of 55 authoritative references on all phases of the subject.

Rainfall and runoff, once calculated, are followed by design of suitable channels to handle the peak discharge with minimum erosion, maintenance and hazard to traffic.

The AASHO *Policy on Geometric Design of Rural Highways* recommends:

"Where terrain permits, roadside drainage channels built in earth should have side slopes not steeper than 4:1 (horizontal to vertical), and a rounded bottom at least 4 ft wide. (Minimum depth 1 ft to 3 ft.) . . . Dimensions can be varied by the use of different types of channel surfacing."

Systematic maintenance is recognized as essential to any drainage channel and therefore should be considered in the design of those channels.

CHEZY EQUATION

A basic hydraulic formula developed by Chezy for determining the flow of water particularly in open channels is written as follows:

$$Q = AV \quad V = c\sqrt{RS} \quad \text{and} \quad Q = Ac\sqrt{RS} \dots\dots\dots\dots(2)$$

in which:

Q = discharge, cfs

A = cross-sectional area of flow in sq ft, at right angles to the direction of flow

V = mean velocity of flow, fps

c = a coefficient of roughness whose value depends upon the character of surface over which water is flowing

R = hydraulic radius in ft $= \dfrac{A}{WP}$

WP = wetted perimeter or length, in ft, of wetted contact between a stream of water and its containing channel measured at right angles to the direction of flow

S = slope, or grade in ft per ft

This fundamental formula is the basis of most capacity formulas.

MANNING'S EQUATION

Manning's formula, published in 1890, gives the value of c in the Chezy formula as:

$$c = \frac{1.486}{n}R^{1/6} \dots\dots\dots\dots\dots\dots(3)$$

the complete Manning formula being:

$$V = \frac{1.486}{n}R^{2/3}S^{1/2} \dots\dots\dots\dots\dots(4)$$

and combining with the Chezy Equation:

$$Q = A\frac{1.486}{n}R^{2/3}S^{1/2} \dots\dots\dots\dots(5)$$

in which:

A = cross-sectional area of flow in sq ft

S = slope in ft per ft

R = hydraulic radius in ft

n = coefficient of roughness (see Tables 4-6, 4-5)

In many computations, it is convenient to group the properties peculiar to the cross section in one term called conveyance (K) or:

$$K = \frac{1.486}{n}AR^{2/3} \dots\dots\dots\dots\dots(6)$$

then

$$Q = KS^{1/2} \dots\dots\dots\dots\dots\dots(7)$$

Uniform flow of "clean" water in a straight, unobstructed channel would be a simple problem but is rarely attained. Manning's formula gives reliable results if the channel cross section, roughness, and slope are fairly constant over a sufficient distance to establish uniform flow.

Table 4-5 Coefficient of Roughness n for Channels

Type of Lining	n (Manning)
Ordinary earth, smoothly graded	.02
Sod, depth of flow over 6 in.	.04
Sod, depth of flow under 6 in.	.06
Type A riprap, rough	.04
Concrete paved gutter	.016

Source: Ohio Hydraulic Treatise, 1947.

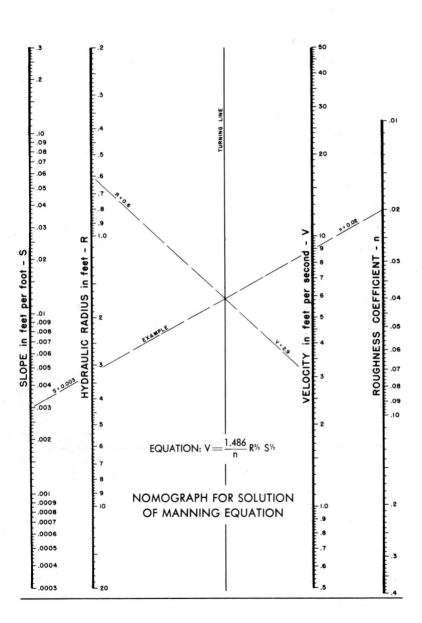

Fig. 4-8. Nomograph for solution of Manning's equation, (4)

Table 4-6 Manning's *n* for Natural Stream Channels
Surface width at flood stage less than 100 ft.

1. Fairly regular section:
    a. Some grass and weeds, little or no brush............................... 0.030—0.035
    b. Dense growth of weeds, depth of flow materially greater than weed height.. 0.035—0.05
    c. Some weeds, light brush on banks.................................. 0.035—0.05
    d. Some weeds, heavy brush on banks................................. 0.05 —0.07
    e. Some weeds, dense willows on banks.............................. 0.06 —0.08
    f. For trees within channel, with branches submerged at high stage, increase all
       above values by... 0.01 —0.02

2. Irregular sections, with pools, slight channel meander; increase values given
   above about.. 0.01 —0.02

3. Mountain streams, no vegetation in channel, banks usually steep, trees and
   brush along banks submerged at high stage:
    a. Bottom of gravel, cobbles, and few boulders........................... 0.04 —0.05
    b. Bottom of cobbles, with large boulders............................. 0.05 —0.07

THE USE OF CHARTS AND TABLES

While design charts[5,6,7] for open-channel flow reduce work, "they cannot replace engineering judgment and a knowledge of the hydraulics of open-channel flow . . . and flow through conduits with a free water surface."[1]

These design charts contain the channel properties (area and hydraulic radius) of many channel sections and tables of velocity for various combinations of slope and hydraulic radius. Their use is explained in the following examples.

Example 1

Given: A trapezoidal channel of straight alignment and uniform cross section in earth, bottom width 2 ft, side slopes 1:1, channel slope 0.003, and normal depth 1 ft.

Find: Velocity and discharge.

Solution:

1. In Table 4-5 for an excavated channel in ordinary earth, *n* is 0.02.

2. Cross-sectional area, *A*, of the channel is 3.0 sq ft and the hydraulic radius is 0.6 ft.

3. Using the nomograph (Fig. 4-8), lay a straightedge between the outer lines at the values of $S = 0.003$ and $n = 0.02$. Mark where the straightedge intersects the turning line.

4. Then place the straightedge so as to line up the point on the turning line and the hydraulic radius of 0.6 ft.

5. Read the velocity 2.9 fps on the velocity line.

6. The discharge, $Q = AV$, is 3.0 sq ft times 2.9 fps or 8.7 cfs.

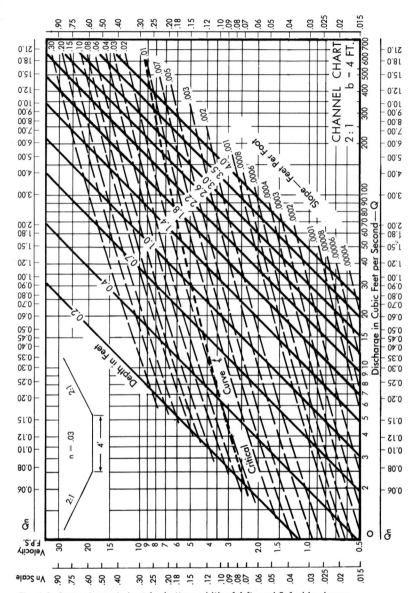

Fig. 4-9. Open-channel chart for bottom width of 4 ft, and 2:1 side slopes.

Example 2

Given: A trapezoidal channel with bottom width 4 ft, side slopes 2:1, $n = 0.03$, channel slope 0.005, and discharge 100 cfs.

Find: Depth d and velocity V.

Solution: (by trial and error)

$$A = (4 + 2d)d$$
$$WP = 4 + 2d\sqrt{5} = 4 + 4.47d$$

Try: $d = 2.5$ ft

$A = (4 + 5) \times 2.5 = 22.5$ sq ft

$WP = 4 + (4.47)(2.5) = 15.2$ ft

$R = 1.48$ ft

From the nomograph, $V = 4.6$ fps

$Q = 22.5 (4.6) = 104$ cfs

This figure is slightly higher than the required 100 cfs, but inasmuch as "exact" solution is $d = 2.45$, the greater refinement does not seem justified. See Fig. 4-9. To the value $d = 2.5$ ft some freeboard should be added.

SAFE VELOCITIES

The ideal situation is one where the velocity will cause neither silting nor erosion. In designing a channel, the approximate grade can be determined from a topographic map, from the plan profiles, or from both.

To prevent the depositing of sediment, the *minimum* gradient for earth and grass-lined channels should be about 0.5 percent and that for smooth paved channels about 0.35 percent. Furthermore it should be kept constant or increasing, if possible, to avoid deposition.

Safe or permissible velocities for erodible channels are given in Table 4-7.

Table 4-7 Comparison of Limiting Water Velocities and Tractive Force Values for the Design of Stable Channels
Straight channels after aging. Canal depth, 3 ft.

Material	n	For Clear Water		Water Transporting Colloidal Silts	
		Velocity ft/sec	Tractive* Force lb/sq ft	Velocity ft/sec	Trac-tive* Force lb/sq ft
Fine sand colloidal	0.020	1.50	0.027	2.50	0.075
Sandy loam noncolloidal	.020	1.75	.037	2.50	0.075
Silt loam noncolloidal	.020	2.00	.048	3.00	0.11
Alluvial silts noncolloidal	.020	2.00	.048	3.50	0.15
Ordinary firm loam	.020	2.50	.075	3.50	0.15
Volcanic ash	.020	2.50	.075	3.50	0.15
Stiff clay very colloidal	.025	3.75	.26	5.00	0.46
Alluvial silts colloidal	.025	3.75	.26	5.00	0.46
Shales and hardpans	.025	6.00	.67	6.00	0.67
Fine gravel	.020	2.50	.075	5.00	0.32
Graded loam to cobbles when non-colloidal	.030	3.75	.38	5.00	0.66
Graded silts to cobbles when colloidal	.030	4.00	.43	5.50	0.80
Coarse gravel noncolloidal	.025	4.00	.30	6.00	0.67
Cobbles and shingles	.035	5.00	.91	5.50	1.10

*"Tractive force" or shear is the force which the water exerts on the periphery of a channel due to the motion of the water. The tractive values shown were computed from velocities given by S. Fortier and Fred C. Scobey and the values of *n* shown.

The tractive force values are valid for the given materials regardless of depth. For depths greater than 3 ft, higher velocities can be allowed and still have the same tractive force. From U.S. Bureau of Reclamation, Report No. Hyd-352, 1952, 60 pp.

Table 4-8 Maximum Permissible Velocities in Vegetal-lined Channels

Cover Average, Uniform Stand, Well Maintained	Slope Range	Permissible Velocity[a]	
	Percent	Erosion Resistant Soils	Easily Eroded Soils
		f p s	f p s
Bermudagrass	0–5 5–10 over 10	8 7 6	6 5 4
Buffalograss Kentucky bluegrass Smooth brome Blue grama	0–5 5–10 over 10	7 6 5	5 4 3
Grass mixture[b]	0–5 5–10	5 4	4 3
Lespedeza sericea Weeping lovegrass Yellow bluestem Kudzu Alfalfa Crabgrass	0–5	3.5	2.5
Common lespedeza[b] Sudangrass[b]	0–5[c]	3.5	2.5

[a]From "Handbook of Channel Design for Soil and Water Conservation," Soil Conservation Service SCS-TP-61, Revised June 1954
[b]Annuals—used on mild slopes or as temporary protection until permanent covers are established
[c]Use on slopes steeper than 5 percent is not recommended.

CHANNEL PROTECTION

If the mean velocity exceeds that permissible for the particular kind of soil, the channel should be protected from erosion. Grass linings are valuable where grass can be supported. Ditch bottoms may be sodded or seeded with the aid of temporary quick growing grasses, mulches, jute bagging or fiberglass. Grass may also be used in combination with other, more rigid types of linings, the grass being on the upper bank slopes.

Linings may consist of stone—dumped, hand placed or grouted, preferably laid on a filter blanket of gravel or crushed stone.

Asphalt and concrete lined channels are used on many steep erodible channels.

Corrugated steel flumes or chutes (and pipe spillways) are favored especially in wet, unstable or frost heaving soils. They should be anchored to prevent undue shifting. Most types of fabricated or poured channels should be protected against buoyancy and uplift, especially when empty. Cutoff walls, half diaphragms, or collars are used to prevent undermining.

Ditch checks (slope-control structures) are used in arid and semi-arid areas where grass won't grow. However, where grass will grow, the use of ditch checks in roadway or toe-of-slope channels is discouraged because they are a hazard to traffic and an impediment to mowing equipment.

High velocity at channel exits must be considered and some provision made to dissipate the excess energy.

Fig. 4-10. Large pipe-arch culvert flowing under *inlet control* condition.

Section C—HYDRAULICS OF CULVERTS

INTRODUCTION

Designing a culvert has not yet reached the stage where two or more individuals will always arrive at the same answer, or where actual service performance matches the designer's anticipation. The reason is that the engineer's interpretation of field data and hydrology is often influenced by personal judgment, based on his own experience in a given locality. However, field data, hydrology and hydraulic research are hopefully closing the gap to move the art of designing a culvert a little closer to becoming a science.

Up to this point, the design procedure has consisted of (1) collecting field data, (2) compiling facts about the roadway, and (3) making a reasonable estimate of flood flow for a chosen frequency. The fourth step is to design an economical culvert to handle the flow (including debris) with minimum damage to the highway, street, railway or adjacent property. Fig. 4-10.

Factors to consider include: type of structure; area and shape of waterway opening; approximate length and slope of culvert barrel; and treatment of inlet and outlet ends.

WHAT MAKES A GOOD CULVERT

An ASCE Task Force on Hydraulics of Culverts offers the following recommendations for "Attributes of a Good Highway Culvert"[8]:

1. The culvert, appurtenant entrance and outlet structures should properly take care of water, bed-load, and floating debris at all stages of flow.

2. It should cause no unnecessary or excessive property damage.

3. Normally, it should provide for transportation of material without detrimental change in flow pattern above and below the structure.

4. It should be designed so that future channel and highway improvement can be made without too much loss or difficulty.

5. It should be designed to function properly after fill has caused settlement.

6. It should not cause objectionable stagnant pools in which mosquitoes may breed.

7. It should be designed to accommodate increased runoff occasioned by anticipated land development.

8. It should be economical to build, hydraulically adequate to handle design discharge, structurally durable and easy to maintain.

9. It should be designed to avoid excessive ponding at entrance which may cause property damage, accumulation of drift, culvert clogging, saturation of fills, or detrimental upstream deposits of debris.

10. Entrance structures should be designed to screen out material which will not pass through the culvert, reduce entrance losses to a minimum, make use of the velocity of approach insofar as practicable, and by use of transitions and increased slopes, as necessary, facilitate channel flow entering the culvert.

11. The design of culvert and outlet should be effective in re-establishing tolerable non-erosive channel flow within the right-of-way or within a reasonably short distance below the culvert.

12. The outlet should be designed to resist undermining and washout.

13. Culvert dissipaters, if used, should be simple, easy to build, economical and reasonably self-cleaning during periods of easy flow.

Fig. 4-11. Large culverts justify careful design with an adequate size factor for the class of roadway and with experience under local conditions.

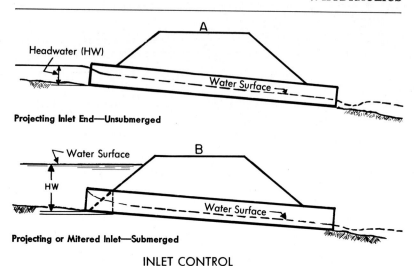

Projecting Inlet End—Unsubmerged

Projecting or Mitered Inlet—Submerged

INLET CONTROL

Fig. 4-12. *Inlet control* is one of the two major types of culvert flow. Condition A with un-submerged culvert inlet is preferred to the submerged end. Slope, roughness and length of culvert barrel are no consideration.

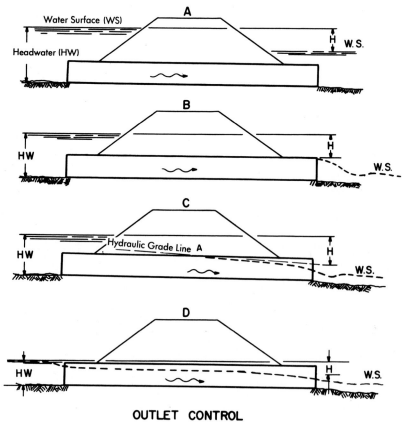

OUTLET CONTROL

Fig. 4-13. *Outlet control* involves these factors: cross-sectional area of barrel; inlet "geometry"; ponding; tailwater; and slope, roughness and length of culvert barrel.

HYDRAULIC CONDITIONS AND DEFINITIONS[9, 10]

Conventional Culverts considered here are circular pipes and pipe-arches, with uniform barrel cross-section throughout.

Inlet Control. There are two major types of culvert flow—with inlet control or outlet control. Under **inlet** control, (1) the cross-sectional area of the barrel, (2) the inlet configuration or "geometry" and (3) the amount of headwater or ponding are of primary importance. (Fig. 4-12)

Outlet Control involves (4) the additional consideration of the tailwater in the outlet channel, and (5) the slope, *roughness* and length of barrel. (Fig 4-13)

Headwater Depth (HW). The headwater depth is the vertical distance from the culvert invert at the entrance (full cross-section) to the energy line of the headwater pool (depth + velocity head). Water surface and energy line at the entrance are assumed to coincide.

$$HW = H + h_0 - LS_0 \dots\dots\dots\dots\dots\dots\dots\dots\dots\dots\dots\dots\dots (8)$$

where: H = head (ft)
  $h_0 = TW$ (under conditions shown here)
  L = length of culvert (ft)
  S_0 = slope of barrel (ft per ft)

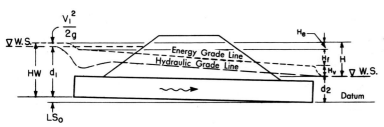

Fig. 4-14. The difference between the energy grade line and the hydraulic grade line is shown here.

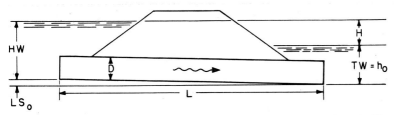

Fig. 4-15. Relationship of headwater to high tailwater and other terms in formula (8).

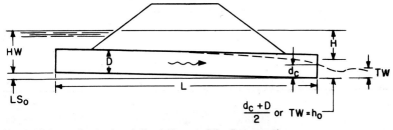

Fig. 4-16. Low tailwater in relation to terms of the flow equation.

Hydraulic Slope. The hydraulic slope or hydraulic grade line, sometimes called the pressure line is defined by the elevations to which water would rise in small vertical pipes attached to the culvert wall along its length. (See Fig. 4-14) The energy line and the pressure line are parallel over the length of the barrel except in the vicinity of the inlet where the flow contracts and re-expands. The difference is the velocity head, $\dfrac{V^2}{2g}$ . . . .(9)

Head (H). The head (Fig. 4–14) or energy required to pass a given quantity of water through a culvert flowing in outlet control (with barrel full) is made up of (1) velocity head $H_v = \dfrac{V^2}{2g}$, (2) an entrance loss H_e, and (3) a friction loss Hf. This energy is obtained from ponding at entrance and slope of pipe, and is expressed in equation form:

$$H = H_v + H_e + H_f \quad \dots \dots \dots \dots \dots \dots (10)$$

Entrance Loss, (H_e) depends upon the geometry of the inlet edge. This loss is expressed as a coefficient k_e multiplied by the barrel velocity head or

$$H_e = k_e \, \frac{V^2}{2g} \quad \dots \dots \dots \dots \dots \dots \dots (11)$$

Table 4-9 Entrance Loss Coefficients for Corrugated Metal Pipe or Pipe-Arch[9]

Inlet End of Culvert	Coefficient k_e
Projecting from fill (no headwall)	0.9
Headwall, or headwall and wingwalls square-edge	0.5
Mitered (beveled) to conform to fill slope	0.7
*End-Section conforming to fill slope	0.5
Headwall, rounded edge	0.2
**Beveled Ring	0.25

*End Sections available from manufacturers.   **See Fig. 4-19.

Friction Loss, (Hf) is the energy required to overcome the roughness of the culvert barrel and is expressed in the following equation:

$$Hf = \frac{(29 \, n^2 L)}{(R^{1.33})} \frac{V^2}{2g} \dots \dots \dots \dots \dots \dots (12)$$

where: n = Manning's friction factor (See Tables 4-10 and 4-11)
L = length of culvert barrel (ft)
V = mean velocity of flow in barrel (ft/sec)
g = acceleration of gravity, 32.2 (ft/sec²)
R = hydraulic radius, or $\dfrac{A}{WP}$ (ft)

Substituting in equation (12) and simplifying (for Bernoulli's Theorem) we get for *full flow:*

$$H = \left(1 + k_e + \frac{29 \, n^2 L}{R^{1.33}}\right)\frac{V^2}{2g} \dots \dots \dots \dots (13)$$

See Fig. 4-14. Nomographs for solving equation (13) are shown in Reference 10.

Table 4-10   Values of Coefficient of Roughness (n)
for Standard Corrugated Steel Pipe
(Manning's Formula)*

Corrugations	Annular 2⅔″ x ½″	Helical						
		1½″ x ¼″[11, 12]	2⅔″ x ½″					
	All Diam.	8″	10″	12″	18″	24″	36″	48″
Unpaved	.024	.012	.014	.011	.014	.016	.019	.020
25% Paved	.021					.015	.017	.020
Fully Paved	.012					.012	.012	.012

Corrugations	Annular 3″ x 1″	Helical—3″ x 1″					
	All Diam.	36″	48″	54″	60″	66″	72″
Unpaved	.027	.021	.023	.023	.024	.025	.026
25% Paved	.023	.019	.020	.020	.021	.022	.022
Fully Paved	.012	.012	.012	.012	.012	.012	.012

*When helically corrugated steel pipe is used for air conduction, the Darcy-Weisbach formula with other values of F (or n) is used. See Table E-1, page 32.

RESEARCH ON VALUES OF n FOR HELICALLY CORRUGATED STEEL PIPE

Tests on helically corrugated pipe demonstrate a lower coefficient of roughness than for annularly corrugated steel pipe when there is a significant amount of helix or spiral in the pipe. For a given diameter, the greater the (angle of) helix, the less the friction factor. For a given helix, the greater the diameter, the less the friction factor.

The values in Table 4-10 are based on standard helical pipe manufactured from a 24-in. net-width strip of steel. However, the pipes tested were of a smaller diameter for a given helix angle. Further research may show even lower values when larger diameters of standard helical pipe for a given helix angle are taken into account.

Most published values of the coefficient of roughness, n, are based on experimental work under controlled laboratory conditions, using clear or clean water. The lines are ordinarily straight and with smooth joints. However, design values should take into account the actual construction and service conditions which vary greatly for different drainage materials. As noted on preceding pages, the friction factor for drainage structure walls is not pertinent for a large percentage of installations.

FIELD STUDIES ON STRUCTURAL PLATE PIPE[14]

Model studies by the U.S. Corps of Engineers and analyses of the same by the Federal Highway Administration have been the basis for friction factors of structural plate pipe for several years. These values shown in the 1967 edition of this Handbook, page 108, ranged from 0.0328 for 5-ft diameter pipe to 0.0302 for 15-ft pipe.

In 1968, full-scale measurements, the first of their kind, were made on a

**Table 4-11. Values of *n* for Structural Plate Pipe[15]
for 6 in. x 2 in. Corrugations
(Manning's Formula)**

Corrugations	Diameters			
6″ x 2″	5 ft	7 ft	10 ft	15 ft
Plain—unpaved	.033	.032	.030	.028
25% Paved	.028	.027	.026	.024

1500-ft long 14-ft diameter structural plate pipe line in Lake Michigan. These measurements indicated a lower friction factor than those derived from model studies on large-size pipe. As a result, the recommended values of Manning's *n* for structural plate pipe of 10-ft diameter and larger have been modified as shown in Table 4-11. The values for the smaller diameters remain as they were.

Design For Culvert Size

The culvert design process shall strive for a balanced result. Pure fluid mechanics should be combined with practical considerations to help assure satisfactory performance under actual field conditions. This includes prospective maintenance and the handling of debris.

The California Division of Highways uses an excellent method of accomplishing this—one that has worked well for more than 25 years. Other states and agencies have used similar approaches. California culvert design practice establishes the following:

Criteria for Balanced Design. The culvert shall be designed to discharge—

(a) a 10-year flood without static head at entrance, and

(b) a 100-year flood utilizing the available head at entrance.

This approach lends itself well to most modern design processes and computer programs such as those published by the Federal Highway Administration. It applies a usable rational control to the elusive matter of minimum waterway area which constitutes good practice. This design method is highly recommended and is followed here in conjunction with the Federal Highway Administration charts.

HYDRAULIC COMPUTATIONS

Minimum Culvert Entrance. From the hydrology data, the 100-year and 10-year discharge have been established for the site.

The pipe size to carry the 10-year storm with no head at entrance is determined from Fig. 4-17. This is the minimum allowable size.

Headwater Depth for Design Discharge. Using the 100-year discharge, determine headwater for inlet and outlet control. Use whichever is greater. Inlet and outlet control flow charts from the Federal Highway Administration are given for common standard sizes of corrugated steel structures. Figs. 4-18 through 4-25 on following pages.

Inlet Control. From Fig. 4-18 through 4-21B the headwater for a given pipe can be determined. Using the minimum size selected for the 10-year flood, determine the headwater (for the entrance condition desired) for the 100-year flood discharge. If this amount of headwater is acceptable for the

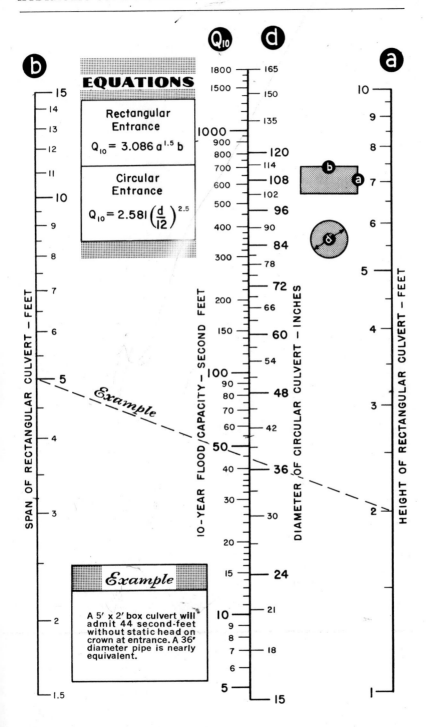

Q₁₀   **d**

EQUATIONS

Rectangular
Entrance

$$Q_{10} = 3.086\, a^{1.5}\, b$$

Circular
Entrance

$$Q_{10} = 2.581 \left(\frac{d}{12}\right)^{2.5}$$

SPAN OF RECTANGULAR CULVERT – FEET

10-YEAR FLOOD CAPACITY – SECOND FEET

DIAMETER OF CIRCULAR CULVERT – INCHES

HEIGHT OF RECTANGULAR CULVERT – FEET

Example

Example

A 5′ x 2′ box culvert will
admit 44 second-feet
without static head on
crown at entrance. A 36″
diameter pipe is nearly
equivalent.

Fig. 4-17. Chart for determining minimum culvert entrance section for 10-year flood.
Water level at crown of culvert. Courtesy California Division of Highways.[17]

culvert in question, the minimum size is satisfactory for the full 100-year design discharged in inlet control. If the headwater is too high, a larger size must be selected corresponding to the maximum permissible headwater. Now check for possible outlet control, as follows.

Outlet Control. Using the size selected for inlet control enter Fig. 4-22, 4-23, 4-24 or 4-25 to determine the headwater depth in outlet control. If the depth here is greater than that for inlet control, the culvert is assumed to be in outlet control and the higher depth applies.

Wall roughness factors used are stated on the flow charts. For other values of "n," use an adjusted value for length, L', calculated by the formula

$$L' = L\left(\frac{n'}{n}\right)^2 \dots\dots\dots\dots\dots\dots\dots\dots\dots\dots\dots (14)$$

where L = Actual length
n' = Actual value of Manning's n
n = Value of Manning's n shown on chart.

Using L' on the length scales in the charts, adjust the result for the Manning's n desired.

The appropriate k_e curve is selected for the entrance condition desired. Typical values of k_e are found in Table 4-9, page 156.

If the culvert is in outlet control and the headwater exceeds the allowable, a larger size can be selected corresponding to acceptable headwater depth. In such a case, alternate solutions should be considered for corrugated steel structures with lower roughness coefficients. See Table 4-10. A smaller size of paved pipe or helical pipe may be satisfactory.

Entrance conditions should also be considered. It may be economical to use a more efficient entrance than planned if a size difference results. Check the lowest k_e curve results.

Structural Plate Factors. Values of Manning's n for Structural Plate Pipe determined in the 1968 full-scale field measurements reported in Table 4-11 are shown for convenience on Figs. 4-24 and 4-25 together with the corresponding adjusted L value to be used. This data was not a part of the Federal Highway Administration charts, which were published in 1963.

OTHER CLASSES OF CULVERTS

This design procedure utilizes 10-year and 100-year flood discharge. Obviously there are culvert requirements of less importance which do not warrant these frequencies. Maximum, or design discharges for less critical culverts may be based on 25 or even 10-year floods. This is a matter of hydrology and is discussed briefly in Section A of this chapter. But, whatever the flood frequency is chosen for the design discharge, the rationale presented here is still usable. The culvert design may be balanced by requiring no static head at entrance for a lower frequency flood discharge than the design discharge frequency.

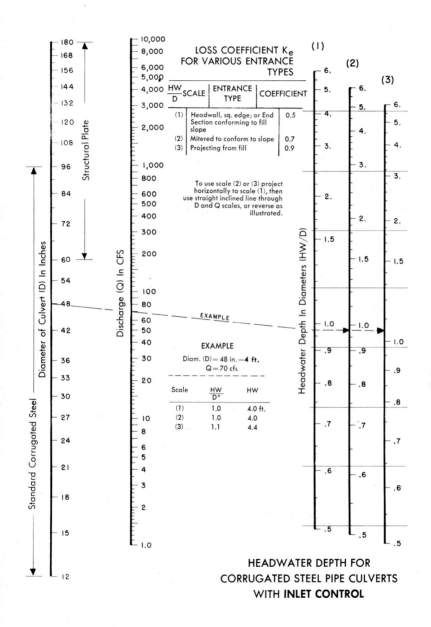

LOSS COEFFICIENT K_e (1)
FOR VARIOUS ENTRANCE
TYPES

HW/D SCALE	ENTRANCE TYPE	COEFFICIENT
(1)	Headwall, sq. edge; or End Section conforming to fill slope	0.5
(2)	Mitered to conform to slope	0.7
(3)	Projecting from fill	0.9

To use scale (2) or (3) project
horizontally to scale (1), then
use straight inclined line through
D and Q scales, or reverse as
illustrated.

EXAMPLE

EXAMPLE

Diam. (D) = 48 in. = **4 ft.**
Q = 70 cfs

Scale	HW/D*	HW
(1)	1.0	4.0 ft.
(2)	1.0	4.0
(3)	1.1	4.4

HEADWATER DEPTH FOR
CORRUGATED STEEL PIPE CULVERTS
WITH **INLET CONTROL**

Fig. 4-18. *Inlet control* nomograph for corrugated steel *pipe* culverts. The manufacturers recommend keeping *HW/D* to a maximum of 1.5 and preferably to no more than 1.0.

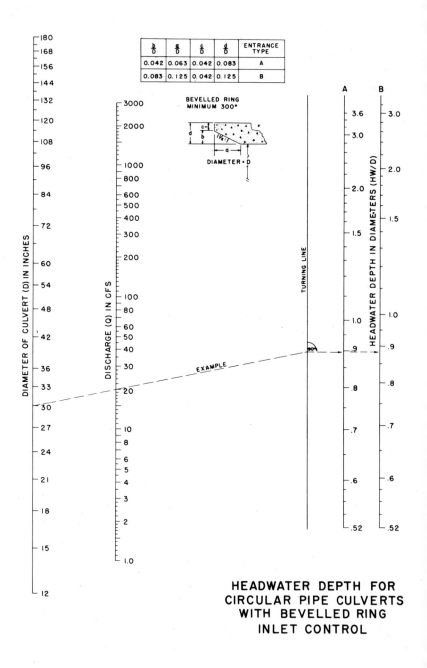

$\frac{b}{D}$	$\frac{a}{D}$	$\frac{c}{D}$	$\frac{d}{D}$	ENTRANCE TYPE
0.042	0.063	0.042	0.083	A
0.083	0.125	0.042	0.125	B

**HEADWATER DEPTH FOR
CIRCULAR PIPE CULVERTS
WITH BEVELLED RING
INLET CONTROL**

Fig. 4-19. *Inlet Control.* Headwater depths for circular *pipe* culverts with beveled ring.

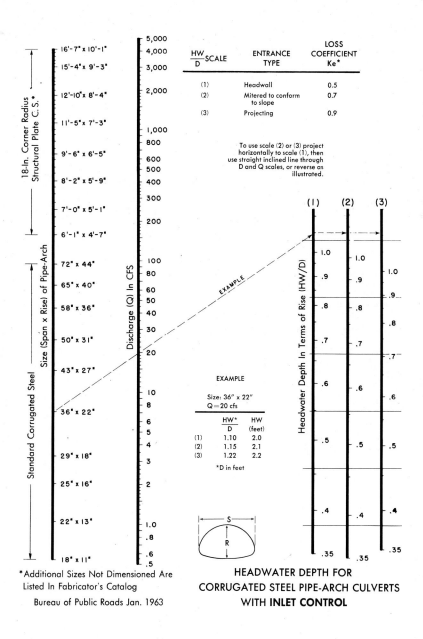

$\frac{HW}{D}$ SCALE	ENTRANCE TYPE	LOSS COEFFICIENT Ke*
(1)	Headwall	0.5
(2)	Mitered to conform to slope	0.7
(3)	Projecting	0.9

To use scale (2) or (3) project horizontally to scale (1), then use straight inclined line through D and Q scales, or reverse as illustrated.

EXAMPLE

Size: 36″ x 22″
Q = 20 cfs

	$\frac{HW^*}{D}$	HW (feet)
(1)	1.10	2.0
(2)	1.15	2.1
(3)	1.22	2.2

*D in feet

*Additional Sizes Not Dimensioned Are
Listed In Fabricator's Catalog

Bureau of Public Roads Jan. 1963

**HEADWATER DEPTH FOR
CORRUGATED STEEL PIPE-ARCH CULVERTS
WITH INLET CONTROL**

Fig. 4-20. *Inlet control* and headwater depths for corrugated steel *pipe-arch* culverts. Headwater depth should be kept low because pipe-arches are generally used where headroom is limited.

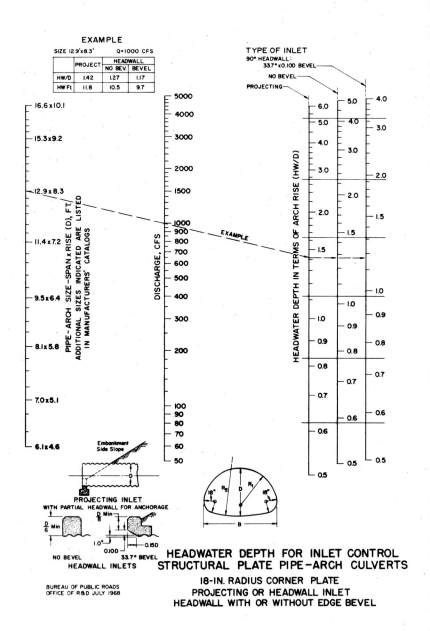

HEADWATER DEPTH FOR INLET CONTROL
STRUCTURAL PLATE PIPE−ARCH CULVERTS
18-IN. RADIUS CORNER PLATE
PROJECTING OR HEADWALL INLET
HEADWALL WITH OR WITHOUT EDGE BEVEL

BUREAU OF PUBLIC ROADS
OFFICE OF R&D JULY 1968

Fig. 4-21A. *Inlet Control.* Headwater depths for structural plate *pipe-arch* culverts with *18-in. radius* corner plate for three types of inlet.

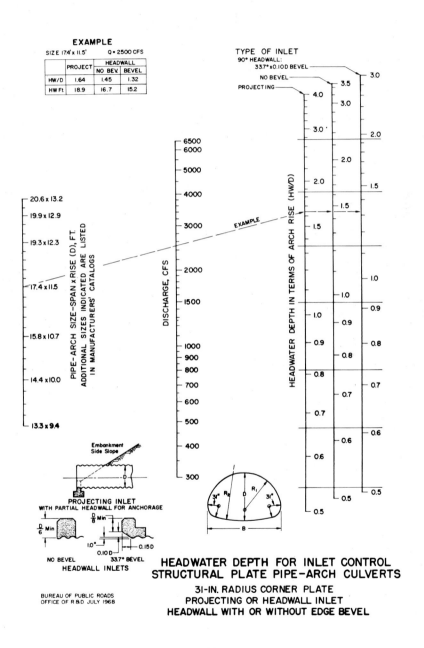

EXAMPLE

SIZE 17.4' x 11.5'   Q = 2500 CFS

	PROJECT	HEADWALL	
		NO BEV.	BEVEL
HW/D	1.64	1.45	1.32
HW Ft	18.9	16.7	15.2

TYPE OF INLET

90° HEADWALL:
33.7° x 0.10D BEVEL
NO BEVEL
PROJECTING

DISCHARGE, CFS

PIPE-ARCH SIZE-SPAN x RISE (D), FT.
ADDITIONAL SIZES INDICATED ARE LISTED
IN MANUFACTURERS' CATALOGS

HEADWATER DEPTH IN TERMS OF ARCH RISE (HW/D)

EXAMPLE

Embankment
Side Slope

PROJECTING INLET
WITH PARTIAL HEADWALL FOR ANCHORAGE

D/6 Min
D/8 Min

1.0"
0.10D
0.15D

NO BEVEL   33.7° BEVEL
HEADWALL INLETS

BUREAU OF PUBLIC ROADS
OFFICE OF R & D JULY 1968

**HEADWATER DEPTH FOR INLET CONTROL
STRUCTURAL PLATE PIPE-ARCH CULVERTS**
31-IN. RADIUS CORNER PLATE
PROJECTING OR HEADWALL INLET
HEADWALL WITH OR WITHOUT EDGE BEVEL

Fig. 4-21B. *Inlet Control.* Headwater depths for structural plate pipe-arch culverts, with 31-in. radius corner plate, for three types of inlet.

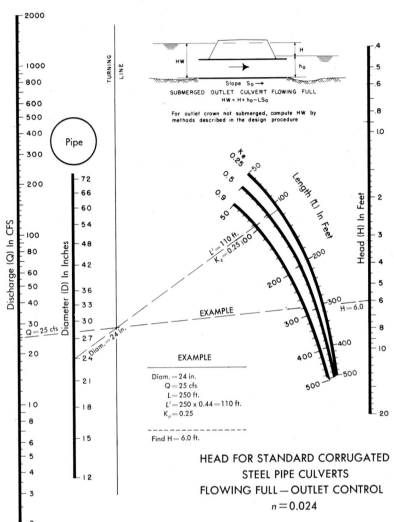

HEAD FOR STANDARD CORRUGATED
STEEL PIPE CULVERTS
FLOWING FULL — OUTLET CONTROL
$n = 0.024$

Fig. 4-22. *Outlet Control.* Head for corrugated steel *pipe* culvert with submerged outlet and culvert flowing full. See note under sketch at top.

Length Adjustment for Improved Hydraulics

Pipe Diameter in Inches	Roughness Factor n' for Helical Corr.*	Length Adjustment Factor $\left(\dfrac{n'}{n}\right)^2$
12	.011	.21
24	.016	.44
36	.019	.61
48	.020	.70

*Other values of roughness, *n*, are applicable to paved pipe, lined pipe and pipe with 3 x 1 in. corrugations. See Table 4-10. To use the above chart for these types of pipe and pipe-arches, use "adjusted length factors" computed per equation 14, page 160.

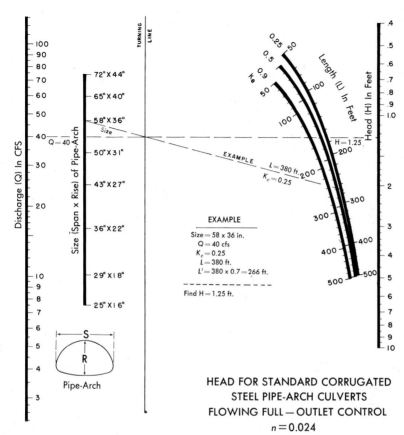

EXAMPLE

Size = 58 x 36 in.
Q = 40 cfs
K_e = 0.25
L = 380 ft.
$L' = 380 \times 0.7 = 266$ ft.

Find H = 1.25 ft.

Pipe-Arch

HEAD FOR STANDARD CORRUGATED
STEEL PIPE-ARCH CULVERTS
FLOWING FULL — OUTLET CONTROL
$n = 0.024$

Fig. 4-23. *Outlet Control.* Head for corrugated steel *pipe-arch* culvert with submerged outlet and flowing full.

Fig. 4-23a. Pipe-arch culvert under limited headroom conditions.

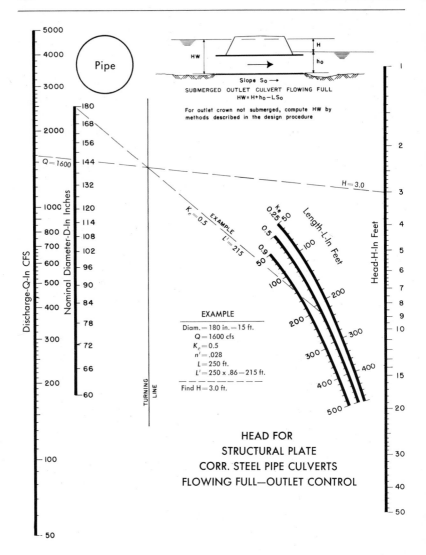

Fig. 4-24. *Outlet Control*. Head for structural plate *pipe* culvert—with submerged outlet and flowing full.

Length Adjustment for Improved Hydraulics

Pipe Diam. in Feet	Roughness Factor		Length Adjustment Factor $\left(\dfrac{n'}{n}\right)^2$
	Curves Based on $n=$	Actual $n' =$*	
5′	.0328	.033	1.0
7′	.0320	.032	1.0
10′	.0311	.030	0.93
15′	.0302	.028	0.86

*See Table 4-11 (page 158)

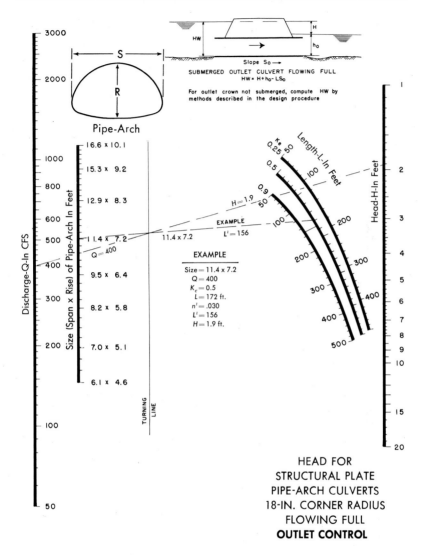

HEAD FOR
STRUCTURAL PLATE
PIPE-ARCH CULVERTS
18-IN. CORNER RADIUS
FLOWING FULL
OUTLET CONTROL

Fig. 4-25. *Outlet Control.* Head for *structural plate pipe-arch* culvert with *18-in.* corner radius—with submerged outlet and flowing full. For 31-in. corner radius, use structure sizes with equivalent areas on the 18-in. corner radius scale.

Length Adjustment for Improved Hydraulics

Pipe-Arch Size in Feet	Roughness Factor		Length Adjustment Factor $\left(\dfrac{n'}{n}\right)^2$
	Curves based on n	Actual n' *	
6.1 x 4.6	.0327	.0327	1.0
8.1 x 5.8	.0321	.032	1.0
11.4 x 7.2	.0315	.030	0.907
16.6 x 10.1	.0306	.028	0.837

*See Table 4-11

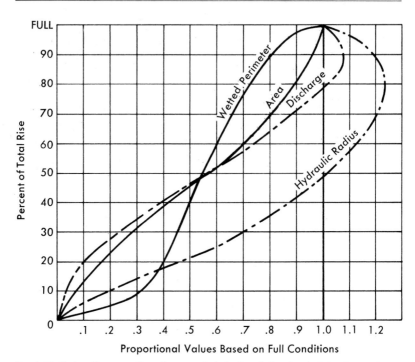

Fig. 4-26. Hydraulic properties of corrugated steel and structural plate pipe-arches.

Table 4-12 Full-Flow Data for Corrugated Steel Pipe-Arches
Corrugations 2⅔ x ½ in.

Dimensions in Inches			Waterway Area in Sq Ft	Hydraulic Radius $A/\pi D$ in Feet
Pipe Diam.	Pipe-Arch			
	Span	Rise		
15	18	11	1.1	0.280
18	22	13	1.6	0.340
21	25	16	2.2	0.400
24	29	18	2.8	0.446
30	36	22	4.4	0.560
36	43	27	6.4	0.679
*42	50	31	8.7	0.791
*48	58	36	11.4	0.907
*54	65	40	14.3	1.012
*60	72	44	17.6	1.120
*66	79	49	21.3	1.233
*72	85	54	25.3	1.342

Corrugations 3 x 1 in.

66	73	55	22	1.273
72	81	59	26	1.379
78	87	63	31	1.518
84	95	67	35	1.592
90	103	71	40	1.698

*These sizes apply to both types of corrugations: 2⅔ x ½ and 3 x 1 in.

Table 4-12A Full-Flow Data for Structural Plate Pipe-Arches

Corrugations 6 x 2 in.

Corner Plates 9 pi   **Radius (Rc) = 18 in.**

Dimensions Ft-In.		Waterway Area in Sq. Ft.	Hydraulic Radius in Feet
Span	Rise		
6′ 1″	4′ 7″	22	1.29′
6′ 4″	4′ 9″	24	1.35′
6′ 9″	4′ 11″	26	1.39′
7′ 0″	5′ 1″	28	1.45′
7′ 3″	5′ 3″	30	1.51′
7′ 8″	5′ 5″	33	1.55′
7′ 11″	5′ 7″	35	1.61′
8′ 2″	5′ 9″	38	1.67′
8′ 7″	5′ 11″	40	1.71′
8′ 10″	6′ 1″	43	1.77′
9′ 4″	6′ 3″	45	1.81′
9′ 6″	6′ 5″	48	1.87′
9′ 9″	6′ 7″	51	1.93′
10′ 3″	6′ 9″	54	1.97′
10′ 8″	6′ 11″	57	2.01′
10′ 11″	7′ 1″	60	2.07′
11′ 5″	7′ 3″	63	2.11′
11′ 7″	7′ 5″	66	2.17′
11′ 10″	7′ 7″	70	2.23′
12′ 4″	7′ 9″	73	2.26′
12′ 6″	7′ 11″	77	2.32′
12′ 8″	8′ 1″	81	2.38′
12′ 10″	8′ 4″	85	2.44′
13′ 5″	8′ 5″	88	2.48′
13′ 11″	8′ 7″	91	2.52′
14′ 1″	8′ 9″	95	2.57′
14′ 3″	8′ 11″	100	2.63′
14′ 10″	9′ 1″	103	2.67′
15′ 4″	9′ 3″	107	2.71′
15′ 6″	9′ 5″	111	2.77′
15′ 8″	9′ 7″	116	2.83′
15′ 10″	9′ 10″	121	2.89′
16′ 5″	9′ 11″	125	2.92′
16′ 7″	10′ 1″	130	2.98′

OTHER HYDRAULIC EFFECTS

Hydraulic capacity of a culvert is affected by factors other than size of opening. In order of consideration here, these include:

1. Flow conditions through culvert
2. Shape of culvert
3. Single vs. multiple opening
4. Slope of culvert
5. Length of culvert
6. Roughness of culvert interior
7. Approach channel
8. Type of culvert inlet
9. Type of culvert outlet
10. Ponding at entrance
11. Height of tailwater

1. Flow Conditions Through Culvert

For culverts on a steep slope, the discharge is controlled at the inlet, depending on headwater depth[9]; on mild slopes, outlet control usually exists.

Table 4-12B Full-Flow Data for Corrugated Steel Pipe-Arches
Corrugations 6 x 2 in.
Corner Plates 15 pi   Radius (Rc) = 31 in.

Span	Rise	Area	Hydraulic Radius
13′ 3″	9′ 4″	97Ft²	2.68′
13′ 6″	9′ 6″	102	2.74′
14′ 0″	9′ 8″	105	2.78′
14′ 2″	9′ 10″	109	2.83′
14′ 5″	10′ 0″	114	2.90′
14′ 11″	10′ 2″	118	2.94′
15′ 4″	10′ 4″	123	2.98′
15′ 7″	10′ 6″	127	3.04′
15′ 10″	10′ 8″	132	3.10′
16′ 3″	10′ 10″	137	3.14′
16′ 6″	11′ 0″	142	3.20′
17′ 0″	11′ 2″	146	3.24′
17′ 2″	11′ 4″	151	3.30′
17′ 5″	11′ 6″	157	3.36′
17′ 11″	11′ 8″	161	3.40′
18′ 1″	11′ 10″	167	3.45′
18′ 7″	12′ 0″	172	3.50′
18′ 9″	12′ 2″	177	3.56′
19′ 3″	12′ 4″	182	3.59′
19′ 6″	12′ 6″	188	3.65′
19′ 8″	12′ 8″	194	3.71′
19′ 11″	12′ 10″	200	3.77′
20′ 5″	13′ 0″	205	3.81′
20′ 7″	13′ 2″	211	3.87′

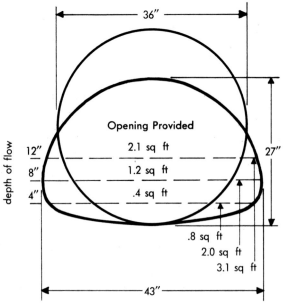

Fig. 4-27. Comparison of waterway cross-sectional areas at equal depths of flow in steel pipe and pipe-arch. The pipe-arch handles a larger volume at the lower levels of flow.

2. Shape of Culvert

The shape of a corrugated metal culvert—circular pipe, vertically elongated pipe, pipe-arch or arch—is generally chosen for reasons of headroom and/or strength rather than for hydraulic reasons. However, as the accompanying chart shows, a pipe-arch carries roughly 50 percent more water at depths up to half full. See Fig. 4-27. This keeps the headwaters at a lower level.

3. Single vs. Multiple Opening

A single culvert opening is, in general, the most satisfactory because of its greater ability to handle floating debris and driftwood. However, in many cases the greater portion of the waterway should be kept low to get the water through quickly without ponding or flooding of the land upstream. In such cases, the solution may consist of using either an arch or pipe-arch, or using a battery of two or more openings, or both. See Fig. 4-28.

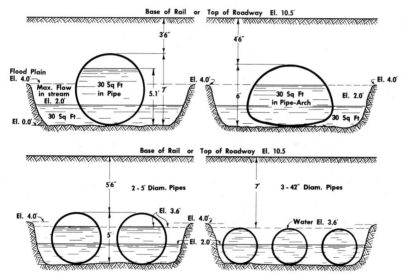

Fig. 4-28. Diagrams showing four choices for a culvert opening. For the assumed conditions, a single large pipe will cause the water to back up and flood the adjacent land. A twin or triple opening, while less efficient hydraulically, offers the best solution.—from *Railway Track & Structures.*

4. Slope of Culvert

Culvert location and length are described and pictured in detail under the subject of Culvert Applications.

For hydraulic and other reasons, a culvert may be installed on the same general grade as the approach and exit channels of the stream or waterway. However, on steeply sloping areas or hillsides, the culvert may be put on the critical slope or a flatter grade to reduce outlet velocities or for other reasons of discharge control.

The use of drop inlets, pipe spillways, paved aprons and cantilevered ends are means of controlling the slope and consequently the outlet velocity.

For culverts flowing with **inlet control,** increasing the barrel slope reduces the headwater depth slightly. The slope is classified as steep, critical or mild;

the flow is uniform on these slopes when the water surface is parallel to the culvert bottom.

For culverts flowing with **outlet control,** the slope of the hydraulic grade line is more important than the slope of the culvert barrel. When the culvert is not flowing full, the slope of the barrel can affect the hydraulic grade line.

5. Length of Culvert

The length of the culvert is influenced not only by the slope and direction of the barrel, but also by the width of roadway, fill height and steepness of fill slopes.

From a hydraulics standpoint, the length of the culvert barrel is a factor only on culvert flow with **outlet control.** It then becomes a factor in the formula for determining the loss of head.

For full flow in culverts on mild slopes, the discharge in long culverts is less than in short culverts. However on steep slopes, if the inlet permits full flow, the discharge in long culverts is **greater** than in short culverts, due to siphoning action.

6. Roughness of Culvert Interior

Laboratory research on models and prototype sizes has in recent years helped to clarify the values of roughness coefficients n as used in Manning's formula and others. Fig. 4-29. These apply to various pipe and pipe-arch sizes and for various materials and shapes.

Fig. 4-29. Test section of structural plate steel pipe, in Laboratory of the Corps of Engineers Waterway Experiment Station at Vicksburg, Mississippi.[15]

Values of the coefficient of roughness *n* for Manning's formula for long pipes and canals are given in Table 4-10 (modified by recent findings).[15]

A large share of culvert installations fall under the classification of flow with inlet control.* Also, designers are aware that on the flatter grade lines, the factor of debris, sediment, boulders and irregular joints can neutralize or offset the hydraulic advantages gained by clear water experiments in the laboratory.

---

*Roughness of culvert interior is not a factor. See Fig. 4-12.

7. Approach Channel

When a culvert is placed either in a natural channel or in a new channel, the alignment should be as direct as possible or follow moderate curvature. Where erosion or eddying of approach channel banks is anticipated, proper revetment, linings or deflectors should be designed to keep the flow as constant as possible.

Where upstream land use is likely to produce driftwood or debris, proper deflectors, screens, racks or risers should pass or divert such materials so they cannot clog the culvert entrance, or so they can be removed by the maintenance crew before the next storm. Drift can create buoyancy that can have a destructive effect, even if not submerged.

If headwater is permitted to pond and submerge the crown of the culvert, more extensive measures must be taken to protect the embankment and channel slopes against erosion and the culvert inlet against possible uplift forces.

A circular[16,17] prepared by the Federal Highway Administration; and based largely on California Culvert Practice[17] describes the purposes of debris control structures and illustrates many different types of such structures. Fig. 4-30.

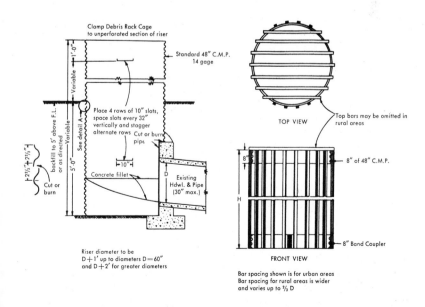

Fig. 4-30. Typical pipe riser with debris rack cage as applied to existing culverts by California Division of Highways.

8. Type of Culvert Inlet

The head required for a culvert has several components: (1) velocity head, (2) entrance loss and (3) friction loss. Streamlining the entrance by rounding or expanding can measurably improve the flow into the culvert and thereby decrease the backwater above the culvert. Inlet improvement is most beneficial for culverts operating under inlet control.[18]

Corrugated steel culverts are ordinarily supplied with "square-cut" ends, but may also be supplied with mitered ends. The end either (1) projects beyond the fill, (2) is flush with a headwall, or (3) is supplemented with a manufactured steel end section. Structural plate pipe and pipe-arches may be supplied with ends beveled or skewed to coincide with the fill slope. These various forms of entrance treatments may be supplemented by means of revetment or slope paving. The purpose is generally for improving the appearance, with hydraulic benefits or cost saving being secondary.

Particularly for large structures, the Federal Highway Administration advocates that provision be made to resist possible structural failure by hydrostatic uplift forces. This trouble can occur where rapid and unprecedented runoff, plus clogging with debris, causes ponding and possible overtopping of the embankment. Inlet protection is suggested in the form of headwalls, collars, slope paving and other means.

Fig. 4-31. Tapered inlet on corrugated steel pipe culvert under an Interstate highway.

9. Type of Culvert Outlet

The principal hydraulic problem at the outlet end of a culvert is to avoid blockage by sedimentation, or damage by undermining of culvert and embankment, or erosion of the downstream channel. High velocities are damaging and should be considered in culvert design.

Greater roughness of the culvert interior is an advantage in reducing outlet velocities, particularly when the pipe is flowing with inlet control, where roughness is not a factor in capacity.

Energy dissipators have been designed and used in some instances, especially in irrigation channels. They add to the cost of the culvert. The FHA suggests computing outlet velocities and comparing with alternate culvert designs, existing culverts in the area, or the natural stream velocities to determine need for channel protection.[19]

Tests have been conducted with impact-type energy dissipators, flared and submerged outlets, and using adverse hydraulic gradients at the culvert exit. Results have been favorable according to the Bureau of Reclamation. Erosion studies[20] have also been made for culverts with a cantilevered outlet, and the effect of riprapping the pool into which the outlet discharges. The energy was effectively dissipated by means of the armor-plated stilling basin shown in Fig. 4-32.

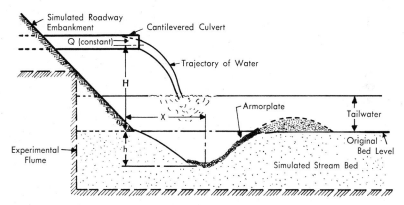

Fig. 4-32. Some variables that can affect the rate of scour caused by outflow from a cantilevered steel culvert into a rectangular channel with rigid sides and an alluvial bed. Armor-plated stilling basin effectively dissipates the energy.

Three conditions of get-away flow are shown in Fig. 4-33 submerged, controlled and free. If get-away is good, the outlet will be free and high velocity will be maintained in the transition. This may require protecting the bed and the banks against scour and eddy action.

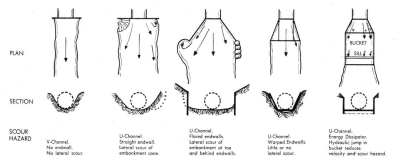

Fig. 4-33. Influence of transition shape on hazard of lateral scour at outlet of culvert—based on California practice.

Section D—HYDRAULICS OF SEWERS

INTRODUCTION

A sewer is defined as a pipe or conduit, generally closed, but normally not flowing full, for carrying storm water, sewage and other waste liquids. The contents generally flow by gravity, but in some instances are pumped.[22]

Sewers may be classified as sanitary, storm, or combined (receiving both surface runoff and sewage). Variations include such classifications as storm overflow sewer, and relief or auxiliary sewer. The use dictates the basis of design as to capacity.

DESIGN FLOW OF SANITARY SEWERS

The flow rates of sewage for which sewer capacity should be provided are based on present and probable future quantities of domestic, commercial and industrial wastes, along with ground water infiltration. Flow may fluctuate from an extreme minimum, or a daily average, to a peak. A sanitary sewer should have adequate capacity for peak flow, and it should move suspended solids so that deposits in the sewer are kept at a minimum.

The design discharge is based on water-use habits of present and anticipated future population. Increases in per capita sewage flows may be expected because of more industries, more household appliances, and increased availability of sewers as against septic tanks and other means of disposal. Sewage flows for various types of businesses or institutions are given in Table 4-13.

Cooling water for air conditioning or industrial processes should be kept out of sanitary sewers by enforced regulations.

Storm water and ground water infiltration into sanitary sewers should be kept within justifiable limits by good design. No commonly accepted rates

Fig. 4-34. Transition from open ditch to corrugated steel pipe sewer.

Table 4-13   Quantity of Sewage Flow[*22]

Type of Operation	Average Flow in Gals. per Capita per Day
Stores, offices, and small business	12 to 25 gals.
Hotels and motels	50 to 150
Schools (without or with showers)	8 to 35
Recreational and summer camps	20 to 25

*Measured or estimated domestic sewage.

Table 4-14   Sewage Flows Used for Design[*22]

Year of data varies from 1943-1949

City	Population in Thousands	Water Consumption	Sewage Flow	Sewer Design Basis	Remarks
		in Gals. per Capita per Day			
Baltimore, Md.	1,300	160	100	135 x (4 to 2)	
Berkeley, Calif.	113	76	60	92	
Boston, Mass.	801	145	140	150	Flowing half full
Dallas, Texas	...	...	150	575	Including storm water and infiltration
Grand Rapids, Mich.	...	178	189.5	200	
Las Vegas, Nev.	45	410	209	250	
Little Rock, Ark.	100	50	50	100	
Los Angeles, Calif.	2,680	165	95	...	
Memphis, Tenn.	450	125	100	100	
Orlando, Fla.	75	150	70	190	
Painesville, Ohio	...	...	125	600	Includes infiltration and roof water
Shreveport, La.	160	135	120	150	

*Measured or estimated domestic sewage.

of infiltration to be used in design have been developed. Excessive amounts of infiltration can make it necessary to increase sewer pipe sizes and increase pumping and treating costs. Faulty joints are the cause of most infiltration, and can also result in in-washing of backfill around a sewer, sometimes with serious settlement of street surfaces and clogging of the sewer itself.

DESIGN FLOW OF STORM WATER

The "rational method," introduced in 1889, recognizes the direct relationship between rainfall and runoff of storm water. A large majority of engineering offices in the United States report the use of this method with satisfactory results for urban drainage.

Improved methods in the science of hydrology deal with the application of a definite design storm pattern to the drainage area and the determination of a runoff hydrograph from total rainfall.

The rainfall frequency used in design of storm sewers in residential areas ranges from 2 to 10 years, with 5 most common. For storm sewers in commercial and high-value districts, the frequency is 10 to 15 years, depending upon economic justification. For flood protection works, 50 years or more.

Time of concentration is discussed on page 143.

Runoff coefficients are given in Tables 4-4, 4-15 and 4-16.

There are other methods of determining runoff, including actual sewer and inlet gagings, principally used in several large cities. Some methods consider such influences as infiltration capacity of pervious areas, depression storage, overland flow detention (such as on airports, where ponding is permitted temporarily), and detention in gutters, catch basins and lateral sewers.

Table 4-15   Runoff Coefficients for Storm Sewers[22]

Description of Area	Runoff Coefficients
Business:	
Downtown areas	0.70 to 0.95
Neighborhood areas	0.50 to 0.70
Residential:	
Single-family areas	0.30 to 0.50
Multi units, detached	0.40 to 0.60
Multi units, attached	0.60 to 0.75
Residential (suburban)	0.25 to 0.40
Apartment dwelling areas	0.50 to 0.70
Industrial:	
Light areas	0.50 to 0.80
Heavy areas	0.60 to 0.90
Parks, cemeteries	0.10 to 0.25
Playgrounds	0.20 to 0.35
Railroad yards	0.20 to 0.40
Unimproved areas	0.10 to 0.30

Tables 4-15 and 4-16 are applicable for storms of 5- to 10-year frequencies. Less frequent higher intensity storms require higher coefficients. Coefficients are based on assumption that the design storm does not occur when ground surface is frozen.

Table 4-16   Runoff Coefficients for Various Surfaces[22]

Character of Surface	Average Runoff Coefficients
Streets:	
Asphaltic	0.70 to 0.95
Concrete	0.80 to 0.95
Drives and walks	0.75 to 0.85
Roofs	0.75 to 0.95
Lawns; Sandy Soil:	
Flat, 2%	0.05 to 0.10
Average, 2 to 7%	0.10 to 0.15
Steep, 7%	0.15 to 0.20
Lawns; Heavy Soil:	
Flat, 2%	0.13 to 0.17
Average, 2 to 7%	0.18 to 0.22
Steep, 7%	0.25 to 0.35

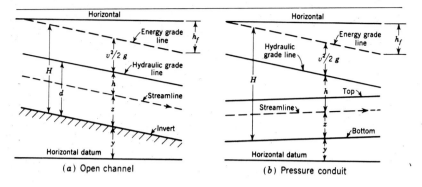

(a) Open channel   (b) Pressure conduit

Fig. 4-35. Hydraulic profiles for uniform flow.

HYDRAULIC CONSIDERATIONS FOR SEWERS

Estimated design flows in sewers are based on assumptions, the accuracy of which is variable. The hydraulic computations for size should be carefully made, but with a factor of allowance for reasonable variations and for anticipated changes in contributing areas.

A number of inter-related factors are involved in sewer hydraulics, including: variation of flow; slope of hydraulic grade line or the invert (which is not parallel to the energy grade line except for uniform flow in an open channel); pipe friction; critical depth, critical flow and critical velocity; drawdown and backwater depths.

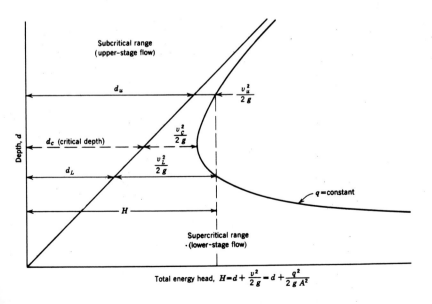

Fig. 4-36. Depth of flow versus total energy head.

Table 4-17. Hydraulic Elements of Pipes (n constant)[22]

$\dfrac{d}{D}$	$\dfrac{A}{D^2}$	$\dfrac{Qn}{D^{8/3}S^{1/2}}$	$\dfrac{Qc}{D^{5/2}}$	$\dfrac{d}{D}$	$\dfrac{A}{D^2}$	$\dfrac{Qn}{D^{8/3}S^{1/2}}$	$\dfrac{Qc}{D^{5/2}}$
0.01	0.0013	0.00007	0.0006	0.51	0.4027	0.239	1.4494
0.02	0.0037	0.00031	0.0025	0.52	0.4127	0.247	1.5041
0.03	0.0069	0.00074	0.0055	0.53	0.4227	0.255	1.5598
0.04	0.0105	0.00138	0.0098	0.54	0.4327	0.263	1.6166
0.05	0.0147	0.00222	0.0153	0.55	0.4426	0.271	1.6741
0.06	0.0192	0.00328	0.0220	0.56	0.4526	0.279	1.7328
0.07	0.0242	0.00455	0.0298	0.57	0.4625	0.287	1.7924
0.08	0.0294	0.00604	0.0389	0.58	0.4724	0.295	1.8531
0.09	0.0350	0.00775	0.0491	0.59	0.4822	0.303	1.9147
0.10	0.0409	0.00967	0.0605	0.60	0.4920	0.311	1.9773
0.11	0.0470	0.01181	0.0731	0.61	0.5018	0.319	2.0410
0.12	0.0534	0.01417	0.0868	0.62	0.5115	0.327	2.1058
0.13	0.0600	0.01674	0.1016	0.63	0.5212	0.335	2.1717
0.14	0.0668	0.01952	0.1176	0.64	0 5308	0.343	2.2886
0.15	0.0739	0.0225	0.1347	0.65	0.5404	0.350	2.3068
0.16	0.0811	0.0257	0.1530	0.66	0.5499	0.358	2.3760
0.17	0.0885	0.0291	0.1724	0.67	0.5594	0.366	2.4465
0.18	0.0961	0.0327	0.1928	0.68	0.5687	0.373	2.5182
0.19	0.1039	0.0365	0.2144	0.69	0.5780	0.380	2.5912
0.20	0.1118	0.0406	0.2371	0.70	0.5872	0.388	2.6656
0.21	0.1199	0.0448	0.2609	0.71	0.5964	0.395	2.7416
0.22	0.1281	0.0492	0.2857	0.72	0.6054	0.402	2.8188
0.23	0.1365	0.0537	0.3116	0.73	0.6143	0.409	2.8977
0.24	0.1449	0.0585	0.3386	0.74	0.6231	0.416	2.9783
0.25	0.1535	0.0634	0.3667	0.75	0.6319	0.422	3.0606
0.26	0.1623	0.0686	0.3957	0.76	0.6405	0.429	3.1450
0.27	0.1711	0.0739	0.4259	0.77	0.6489	0.435	3.2314
0.28	0.1800	0.0793	0.4571	0.78	0.6573	0.441	3.3200
0.29	0.1890	0.0849	0.4893	0.79	0.6655	0.447	3.4111
0.30	0.1982	0.0907	0.5226	0.80	0.6736	0.453	3.5051
0.31	0.2074	0.0966	0.5569	0.81	0.6815	0.458	3.6020
0.32	0.2167	0.1027	0.5921	0.82	0.6893	0.463	3.7021
0.33	0.2260	0.1089	0.6284	0.83	0.6969	0.468	3.8062
0.34	0.2355	0.1153	0.6657	0.84	0.7043	0.473	3.9144
0.35	0.2450	0.1218	0.7040	0.85	0.7115	0.477	4.0276
0.36	0.2546	0.1284	0.7433	0.86	0.7186	0 481	4.1466
0.37	0.2642	0.1351	0.7836	0.87	0.7254	0.485	4.2722
0.38	0.2739	0.1420	0.8249	0.88	0.7320	0.488	4.4057
0.39	0.2836	0.1490	0.8672	0.89	0.7384	0.491	4.5486
0.40	0.2934	0.1561	0.9104	0.90	0.7445	0.494	4.7033
0.41	0.3032	0.1633	0.9546	0.91	0.7504	0.496	4.8724
0.42	0.3130	0.1705	0.9997	0.92	0.7560	0.497	5.0602
0.43	0.3229	0.1779	1.0459	0.93	0.7612	0.498	5.2727
0.44	0.3328	0.1854	1.0929	0.94	0.7662	0.498	5.5182
0.45	0.3428	0.1929	1.1410	0.95	0.7707	0.498	5.8119
0.46	0.3527	0.201	1.1900	0.96	0.7749	0.496	6.1785
0.47	0.3627	0.208	1.2400	0.97	0.7785	0.494	6.6695
0.48	0.3727	0.216	1.2908	0.98	0.7817	0.489	7.4063
0.49	0.3827	0.224	1.3427	0.99	0.7841	0.483	8.8261
0.50	0.3927	0.232	1.3956	1.00	0.7854	0.463	—

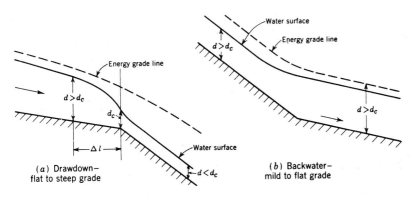

Fig. 4-37. Hydraulic profiles for non-uniform flow.

HYDRAULIC DESIGN OF SEWERS

There are many excellent textbooks available on hydraulics fundamentals and their application to sewer design.[5, 22] We cannot explain here the mechanics of the various calculations just referred to and can only direct the neophyte designer to the referenced texts for this knowledge. However, for the convenience of those calculating the more complex flow factors involving flow stability, stage and backwater, and drawdown, Figs. 4-39, 4-40, 4-41 provide critical depths of common sizes and shapes of pipe; Fig. 4-42 can be used for circular and rectangular shapes to obtain critical depths and specific energy heads. Table 4-17 provides tabular values of hydraulic factors for open-channel flow in circular pipes.

(*Text continued, page 188*)

Fig. 4-38. Installing 6500 ft of 84-in. spun-lined corrugated steel pipe as subaqueous outfall sewer into Raritan Bay along New Jersey seacoast.

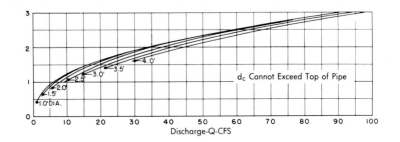

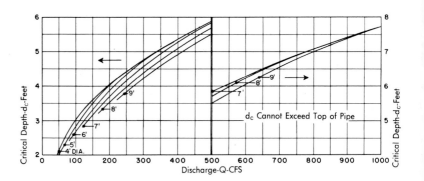

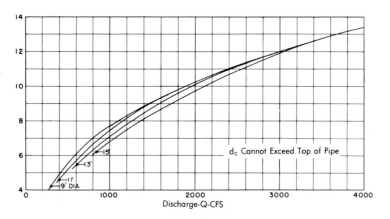

Fig. 4-39. Critical depth curves for circular *pipe*. Same for corrugated steel and other types of pipe.

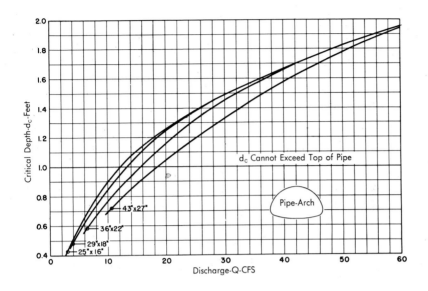

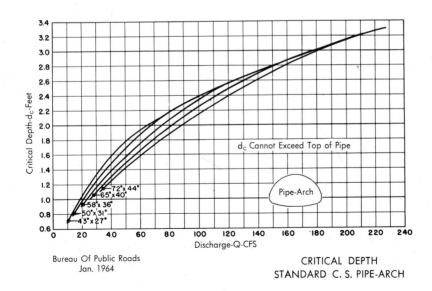

Bureau Of Public Roads
Jan. 1964

CRITICAL DEPTH
STANDARD C. S. PIPE-ARCH

Fig. 4-40. Critical depth curves for standard corrugated steel pipe-arch. See d_c in Fig. 4-16.

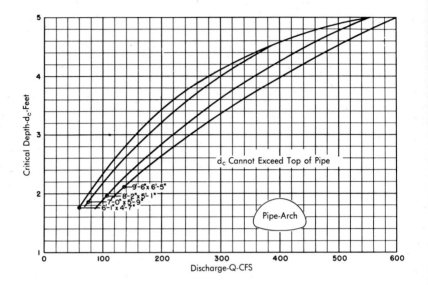

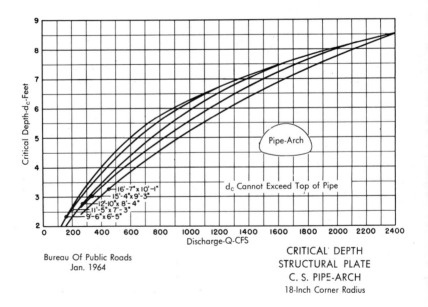

Bureau Of Public Roads
Jan. 1964

CRITICAL DEPTH
STRUCTURAL PLATE
C. S. PIPE-ARCH
18-Inch Corner Radius

Fig. 4-41. Critical depth curves for *structural plate pipe-arch* with *18-in.* corner radius.

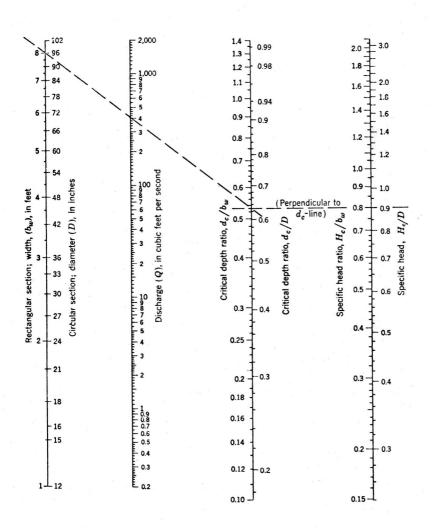

Fig. 4-42. Critical depth of flow and specific head in rectangular and circular conduits.[22]

(*Text continued from page 183*)

The design of a sewer system is based on the total available energy and the losses of that energy that will occur from all causes in the total system. Conduit wall friction losses are usually a major source of energy loss, but the design of the pipe sizes cannot be properly based on this loss alone. The influence of other energy losses must be calculated and included in the overall design. In some systems such losses can be quite significant.

These "other" energy losses are commonly referred to as minor losses. Perhaps this terminology has caused them to be overlooked by designers on some occasions. These "minor" losses are caused by entrances, transitions, manholes and other junctions, elbows, bends, grade breaks, joints and mis-alignments. The energy lost is a function not only of geometry but water velocity. Thus, the velocity in the system will affect these energy losses.

A conduit with a higher n factor will have a higher energy loss in wall friction. However, this "rougher" conduit will also have a lower velocity of flow. The lower velocity will result in less energy loss from other sources. This should be taken into account in final sizing of the conduit rather than basing final pipe sizes only on wall friction charts.

Energy Losses

A. CHANGE IN DIRECTION OR MAGNITUDE

Energy losses will result from changes in magnitude or direction of flow, owing to various appurtenances in the line:

1. Entrance Losses

$$H_e = k_e \frac{V^2}{2g} \dots\dots\dots\dots\dots\dots\dots\dots\dots\dots\dots (11)$$

Values of k_e for various entrances have been given in Culvert Design. See Table 4-9 (p. 156).

2. Transitions

    (a) Open channel flow

$$H_L = k \triangle \frac{V^2}{2g} \dots\dots\dots\dots\dots\dots\dots\dots\dots\dots (17)$$

Simple transitions in size in a manhole with straight-through flow may be analyzed with the above equation. The term $\triangle \left(\dfrac{V^2}{2g} \right)$ refers to the change in velocity head in the upstream and downstream conduits. k varies from 0.1 for increasing velocity to 0.2 for decreasing velocity if flow is sub-critical. For super-critical flow, greater values of k are probable.

    (b) Pressure flow

    (1) For an expansion $\quad H_L = k \dfrac{(V_1 - V_2)^2}{2g} \dots\dots\dots\dots\dots\dots\dots\dots (18)$

in which H_L is the energy loss, k is equal to about 1.0 for a sudden expansion and about 0.2 for a well designed transition.

(2) For a contraction $H_L = k \dfrac{V_2^2}{2g} \left[1 - \dfrac{A_2^2}{A_1} \right]^2$ ....(19)

k is equal to 0.5 for a sudden contraction and about 0.1 for a well designed transition.

3. Bends

$$H_b = k_b \frac{V^2}{2g}.$$ ....(20)

For estimating purposes a value of k_b of 0.4 is suggested for 90° circular bends in which the centerline radius of curvature exceeds the pipe diameter. For 45° bends a k_b value of 0.32 is proposed with linear proportioning in between.

4. Junctions

A junction occurs where one or more branch sewers enter a main sewer. The energy loss of junctions involves the loss in two or more transitions, one for each flow path. Values for loss coefficients are not readily available. Reference 22 contains information on their design for open channel and pressure flow.

B. FRICTION LOSS

Several formulas for conduit flow are available. Manning's, Kutter's or Hazen-Williams are all applicable under certain conditions. However, the Manning equation is the most widely used and familiar to the engineer. This text confines itself to the Manning equation for computing energy loss in the pipe from friction.

The Manning equation is $V = \dfrac{1.49}{n} (R^{2/3} S^{1/2})$ ....(4)

This is the flow equation to determine the mean velocity in a given pipe with an available energy of S ft per foot. Following the original premise of computing energy losses for all parts of the sewer system, it is logical and convenient to express the formula in terms of energy loss.

In a pipe flowing at mean velocity, discharge is

$$Q = VA, \text{ or } V = \frac{Q}{A}$$ ....(2)

Substituting $\dfrac{Q}{A}$ for V and rearranging the terms, Manning's equation for energy loss in pipe friction is

$$H_p(S) = \left(\frac{Qn}{1.49 A R^{2/3}} \right)^2 \text{ in ft/ft pipe}$$ ....(21)

The charts in Figs. 4-44 through 4-49 can be used to find the friction energy loss for standard sizes of corrugated steel pipe for wall friction coefficients of 0.012 to 0.027. The charts, Fig. 4-43 and Table 4-18 are useful in obtaining individual solutions with the Manning formula.

COEFFICIENTS FOR FRICTION FORMULAS AND FACTORS AFFECTING THEM

The ASCE Manual[22] "Design and Construction of Sanitary and Storm

Sewers (1969)" states the following with reference to "Coefficients for Friction Formulas and Factors Affecting Them":

"There have been many experiments in both the laboratory and the field to determine the friction coefficients for various materials and conditions. In the laboratory accurate measurements can be obtained, but it is difficult to duplicate conditions of flow equivalent to those in a sewer. On the other hand, field measurements in existing sewers may reflect unknown variables peculiar to the particular sewer being investigated, as well as errors in measurement and an inability to control identifiable variables.

"Factors which affect the choice of a coefficient are conduit material, Reynolds number, size and shape of conduit, and depth of flow. In addition to these interrelated factors the following should be considered:

(a) Rough, opened, or offset joints,
(b) Poor alignment and grade due to settlement or lateral soil movement,
(c) Deposits in sewers,
(d) Amount and size of solids being transported,
(e) Coatings of grease or other matter on interior of sewer,
(f) Tree roots, joint compounds, and mortar dams resulting from poor or deteriorated jointing and other protrusions, and
(g) Flow from laterals disrupting flow in the sewer.

"Where deposition will not be a problem, the designer may be justified in using values of coefficients which will result in somewhat lower predicted friction losses for storm sewers over those used for sanitary or combined sewers. For conduits of minimal slope and velocity, deposition may be aggravated so that a higher than normal friction loss allowance may be justified."

Table 4-19 is a summary of commonly used values of Manning's n for many materials as given in the ASCE Manual.[22]

Table 4-10A, friction factors for corrugated steel pipe is a repeat of the data given in culvert design (Table 4-10) provided here for convenience.

For example of sewer size computations, see page 200.

Table 4-10A. Values of Coefficient of Roughness (n) for Standard Corrugated Steel Pipe (Manning's Formula)

Corrugations	Annular 2⅔" x ½"	Helical						
		1½" x ¼"[11, 12]	2⅔" x ½"					
	All Diam.	8"	10"	12"	18"	24"	36"	48"
Unpaved	.024	.012	.014	.011	.014	.016	.019	.020
25% Paved	.021					.015	.017	.020
Fully Paved	.012					.012	.012	.012

Corrugations	Annular 3" x 1"	Helical—3" x 1"					
	All Diam.	36"	48"	54"	60"	66"	72"
Unpaved	.027	.021	.023	.023	.024	.025	.026
25% Paved	.023	.019	.020	.020	.021	.022	.022
Fully Paved	.012	.012	.012	.012	.012	.012	.012

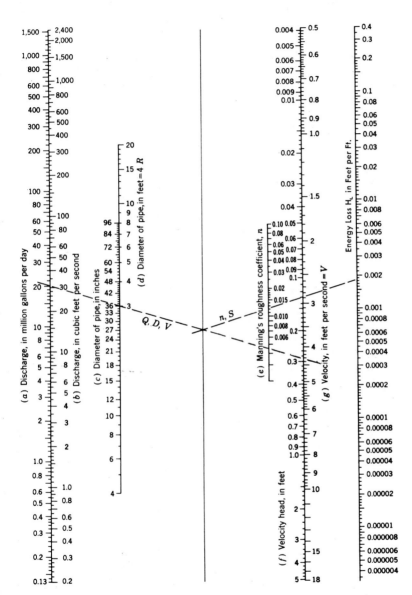

Fig. 4-43. Alignment chart for energy loss in pipes, for Manning's formula.

Note: Use chart for flow computations, $H_L = S$

Table 4-18. Energy-Loss Solution by Manning's Formula for Pipe Flowing Full

Diam. in Inches	Area in Square Feet A	Hydraulic Radius R	$R^{2/3}$	$AR^{2/3}$	$\left(\dfrac{n}{1.486AR^{2/3}}\right)^2 \times 10^{-7}$				
					n=0.012	n=0.015	n=0.019	n=0.021	n=0.024
6	.196	.125	.250	.049	271,600.	424,420.	681,000.	831,940.	1,086,350.
8	.349	.167	.303	.106	58,000.	90,703.	145,509.	177,730.	232,164.
10	.545	.208	.351	.191	17,879.	27,936.	44,802.	54,707.	71,455.
12	.785	.250	.397	.312	6,698.	10,466.	17,797.	20,605.	26,791.
15	1.227	.3125	.461	.566	2,035.6	3,180.8	5,102.5	6,234.4	8,144.6
18	1.767	.375	.520	.919	772.2	1,206.5	1,935.5	2,364.7	3,088.7
21	2.405	.437	.576	1.385	340.00	531.24	852.60	1,041.0	1,359.98
24	3.142	.50	.630	1.979	166.5	260.04	417.31	510.20	666.39
30	4.909	.625	.731	3.588	50.7	79.126	127.01	155.12	202.54
36	7.069	.75	.825	5.832	19.20	29.953	48.071	58.713	76.691
42	9.621	.875	.915	8.803	8.40	13.148	21.096	25.773	33.667
48	12.566	1.00	1.00	12.566	4.130	6.452	10.353	12.647	16.521
54	15.904	1.125	1.082	17.208	2.202	3.440	5.520	6.741	8.817
60	19.635	1.25	1.16	22.777	1.257	1.965	3.337	3.848	5.030
66	23.758	1.375	1.236	29.365	0.756	1.182	1.895	2.316	3.026
72	28.274	1.50	1.310	37.039	0.475	0.743	1.192	1.456	1.902
78	33.183	1.625	1.382	45.859	0.310	0.485	0.777	0.950	1.241
84	38.485	1.75	1.452	55.880	0.209	0.326	0.524	0.640	0.835
90	44.179	1.875	1.521	67.196	0.144	0.226	0.362	0.442	0.578
96	50.266	2.00	1.587	79.772	0.102	0.160	0.257	0.314	0.410
108	63.617	2.25	1.717	109.230	0.055	0.085	0.137	0.167	0.219
114	70.882	2.375	1.780	126.170	0.041	0.064	0.103	0.125	0.164
120	78.54	2.5	1.842	144.671	0.031	0.049	0.078	0.098	0.125

Manning Flow Equation: $Q = \left(A \times \dfrac{1.486}{n} \times R^{2/3}\right) \times S^{1/2}$

Energy Loss $= S = Q^2 \left(\dfrac{n}{1.486\ AR^{2/3}}\right)^2$

To find energy loss in pipe friction for a given Q . . .

Table 4-19. Effective Absolute Roughness and Friction Formula Coefficients[22]

Conduit Material	Manning n (ft⅙)
Closed conduits	
Asbestos-cement pipe	0.011–0.015
Brick	0.013–0.017
Cast iron pipe	
Uncoated (new)	—
Asphalt dipped (new)	—
Cement-lined & seal coated	0.011–0.015
Concrete (monolithic)	
Smooth forms	0.012–0.014
Rough forms	0.015–0.017
Concrete pipe	0.011–0.015
Plastic pipe (smooth)	0.011–0.015
Vitrified clay	
Pipes	0.011–0.015
Liner plates	0.013–0.017
Open channels	
Lined channels	
a. Asphalt	0.013–0.017
b. Brick	0.012–0.018
c. Concrete	0.011–0.020
d. Rubble or riprap	0.020–0.035
e. Vegetal	0.030–0.40
Excavated or dredged	
Earth, straight and uniform	0.020–0.030
Earth, winding, fairly uniform	0.025–0.040
Rock	0.030–0.045
Unmaintained	0.050–0.14
Natural channels (minor streams, top width at flood stage < 100 ft)	—
Fairly regular section	0.03 –0.07
Irregular section with pools	0.04 –0.10

Fig. 4-43A. Aerial sewer of corrugated steel pipe with smooth lining is hydraulically efficient.

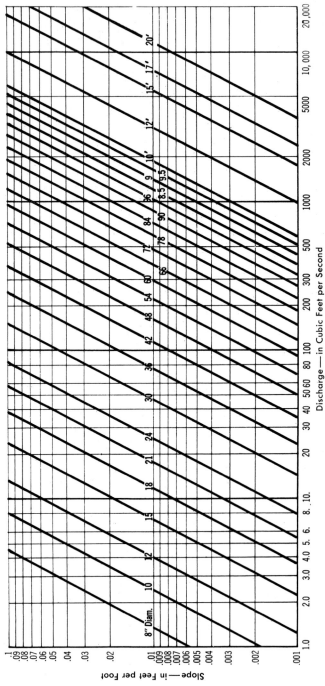

*Note: A pipe-arch flowing full has 84% of the capacity of a round pipe flowing full when periphery, n and slope are equal.

**Energy loss for pipe friction only. Compute losses from all sources in selecting final pipe sizes.

Hp — in Feet per Foot

Fig. 4-44. Energy Head Loss Based on Manning's Formula.

Pipe* Flowing Full $n = .012$**

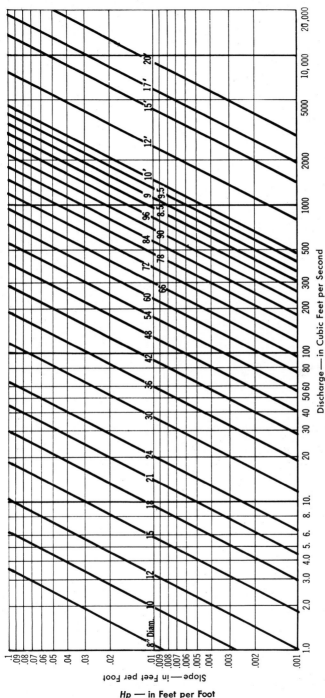

*Note: A pipe-arch flowing full has 84% of the capacity of a round pipe flowing full when periphery, n and slope are equal.
**Energy loss for pipe friction only. Compute losses from all sources in selecting final pipe sizes.

Discharge — in Cubic Feet per Second

Slope — in Feet per Foot

Hp — in Feet per Foot

Fig. 4-45. Energy Head Loss Based on Manning's Formula.

Pipe* Flowing Full $n = .015$**

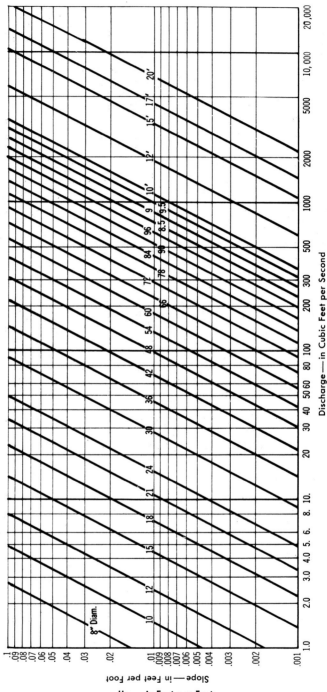

*Note: A pipe-arch flowing full has 84% of the capacity of a round pipe flowing full when periphery, *n* and slope are equal.
**Energy loss for pipe friction only. Compute losses from all sources in selecting final pipe sizes.

Discharge — in Cubic Feet per Second

Slope — in Feet per Foot

Hp — in Feet per Foot

Fig. 4-46. Energy Head Loss Based on Manning's Formula.

Pipe* Flowing Full   *n* = .019**

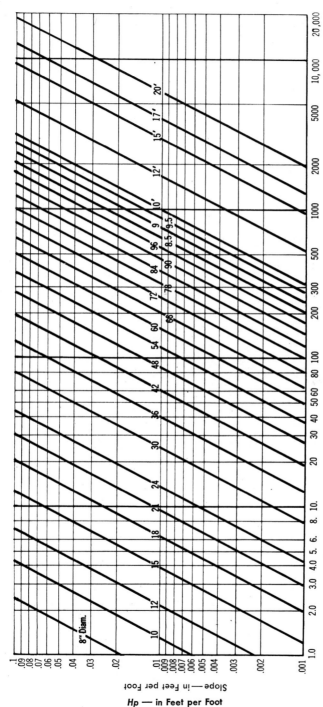

*Note: A pipe-arch flowing full has 84% of the capacity of a round pipe flowing full when periphery, n and slope are equal.
**Energy loss for pipe friction only. Compute losses from all sources in selecting final pipe sizes.

Discharge — in Cubic Feet per Second

Slope — in Feet per Foot

Hp — in Feet per Foot

Fig. 4-47. Energy Head Loss Based on Manning's Formula.
Pipe* Flowing Full $n = .021$**

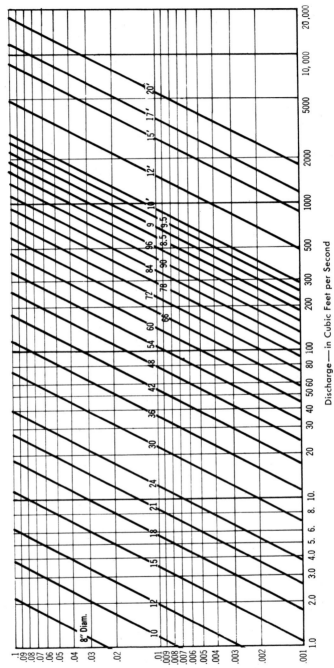

Fig. 4-48. Energy Head Loss Based on Manning's Formula.
Pipe* Flowing Full $n = .024$**

*Note: A pipe-arch flowing full has 84% of the capacity of a round pipe flowing full when periphery, n and slope are equal.
**Energy loss for pipe friction only. Compute losses from all sources in selecting final pipe sizes.

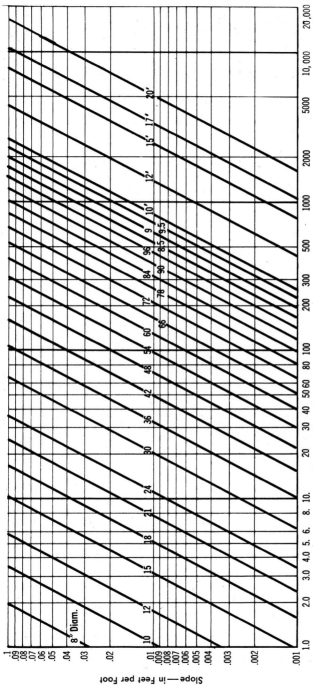

*Note: A pipe-arch flowing full has 84% of the capacity of a round pipe flowing full when periphery, n and slope are equal.
**Energy loss for pipe friction only. Compute losses from all sources in selecting final pipe sizes.

Discharge—in Cubic Feet per Second

Slope—in Feet per Foot

Hp — in Feet per Foot

Fig. 4-49. Energy Head Loss Based on Manning's Formula.

Pipe* Flowing Full   *n* = .027**

Example

Given: Storm drain with three elbows and square-edge entrance box.
Length = 750 feet
Discharge = 30 cfs
Maximum available head = 3.75 ft at 0.005 ft/ft
Loss coefficients $k = 0.25$ for elbow
$k = 0.5$ for entrance box

Required: Various alternate required sizes of smooth, annular and helical corrugated pipe.

Solution: 1. *Smooth Pipe:* reinforced concrete or fully-lined corrugated steel pipe, $n = 0.012$
From Fig. 4-44, Select tentative size of 30 in.
For 30-in., pipe friction energy loss = $750 \times .0043 = 3.2$ ft loss

$$V = \frac{Q}{A} = \frac{30}{4.9} = 6.1 \text{ fps}$$

$$\text{Total of other losses} = \sum k \left(\frac{V^2}{2g}\right)(3 \times 0.25 + 0.5)\left(\frac{6.1^2}{64.4}\right) = 0.72 \text{ ft loss}$$

Total loss = $3.2 + 0.7 = 3.9$ ft
This exceeds the available head (3.75); try 36-in.
From Fig. 4-44, 36-in. pipe has loss = $750 \times .0018 = 1.33$ ft
Other losses will be less than for 30-in (0.72 ft)
Available head is 3.75 ft, so 36-in. pipe is obviously OK.

Result: *Use 36-in. smooth pipe.*

Solution: 2. *Annular Corrugated Pipe,* $n = 0.024$
From Fig. 4-48, select tentative size of 42-in.
For 42-in., pipe friction loss = $750 \times 0.0032 = 2.4$ ft loss

$$\text{For 42-in., } V = \frac{Q}{A} = \frac{30}{9.6} = 3.1 \text{ fps}$$

$$\text{Total of other losses } H_L = \sum k \left(\frac{V^2}{2g}\right) = 1.25 \times \left(\frac{3.1^2}{64.4}\right) = 0.19 \text{ ft loss}$$

Total loss = $2.4 + 0.19 = 2.6$ ft

Result: Loss is less than available head. 42 in. is OK.

Solution: 3. *Helical Corrugated Pipe,* n varies with diam.
Since 42-in. pipe with $n = 0.024$ is OK, try 36-in. in helical
For 36-in. helical, from Table 4-10, $n = 0.019$
From Fig. 4-46, pipe friction loss = $750 \times 0.0045 = 3.4$ ft loss

$$\text{For 36-in., } V = \frac{Q}{A} = \frac{30}{7.07} = 4.24$$

$$\text{Other losses} = \sum k \left(\frac{V^2}{2g}\right) = 1.25 \times \left(\frac{4.24^2}{64.4}\right) = 0.35 \text{ ft loss}$$

Total loss = $3.4 + 0.35 = 3.75$ (same as available head)

Result: *Use 36-in. helical pipe.*

Section E—HYDRAULICS OF SUBDRAINS

FREE WATER

Ground water may consist of an underground reservoir (perched) or it may be flowing through a thick seam of pervious material like an underground river, i. e., a well field. Likewise, it may be seeping or percolating through a thin seam between impervious strata, or be concentrated in the form of a spring.

Free water enters or leaves a subgrade by gravity. It may consist of storm water seeping through cracks in the pavement or along the edges. Or it may be ground water percolating from a higher water-bearing stratum, as in a cut or sidehill excavation. See Subdrainage Applications pages, 15-21.

Especially noticeable in springtime, this seepage is also visible shortly after rains when the remainder of the road has dried off. Passing traffic also serves to "pump" some of this water plus subgrade soil up through the cracks or joints onto the road surface. Fig. B-1. p. 15.

This water is harmful not only because it lowers the bearing power and stability of the subgrade, but because it may freeze on the surface and become an unexpected traffic hazard. It can and should be removed to establish a stable subgrade and prevent possible trouble.

SUBSURFACE RUNOFF COMPUTATION

The amount of subsurface runoff in general equals that which soaks into the ground from surface applications, less that lost by evaporation or used by plants. The nature of the terrain, its size, shape and slopes, as well as the character and slopes of the substrata are contributing factors.

A practical way to determine flow is to dig a trench or test pit. This is especially helpful where an *intercepting* drain (Fig. 4-50) is to be placed across a seepage zone to divert the flow.

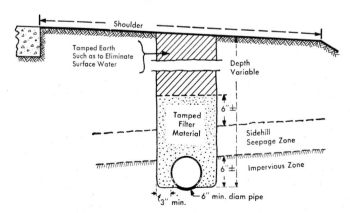

Fig. 4-50. An intercepting drain placed in the impervious zone is effective for keeping free water out of the roadway and subgrade.

**Table 4-20   Constants for Subsurface Runoff for
Various Soil Permeability Types**

Depths of Water Removed in 24 Hours

Soil Permeability Type	Depth in Inches		Quantity of Water Per Lateral (cubic feet per second per acre)
	Fraction	Decimal	Constant C
Slow to Moderate	1/16	0.0625	0.0026
Slow to Moderate	1/8	0.1250	0.0052
Slow to Moderate	3/16	0.1875	0.0079
Slow to Moderate	1/4	0.2500	0.0105
Moderate	5/16	0.3125	0.0131
Moderate	3/8	0.3750	0.0157
Moderate	7/16	0.4375	0.0184
Moderate	1/2	0.5000	0.0210
Moderate	9/16	0.5625	0.0236
Moderate to Fast	5/8	0.6250	0.0262
Moderate to Fast	11/16	0.6875	0.0289
Moderate to Fast	3/4	0.7500	0.0315
Moderate to Fast	13/16	0.8125	0.0341
Moderate to Fast	7/8	0.8750	0.0367
Moderate to Fast	15/16	0.9375	0.0394
Moderate to Fast	1	1.0000	0.0420

Determining correct size for subdrainage pipe requires an indirect approach. For problems other than those involving large flat areas, size determination becomes almost a matter of personal judgment or local experience. The following procedure applies mostly to flat areas.

Example: Rate of runoff for average agricultural soils has been determined by agricultural engineering experiment stations as about 3/8 in. in 24 hours. For areas of heavy rainfall or more pervious soils, this factor may be increased to 3/4 or 1 in. Such runoff is converted to cubic feet per second per acre. See conversion table (Table 4-20).[24] The following simple formula is given:

$$Q = CA \dotfill (1)$$

in which Q = discharge or required capacity, in cu ft per sec.

A = area to be subdrained, in acres

C = subsurface runoff factor, converted to cu ft per sec. per acre

Assuming a drainage coefficient of 3/8 in. in 24 hrs. (C = .0157) and laterals 600 ft long, spaced on 50-ft centers, the following result is obtained:

$$Q = .0157 \times \frac{600 \times 50}{43,560} = .0108 \text{ cu ft per sec.}$$

SIZE OF PIPE

The size of pipe can be determined by the use of the Manning Formula, or by the use of a nomograph.[24] For normal subdrainage, approximately 500 ft of 6-in. perforated steel pipe may be used before increasing to the next size.

Where possible, a minimum slope of 0.15 ft per 100 ft should be used for subdrainage lines. It is sometimes permissible to use an even flatter slope where necessary to obtain a free outlet. A steeper slope helps to provide a self-cleansing velocity.

THE TRENCH

The principal parts of a subdrain are: trench, perforated pipe, backfill or filter, top seal, and outlet.

Proper location of the trench presumes a knowledge of the depth of the

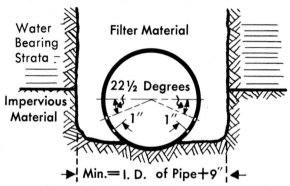

Fig. 4-51. The bottom of a subdrain pipe should be deep enough to effect complete removal of the free water.

impervious stratum and the water table, the kind of soil, the source (direction) and the volume of flow, and the depth of frost penetration.

There is no standard depth of trench. It may vary from 2 to 10 ft. It should be about 2 ft below average frost penetration under a bare pavement. The important thing for complete interception is to go deep enough so the pipe can lie in the impervious zone (Fig. 4-51). Width should be 8 to 10 in. more than the pipe diameter.

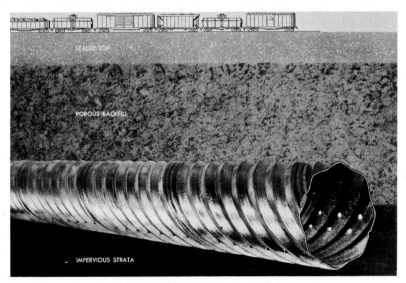

Fig. 4-52. In helically corrugated perforated steel pipe, a blank space in the bottom helps to keep ordinary seepage flow within the pipe.

PERFORATED PIPE

Perforated corrugated steel pipe is used widely to control ground water (Fig. 4-52). Advantages cited are long lengths, light weight, flexibility, strength, simple joints, ample infiltration but with exclusion of many solids.
Diameters range from 6 to 24 in. See Table 1-14, page 49.

BACKFILL MATERIAL: FILTERS

Early subdrains consisted of a trench filled with brush or coarse rock ("french" drains) which quickly silted up. Extensive research by the U. S. Waterways Experiment Station at Vicksburg, Mississippi, shows that a graded material roughly equal to concrete sand (AASHO Specs) has been found most suitable. See Table 4-21 and Fig. 4-53 for a typical analysis. Such material gives better support to the sidewall of the trench and thereby reduces erosion and silting. Filter material should be placed in layers and be tamped.

Tests by the Corps of Engineers showed least clogging occurs with porous or perforated walls rather than through open joints of rigid pipe.[25] Other experiments showed that with the use of finely graded backfill, least clogging occurs when the perforations are in the bottom half of the pipe, at least 22½ degrees below the horizontal axis. A minimum of 16 perforations ¼ in.* in diameter, per linear foot of pipe is desirable for all pipe sizes.

Where portions of the line are used as a water conductor rather than interceptor, perforations may be turned up or omitted. Pervious backfill should be eliminated beyond the point where seepage occurs.

---

*AREA Specification 1-4-11 requires ⅜-in. perforations for railway use.

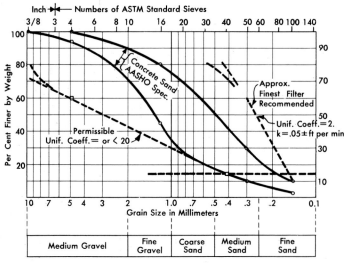

Fig. 4-53. Chart showing range and gradation of granular material for most suitable subdrain backfill. AASHO concrete sand falls within the recommended limits. Maximum size is ¾-in. gravel.

Table 4-21   Size of Filter Material for Subdrains

Standard ASTM Sieve	Percent
Passing a ⅜-in. sieve	100
Passing a No. 4 sieve	95–100
Passing a No. 16 sieve	45–80
Passing a No. 50 sieve	10–30
Passing a No. 100 sieve	2–10

AASHO Spec. M6-51, Gradation limits of concrete sand.

When subdrain pipes with open joints or with perforations turned up are used, it is generally necessary to use two different backfill materials. A coarser filter material (No. 2 in Fig. 4-54) is placed around the pipe to prevent the entrance of fine material into the pipe. Second, the fine filter material must be used to prevent washing of soil fines from the trench walls.

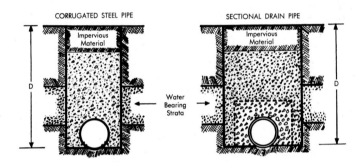

Depth "D" should be varied to suit installation conditions.

Filter Gradation	Percent Passing Std. ASTM Sieve							
	1½	1	⅜	No. 4	No. 8	No. 16	No. 50	No. 100
No. 1	—	—	100	95-100	—	45-80	10-30	0-10
No. 2	100	90-100	25-60	5-40	0-20	—	—	—

Fig. 4-54. Perforated corrugated steel pipe with positively connected joints requires only a single grade of filter material (left). Short sectional pipe with open joints requires two grades of backfill (right) to keep the trench wall fines from clogging the pipe.

TOP SEAL

Use of a sealed trench keeps out surface water which may carry silt and clog the backfill. The material used may be clay or a mixture using asphalt or other binder.

On ordinary construction it is advisable to remove the surface water by means of gutters and catchbasins or drop inlets rather than through the trench backfill. However, if the subdrain is adequate in size and can be cleaned out when necessary, surface water can safely be admitted through the backfill or inlets.

OUTLETS

Pipe outlets should be high enough so they cannot clog with silt or snow. Cantilevering the end of the pipe and deflecting it to enter the stream at an angle will generally protect against undermining. A suitable screen or a flap gate will keep rodents from building their nests in the pipe.

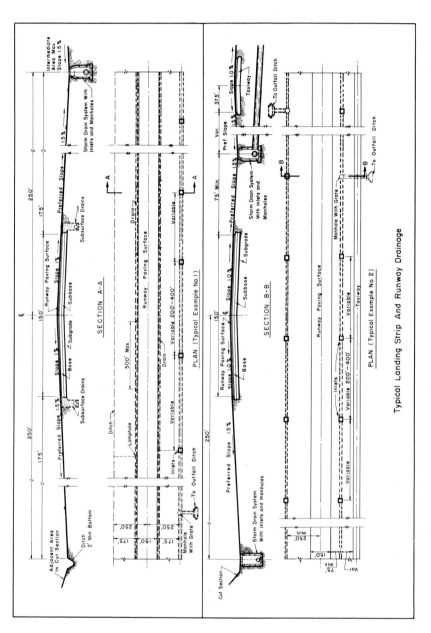

Fig. 4-55. Typical runway drainage layout as designed by Federal Aviation Agency.

REFERENCES AND BIBLIOGRAPHY

1. Searcy, J. K., *Design of Roadside Drainage Channels*, U. S. Bureau of Public Roads, Hydraulic Design Series No. 4, U. S. Gvmt. Printing Office, Washington, D. C., 1965, 56 pp. (Contains a list of 55 helpful references.)

2. ASCE, *Hydrology Handbook*, American Society of Civil Engineers. Manual No. 28, 1949, 184 pp.

3. U. S. Weather Bureau, *Rainfall-Frequency Atlas of the United States*, Tech. Paper 40, U. S. Gvmt. Printing Office, Washington, D. C., 1961.

4. U. S. Weather Bureau, *Rainfall Intensity—Duration—Frequency Curves for Selected Stations in the U. S.*, Tech. Paper 25, U. S. Gvmt. Printing Office, Washington, D. C., 1955, 53 pp.

5. King, H. W., *Handbook of Hydraulics*, McGraw-Hill Book Co., Inc., New York, 4th ed., 1954.

6. Department of Defense, U. S. Corps of Engineers, *Hydraulic Tables*, U. S. Gvmt. Printing Office, Washington, D. C., 1944, 565 pp.

7. U. S. Bureau of Reclamation, *Hydraulic and Excavation Tables*, U. S. Gvmt. Printing Office, Washington, D. C., 10th ed., 1950, 173 pp.

8. Jones, C. W., *Design of Culverts*, Supv. Bridge Engineer, Calif. Div. of Highways and Chairman of ASCE Task Force, 1961.

9. Herr, L. A. and Bossy, H. G., *Hydraulic Charts for the Selection of Highway Culverts*, U. S. Bureau of Public Roads, Hydraulic Eng. Circular No. 5, U. S. Gvmt. Printing Office, Washington, D. C., 1964, 54 pp.

10. Herr, L. A. and Bossy, H. G., *Capacity Charts for the Hydraulic Design of Culverts*, Hydraulic Eng. Circular No. 10, U. S. Gvmt. Printing Office, Washington, D. C. 1965, 90 pp.

11. Rice, C. E., *Friction Factors for Helical Corrugated Pipe*, ARS 41-119, Agricultural Research Service, U. S. Dept. of Agri., Feb., 1966.

12. Chamberlain, A. R., Discussion of Proc. Paper 2148 in Jnl. of Hydraulics Div., ASCE, Vol. 85, 1959.

13. Silberman, Edward, *Effects of Helix Angle on Flow in Corrugated Pipes*, Jnl. of Hydraulics Div., ASCE, Vol. 96, 11 pp., Nov. 1970.

14. Bauer, W. J., *Determination of Manning's n for 14-ft Corrugated Steel Pipe*. Report of Consulting engineers of Bauer Engineering, Inc., Chicago, 27 pp., April 1969.

15. Grace, J. L., Jr., Department of Defense, U. S. Corps of Engineers, *Friction Factors for Hydraulic Design of Corrugated Metal Pipe*, U. S. Waterways Exp. Sta., Vicksburg, Miss., Highway Research Board, Proc. Vol. 44, 1965.

16. *Debris Control Structures*, Hydraulic Eng. Circular No. 9, Washington, D. C., Feb., 1964, 37 pp.

17. Calif. Div. of Highways, *California Culvert Practice*, Sacramento, Bulletin, 1944, 119 pp.

18. French, John L., *Tapered Inlets for Pipe Culverts*, ASCE, Proc. Paper 3845, Vol. 90, No. HY2, March, 1964, pp. 255-299.

19. Highway Research Board, *New Developments for Erosion Control at Culvert Outlets*, Bull. 286, 1960.

20. U. S. Bureau of Reclamation, *Progress Report on Results of Studies on Design of Stable Channels*, Report No. Hyd-352, U. S. Gvmt. Printing Office, Denver, Colo., 1952, 60 pp.

21. U. S. Bureau of Public Roads, *Design Charts for Open Channel Flow*, Hydr. Design Series No. 3, 1961.

22. American Society of Civil Engineers; Water Pollution Control Federation, New York, N. Y., *Design and Construction of Sanitary and Storm Sewers*, Manuals of Engineering Practice, Nos. 37 and 9, respectively, 1969, 332 pp.

23. *Corrugated Steel Pipe Storm Sewers*, National Corrugated Steel Pipe Assn. Manual, 1968, 32 pp.

24. *Solving Drainage Problems*, Bethlehem Steel Corporation, Bethlehem, Pa., Booklet 425-B, 1959, 80 pp.

25. *Investigation of Filter Requirements for Underdrains*, Technical Memorandum No. 183-1, U. S. Army Engineer Waterways Experiment Station, Vicksburg, Mississippi 39181, Nov. 1941, 48 pp. (out of print, loan copies available).

Fig. 5-1. Inspecting an 84-in. bituminous-coated steel sewer pipe 33 years after it was installed across a peat bog. Same structure is shown below.

Fig. 5-2. The pipe was in good structural and material condition.

CHAPTER 5

Design Against Corrosion and Abrasion

BACKGROUND

Metallic corrosion is defined as an electro-chemical process. Corrosion occurs on the surface of metals when a corrosion cell is formed: that is, a spot or place on the metal surface where a difference in electrical potential generates a flow of current from the metal surface, causing metallic ions to go into solution and combine with hydroxyl ions to form corrosion products. Four things are needed for metal to corrode:

1. A metal surface called the *anode* where corrosion occurs
2. A solution called the electrolyte, (to complete the electrical circuit) which may be water or wet soil. In the ordinary case oxygen must also be present in the electrolyte for corrosion to occur.
3. Another metal surface called the *cathode.*
4. A metallic electrical path from the anode to the cathode to permit the flow of electrons.

There are a number of conditions in both soil and water environments that can cause corrosion cells to form.

On the soil side, corrosion cells can be formed by a mixture of different soils that may be used in the backfill. Corrosion cells may also be caused by the differences in air and moisture content of the soils in the backfill, or corrosion cells may be formed due to cinders or salts that may be contained in the backfill. These are three examples of several conditions that could form corrosion cells in the soil environment. There are a number of others.

Soils can be divided into four groups for visual classification as to potential corrosiveness as shown in Table 5-1.

Table 5-1   Corrosiveness of Soils[1]

Soil Group Number	Types of Soil	Aeration	Drainage	Color	Water Table
I Lightly Corrosive	1. Sands or sandy loams 2. Light textured silt loams 3. Porous loams or clay loams thoroughly oxidized to great depths	Good	Good	Uniform color	Very low
II Moderately Corrosive	1. Sandy loams 2. Silt loams 3. Clay loams	Fair	Fair	Slight mottling	Low
III Badly Corrosive	1. Clay loams 2. Clays	Poor	Poor	Heavy texture—Moderate mottling	2'-3' below surface
IV Unusually Corrosive	1. Muck 2. Peat 3. Tidal marsh 4. Clays & organic soils 5. Adobe clays	Very poor	Very poor	Bluish-grey mottling	At surface; or extreme impermeability

ELECTRICAL RESISTANCE

In identifying the potential corrosiveness of soils, corrosion engineers have determined that the electrical resistance of the soil, measured in ohms per cubic centimeter, is the best measure of the aggressiveness of a given soil.

Electrical resistance is directly related to moisture content and the quantity of dissolved salts and other deteriorative compounds in the soil. The general relation of soil corrosion to resistivity is shown in Table 5-2, where the soils are divided into four classes.

Table 5-2   Relationship of Soil Corrosion To Electrical Resistivity[1]

Soil Class	Corrosion Resistance	Electrical Resistance ohm/cm
1	Excellent	10,000–6000
2	Good	6000–4500
3	Fair	4500–2000
4	Bad	2000–0

There are three principal corrosion cells that can attack a pipe on the inside. These are (1) the oxygen concentration cell, (2) the salt concentration cell, and (3) the hydrogen cell. These cells are formed by differential concentration of dissolved oxygen and salt in the electrolytes.

1. *The oxygen concentration cell* is always present to some extent in water flowing through a pipe.

2. *Salt concentration cells* are a factor in runoff waters containing significant quantities of dissolved salt compounds, which in most parts of the United States are relatively low. Electrical resistivity of water is the best indicator of salt concentration. For example, sea water has a resistivity of about 90 ohm centimeters whereas ordinary tap water will usually be in the range of 10,000 ohm centimeters or higher. The same relationship of corrosion and resistivity as used for the soil side of the structure would be satisfactory in evaluating the severity of salt concentration cell corrosion inside a pipe.

3. *Hydrogen cells* develop in acid solutions in proportion to the hydrogen ion concentration, or pH. Hydrogen cells will also be more aggressive in water of low resistivity.

These are the corrosion principles that govern the material performance of underground steel conduits. Understanding them and investigating their application and relative significance to corrugated steel conduits has been a significant forward step of the last ten to fifteen years.

PIPE INVESTIGATIONS

Many studies were made of corrugated culverts in the 1920's and 1930's by various state and federal agencies and pipe producers. These early investigations established general guidelines but did not provide a solid scientific basis for material service design. The studies most significant to our modern criteria are those made after 1950.

From this period came the important developments, and this text is limited to this period.

1. California (1954–1962)[2]

The most extensive and comprehensive study made included over 7000 pipes in every type of environment in California. The possible factors influencing corrosion were correlated with the observed corrosion rates. It was found that all the significant factors interrelated with the resistivity and pH of the soil and water. A method was developed to provide an estimate of the corrosion rate at a given site by using pH and resistivity values of soils and waters.

2. New York (1967)[4]
   Approximately 800 pipes were inspected, with the possible corrosion factors and corrosion rates measured at each site. Site conditions throughout New York were found to be quite similar and fell within a narrow range of pH and resistivity. As a result, New York found little significance to individual site conditions other than water hardness. Plain galvanized steel pipe had an observed average metal loss rate of .00137 inch per year.

3. Idaho (1965)
   Idaho inspected over 100 pipes throughout the state, checking the observed corrosion against the California test. Idaho found the California test method to be "satisfactory and the estimated life therefrom conservative in all but a few installations."

4. Washington (1965)
   Investigating culverts throughout the state, Washington established a geographical criteria. Plain galvanized pipe was generally satisfactory east of the Cascade Mountains while coated or coated-and-paved pipe was required west of the mountains.

Fig. 5-3. Under the famous Pennsylvania Turnpike built over 30 years ago, an inspector found this asphalt coated-and-paved culvert in very good condition.

```
┌─────────────────────────────────────────────────────────────────────────────────┐
│          CORRUGATED STEEL PIPE INSPECTION REPORT          │ Fig.          │
│                                                                                   │
│                    Plain Galv.   _____   Size _____ Length _____    │
│  Riveted      _____  Asph. Coated _____                                   │
│  Helical      _____  Paved Invert _____   Wall Thickness _____   │
│  Struct. Plate _____ 100% Lined  _____                                    │
│                          Other       _____   Corrugation Depth – (1/2") (1") (2") │
│                                                                                   │
│                                                  Spelter Weight _____ oz.     │
│                                                                                   │
│                                                  Date Installed _____         │
│───────────────────────────────────────────────────────────────────────────────  │
│  State _____ County _____ Road _____                   │
│                                                                                   │
│  Location by Station                                                              │
│  or Speedometer Reference _____│
│                                                                                   │
│  Date of Inspection _____  Age of Structure _____ Yrs.     │
│                                                                                   │
│  (Culvert) _____ (Storm Drain) _____ (Sanitary Sewer) _____ (Other _____ )    │
│                                                                                   │
│  Flow – (Constant)     (Prolonged)     (Occasional)     (Stagnant)   (Other ____ )│
│          (Scouring)    (Filling)                                                  │
│                                                                                   │
│  Nature of Watershed _____ Bed Load – (Abrasive) (Non-abrasive)│
│                                                                                   │
│  Slope _____  Severe Erosion Evident – (Yes)  (No)      │
│───────────────────────────────────────────────────────────────────────────────  │
│                          VISUAL EVALUATION                                        │
│                                                                                   │
│              Rating              Comments            Visual Rating Scale          │
│                                                                                   │
│  Top     _____  90-Galvanizing intact                    │
│                                                                                   │
│  Sides   _____  75-Galvanizing partly gone, some rust    │
│                                                                                   │
│  Invert  _____  50-Galvanizing gone, significant metal loss│
│                                                                                   │
│  Pipe Exterior _____ 25-Deep pitting, heavy metal loss, metal perforated│
│                                                                                   │
│  Condition of:  Coating _____ 0-Metal perforated                       │
│                                                                                   │
│                 Paving _____                                         │
│───────────────────────────────────────────────────────────────────────────────  │
│  Field Samples Taken                       Field Measurements                     │
│                                                                                   │
│  Water _____  Soil _____  Water pH _____  Soil Resistivity _____ │
│                                                                                   │
│  Pipe Invert _____  Pipe Side _____  Soil _____  Original Pipe Thickness __ │
│───────────────────────────────────────────────────────────────────────────────  │
│                          LABORATORY DATA                                          │
│                                                                                   │
│  Pipe Sample                               Minimum Soil Resistivity _____ ohm/cm │
│                                                                                   │
│             Thickness   % Loss             Water Resistivity _____ ohm/cm    │
│                                                                                   │
│  Invert     _____   _____         ┌──────────────────────────────────────┐   │
│                                       │ REPORT NO.        Date _____       │   │
│  Side       _____   _____         │ By _____       │   │
│                                       └──────────────────────────────────────┘   │
└─────────────────────────────────────────────────────────────────────────────────┘
```

Fig. 5-4. Inspection report form for corrugated steel pipe structures.

5. **Minnesota (1967)[6]**

The local manufacturers' association investigated culverts and established a correlation between Marbut's Great Soil Groups[5] and service life. The state's own investigation checked these findings. Dividing the state into four zones, according to soil type, has provided simple and straightforward design criteria. See Table 5-3.

6. **Iowa (1968)[7]**

Local manufacturers' association established the same correlation for Iowa as had been discovered in Minnesota.

Table 5-3 Projected Typical Years To Perforation At Ends Of Galvanized Corrugated Steel Pipe Culverts In Minnesota

Soil Group		Dry & Storm Installations	Standing Water and Silted Installations
I. PODSOL	Strongly acid	55–85 years	30–55 years
II. GREY-BROWN PODSOLIC	Acid	65–95	45–75
IV. PRAIRIE	Slightly acid surface w/neutral to alkaline subsoil	70–100	55–85
V. CHERNOZEM	Alkaline	100+	70–100+

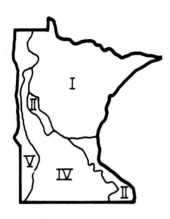

Fig. 5-5. Minnesota durability-design guide map showing four major soil groups.

7. Kansas (1971)[8]

Kansas State Highway Department investigated approximately 800 pipes with results similar to those in New York. A narrow range of pH and resistivity was involved, with no correlation between these factors and pipe life. Corrugated steel pipe was found to last approximately 50 years or longer. The California Test Method was found unsuitable for Kansas because it frequently predicted too short a life.

Each comprehensive investigation has shown that the majority of sites are mild in nature and not aggressive toward galvanized steel. However, there are individual locations as well as general geographic areas that are corrosive for steel. A lack of knowledge as to where such areas exist has, in the past, resulted in corrosion problems with corrugated steel pipe. Designers have often been seriously hampered by a lack of reliable corrosion criteria.

Thanks to the scientific inspections and analyses made in the last two decades, there is now available criteria with which the designer can evaluate the corrosion potential. With the guesswork eliminated, the right material for the job can be specified with confidence.

Corrosion–Abrasion
Design Procedure

A. CHECK FOR OLD EXISTING STRUCTURES

The most reliable information is still to be found in an old corrugated steel structure in the same location on the same watercourse. Old installations of this type are invaluable and should be the first consideration in any corrosion investigation for a proposed project. Oftentimes a little investigating upstream and downstream in the area will reveal useful installations under old roads, steets or parking lots.

Investigations of existing structures should be uniform and standardized for most useful results. The form shown in Fig. 5-4 has been adopted by the National Corrugated Steel Pipe Association and is suggested for use.

B. CLASSIFY ENVIRONMENT, "NORMAL" OR "ACIDIC"

The environment, that is the natural soil and water, in the region in question may be classified by the level of hydrogen ion concentration, or "pH". In many states a single classification will apply to the entire state with the exception of obvious unusual conditions such as salt water marshes, coal mining runoff and concentrated industrial effluents. In most sections of the United States the pH of the natural soil and water is fairly well established and the information available in the form of iso maps. Typical sources for this information are the U.S. Geological Survey, state departments of commerce, health and agriculture and the U. S. Soil Conservation Service.

Sites with a pH of 5.8 or more are classified as "*NORMAL*". Sites with a pH of less than 5.8 are classified as "*ACIDIC*".

C. METAL LOSS RATE

1. "*NORMAL*", *pH=5.8 or more*
   (a) For ordinary installations of plain galvanized pipe, use a corrosion-abrasion rate of 0.0013 in. per year.
   (b) For unusually soft water installations, increase the above rate to 0.0030 in. for plain galvanized pipe as shown in Table 5-4.

Table 5-4   Estimated Years to Perforation of Invert of Plain Galvanized Corrugated Steel Pipe

For NORMAL Conditions (pH $\gtreqless$ 5.8)

Wall Thickness in Inches	Normal Water .0013 In. per Year	Very Soft Water .003 In. per Year
.064	49 years	22 years
.079	60	26
.109	84	36
.138	106	46
.168	over 100	56
.188	over 100	63
.218	over 100	73
.249	over 100	83
.280	over 100	93

2. *"ACIDIC", pH less than 5.8*
   (a) Follow the sampling and testing procedures on pgs. 220–223.
   (b) Use Chart in Fig. 5-6 to estimate time to invert perforation.

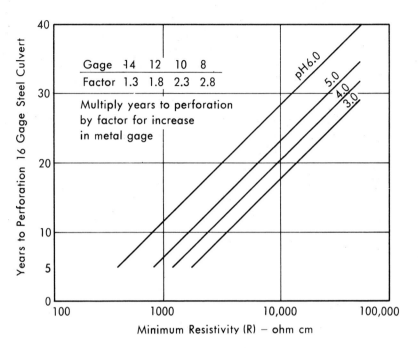

Fig. 5-6. Method of estimating time to first perforation for 16 ga. steel pipe. Excerpted from California Division of Highways Test Method 643-B.

D. PROTECTIVE COATINGS AND PAVING

1. *Asphalt Coated Only* (no pavement)

Asphalt coatings are quite useful in protecting pipe under many circumstances. Such coating is very effective on the pipe exterior. In those applications in which the exterior of the pipe determines its life, such coatings add approximately 25 years. Arid regions represent a typical environment in which pipe exteriors can determine pipe life.

The usefulness of coatings alone on the pipe interior is limited. Abrasive flow may remove the coating in the invert. New York observed approximately 10 years of added life for coatings alone while California found a 6-year addition. It is recommended that coatings (without invert paving) only be used for:

   (a) Protection of pipe *exteriors*. Add 25 years.
   (b) Pipe *interiors* in non-abrasive flows, free of ice action. Add 6 to 10 years.

2. *Asphalt Coating and Paving*

Asphalt coating and invert-paving affords a much higher degree of interior protection to pipe than asphalt coating alone. For factory-made pipe, the poured asphalt pavement protects the critical invert area with a resilient mass. There is a limit to the performance of such paving as it is not suitable for very severe erosion situations such as those in which the bottom is torn out of normal structures in a season or two.

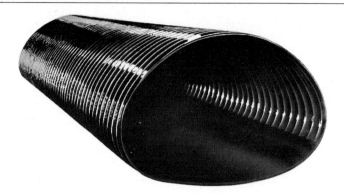

Fig. 5-7. A thick pavement covers the bottom of the pipe or pipe-arch to a minimum depth of ⅛ in. Such pavement protects against abrasion and the impact of gravel and boulders.

California found up to 15 years of added life for asphalt pavements. However, this was based on a small number of installations, and most of these installations represented highly abrasive flow conditions and/or steep slopes. On the other hand, in New York, pavements extended pipe life "beyond practical limits of design life." It seems obvious that engineering judgment must be exercised in evaluating paving and assigning some number of years of life for it. The following guideline is recommended:

Table 5-5 Years of Life Added to Structures with Asphalt Paved Invert

Slope of Pipe	Abrasion	Added Years
Less than 1%	Mild	35
	Significant	25
1%–2%	Mild	30
	Significant	20
3%–4%	Mild	25
	Significant	20
Greater than 4%	Mild	20
	Significant	15

E. CULVERT GRADE STAINLESS STEEL, TYPE 409

Sites of aggressive corrosion and abrasion are potential applications for this relatively new type steel pipe. Using the corrosion design methods previously described or those published by the American Concrete Institute for rigid pipe may indicate prohibitively short service life. In these cases the first cost becomes much less significant than for normal applications. Typical sites or applications are listed here.

1. *Acid Mine Water Drainage.* Conventional concrete and metal pipes have in some instances shown a life of less than a year in acid mine water drainage. However, test installations of culvert-grade stainless steel, placed in 1966, have under these conditions shown no observable corrosion. There is every reason to believe that an indefinite service life may be assigned.

2. *Salt Water.* This environment has proved most severe for conventional pipe materials. After three years of exposure to tidal salt water, culvert-grade stainless steel pipe is still in excellent condition with only superficial staining but no loss of metal.

3. *Abrasion.* Stainless steel, type 409, has been thoroughly tested for pipe line transmission of coal slurries and other highly abrasive materials. In this service it has provided many times the life of other pipe line materials. Culvert test pipes of this stainless steel installed under highly abrasive conditions have shown virtually no metal loss over a period of years.

For these three conditions—acid mine water drainage, salt water and abrasive flow—culvert grade stainless steel pipe can be a sound economic choice even though the first cost may be as much as three times that of galvanized steel pipe. Structural design should be based on minimum thickness required, as in Chapter 3. The service life is provided by the premium material, stainless steel. It defeats the economic purpose to also increase thickness beyond the structural requirement.

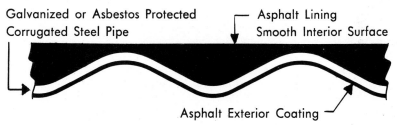

Galvanized or Asbestos Protected Corrugated Steel Pipe — Asphalt Lining Smooth Interior Surface

Asphalt Exterior Coating

Fig. 5-8. Cross section of bituminous spun lining over the complete interior periphery of corrugated steel pipe.

F. "DESIGN LIFE"

The foregoing parameters may be applied to the minimum structural design obtained in Chapter 3 to determine the average number of years before perforation may be expected in the pipe invert. This figure establishes the length of time the structure is likely to operate without material maintenance. After that it is quite possible to extend the useful life of the structure with a field-applied pavement or lining.

What is the required "time to invert perforation" of a particular structure? Logically it is quite variable, being a matter of economic comparisons of initial cost and interest on investment vs repair costs at future dates. However, it is common practice to establish a standard DESIGN LIFE for drainage structures commensurate with the importance of the facility.

The term DESIGN LIFE *refers to the period of service without major repairs.* For example, the Federal Highway Administration requires a 50-year design life for Interstate Highways and this applies also to the culverts. Most state highway departments have comparable requirements for their highest level of construction. For less important installations a shorter design life is acceptable.

It is important to recognize that the structure does not crumble and collapse at the end of its DESIGN LIFE. This merely marks the estimated average time without repair costs.

G. SELECTION OF FINAL PIPE DESIGN

From the appropriate chart (Table 5-4 or Fig. 5-6), check the "time to invert perforation" for the pipe wall thickness required for structural design. If this equals or exceeds the established DESIGN LIFE for the structure, the minimum structural thickness is satisfactory for the final design.

If the time to perforation is less than DESIGN LIFE, there are several solutions possible. The most economical one is usually the most desirable.

To find this, follow the procedure outlined below. Do not fall into the easy trap of arbitrarily increasing the metal thickness.
1. Check the possible alternatives required for hydraulic design. That is, possible size differences, applicable to invert paved or fully paved pipe. Clearly, if paving also assists in hydraulic requirements, it should be chosen to provide the added years required.
2. Consider the erosion factor at the site. If it is significant, again paving will be a logical first choice solution.
3. If a structural plate pipe is involved, additional metal thickness of the *invert plate* is normally the most economical solution.
4. For standard corrugated steel pipe, use this guideline: The combination of least metal thickness and invert paving that provides the required "time to perforation" will be the most economical solution.

Example 1

From Chapter 3, *Structural Design*, Example No. 1, a 48″ culvert under 60′ of fill required a wall thickness of 0.064″ in either a 2⅔″ × ½″ or 3″ × 1″ corrugation. Assume the following corrosion-abrasion conditions for this installation:

Environment: In this whole general area, the pH of soil and water is above 5.8. However, the water is very soft.

Slope of Pipe: $S = 0.008$ ft per ft
Abrasion: Silty bedload, no sharp, abrasive detritus.
General: Midwestern area, hilly, average rainfall

SOLUTION

A. No old existing structures available
B. Environment classifies as "Normal"
C. Metal Loss Rate. For very soft water, from Table 5–4, a loss rate of .003 in. per year will apply.
D. Coatings and Paving. Add 6 years for asphalt coating alone. From Table 5–5 add 35 years for coating and paving for mild abrasion and less than 1% slope.
E. Design Life. Culvert under Interstate Highway. Requires 50 years without major repair.
F. Selection of Final Design: From Table 5–4, .064″ wall = 22 yrs
                                                    .138″ wall = 46 yrs
   Alternatives:
     1. .064″ wall + coating and paving = 22 + 35 = 57 yrs
     2. .138″ wall + coating = 46 + 6 = 52 yrs
   Select .064″ wall, coated and paved, as most economical solution.

Example 2

From Chapter 3, Example 2, a 120″ diam. pipe in 3″ × 1″ or 6″ × 2″ corrugation under 65′ of fill requires 0.168″ wall thickness. Assume the following abrasion-corrosion design factors:

Environment: pH of soil and water is 5.0 in this area
Slope: $S = .015$ ft per ft
Abrasion: Small fractured rock and sharp sand bedload plus evidence of abrasion
General: Mountainous area; heavy rainfall

SOLUTION

A. No existing steel structures on same water course. Ten-year old concrete box upstream shows significant abrasion in invert.
B. Site classifies as "Acidic"
C. Metal Loss Rate   1. Soil resistivity at site measured 4500 ohm-cm

2. From Fig. 5–6, time to perforation for .064″ thickness = 18 yrs Metal thickness factor for 0.168″ is 2.8. Years for 0.168″ = 2.8 ×18 = 50.4 yrs

D. **Coating and Paving.** Asphalt paving not available in 120″ pipe. Asphalt coating not recommended for interior protection in abrasive conditions.

E. **Design Life.** Major highway, requires 50 years

F. **Final Design:** The structural design thickness of 0.168″ provides the required design life. However, the evidence of significant abrasion indicates added invert protection. Recommend heavy invert plate of 0.218″ thickness for 6″ × 2″ structural plate pipe or field-installed concrete pavement for a 3″ × 1″ pipe.

SUMMARY

The tools are available for confident design of galvanized corrugated steel structures for corrosive and abrasive effects. Modern comprehensive investigations in such states as California, New York, Washington, Minnesota and Kansas are the basis for the recommended design procedure presented.

MAINTENANCE

The following quotation is taken from the U.S. Soil Conservation Design Manual: "All structures need maintenance for satisfactory operation and to prolong their life, thereby reducing replacement cost. Owners should be urged to inspect structures at least once annually and at other opportune times. Cracks that develop should be sealed, protective coatings applied where needed, and modifications, riprap, or repairs made where and when they are necessary. Often a small repair job will prevent a large repair job, or even complete failure, later on. Debris or obstructions at the inlet or outlet of structures should be removed immediately."

REFERENCES

1. American Water Works Association, *Steel Pipe Design and Installation*, Manual M 11, 286 pp. 1964.
2. Beaton, J. L. and Stratfull, R. F., *Field Test for Estimating Service Life of Corrugated Metal Pipe Culverts*, Calif. Div. of Highways, Highway Research Board, Proc. Vol. 41, 1962, p. 258.
3. California Div. of Highways, *Planning Manual of Instructions, Part 7—Design, Section 7-800.*.
4. New York Dept. of Transportation, *Durability of Corrugated Metal Culverts*, Research Report 66-5, 84 pp., Nov. 1967.
5. Marbut, C. F., *Great Soil Groups.* Identification of soil groups is by the classification originated by C. F. Marbut and published in "Atlas of American Agriculture, Part III, Soils of the U.S.," . . . U.S. Gvmt. Printing Office, 1935. This method was utilized by the National Bureau of Standards in "Underground Corrosion," U.S. Dept. of Commerce, Circular 579, 1957. (Covers 44 years of tests.)
6. Holt, A. Roland, *Durability Design Method for Galvanized Steel Pipe in Minnesota.* Report sponsored by Minnesota members of National Corrugated Steel Pipe Association, Minneapolis, 34 pp., 1967.
7. Malcom, W. J., *Durability Design Method for Galvanized Steel Pipe in Iowa.* Report sponsored by Corrugated Metal Pipe Association of Iowa and Nebraska, 24 pp., 1968.
8. Worley, H. E., *Corrosion of Corrugated Metal Pipe*, Report of State Highway Commission of Kansas, 38 pp., 1971.
9. Stratfull, R. F., *Field Method of Detecting Corrosive Soil Conditions*, Calif. Div. of Highways, Proc. 15th Annual Street & Highway Conf., Jan. 1963.

APPENDIX A

SAMPLING AND TESTING PROCEDURE*

PART I. Method of Field Resistivity Survey and Sampling for Corrosion Tests

Scope

The field resistivity test is an indication of the soluble salts in the soil or water, and is used primarily as a guide for selecting samples that will be further tested in the laboratory to obtain data for estimating the service life of culverts. The natural soil in each channel or culvert location and the structural backfill material are tested by a portable earth resistivity meter, and samples are selected on the basis of these tests.

Procedure

A. Apparatus

1. Portable earth resistivity meter, suitable for rapid in-place determinations of soil resistivity.
2. Field probe.
3. Steel starting rod, for making hole (in hard ground) for inserting probe.
4. Sledge hammer (4 lbs.)

B. Materials

Distilled, de-ionized or other clean waters that measure greater than 20,000 ohm/cm^3.

C. Recording Data

Record test data in a field note book for use in selecting samples and also for use as needed in analyzing laboratory test data.

D. Test Procedure

1. In the channel of a proposed culvert site, insert the field probe into the soil for a depth of between 6″ and 12″ and measure resistivity. Remove the field probe and pour about 2 ounces of clean water into the hole.
2. Re-insert the probe, while twisting to mix the water and soil, then measure the resistivity. Follow manufacturer's instructions for correct use of meter.
3. Withdraw the field probe and add an additional 2 ounces of clean water.
4. Re-insert the probe and again measure the resistivity of the soil.
5. Record the lowest of the readings as the field resistivity of the soil.

E. Selection of Soil Samples for Laboratory Tests

1. Make sufficient resistivity determinations at various locations in the channel or culvert site area to represent adequately the entire area.
2. If the resistivity is reasonably uniform within the limits of the project, three soil samples from different locations will be sufficient. If, however, some locations show resistivities that differ significantly from the average of the determinations for the area being surveyed, additional soil samples should be taken to represent these locations,—particularly those with resistivities significantly below the average.

   a. For example, if the soil resistivities throughout the surveyed area are all at or near an average value of 2000 ohm/cm^3, three samples will be enough. If any of the locations tested have resistivities markedly below this average, for example 800 ohm/cm^3, then these "hot spots" should definitely be represented by additional samples. Scattered locations of

*From California Test Method 643-B[9]

higher resistivity, for example 3000 ohm/cm^3 or more, do not necessarily require additional samples.

b. Judgment must be exercised both in the field testing and sampling and in evaluating the laboratory tests.

c. In all cases, do not take less than 3 samples.

F. Precautions

In field testing and sampling, follow very carefully the test method instructions and also the manufacturer's instructions for use of meters.

PART II. Preliminary Field Method of Determining pH of Water Samples

Scope

This method is suitable for use in the field or laboratory for determining the pH of water samples.

Procedure

A. Apparatus and Materials

1. 2 oz. or larger wide-mouth container, e.g. glass jar, beaker, or dry wax paper cup.
2. pH meter, suitable for either field or laboratory testing.
3. pH standard solution of pH 7.

B. Recording Data

Record test data in a field notebook.

C. Method of Sampling

1. Dip the wide-mouth container into the water to be tested. Swirl to rinse and pour out contents to avoid contamination from container.
2. Dip into the water again for obtaining a sample.
3. Pour off any film which is on the surface of the sample before testing.

D. Standardizing pH Meter

Follow the instructions provided with the type of pH meter being used.

E. Use of pH Meter to Determine pH of Water

Follow the instructions provided with the type of pH meter being used.

F. Precautions

Follow the manufacturer's instructions for use of the meter and observe the usual precautions for making chemical tests.

Notes

pH readings may be taken at any period other than flood flow. All waters which have a pH of less than 6 should be sampled for further analysis, in one quart bottles.

PART III. Method of Determining pH of Soils

Scope

This method is suitable for use in determining the pH of soil samples.

Procedure

A. Apparatus and Materials

1. Paper cups, 2 oz. wax coated type.
2. Teaspoon or small metal scoop.

3. Wash bottle containing distilled water.
4. pH meter suitable for field or laboratory testing.
5. pH Standard solution of pH 7.

B. Recording Data

Record data in a field notebook or on Form T-619.

C. Preparation of Test Specimens

1. Place 2 rounded teaspoonfuls of the soil to be tested into a 2-oz. paper cup.
2. Add about 2 teaspoonfuls of distilled water to the sample in the cup.
3. Disperse soil in water by stirring. The specimen is now ready for testing.

D. Standardization of pH Meter

Follow the instructions provided with the pH meter.

E. Use of pH Meter to Determine pH of Soil

Follow the instructions provided with the pH meter.

F. Precautions

Carefully follow the above procedure and the manufacturer's instructions.

If the pH reading is unstable when the electrode is immersed in the soil slurry, leave the electrode immersed until the pH reading has stabilized. In some cases this waiting period for the stabilization of the pH reading may take 5 minutes.

PART IV. Laboratory Method of Determining Minimum Resistivity

Scope

This method covers the procedure for determining the minimum resistivity of soil or water samples selected as indicated in PART I. These resistivity values are used in estimating culvert life as described in PART V.

Procedure

A. Apparatus

1. Resistivity meter suitable for laboratory testing.
2. Soil box calibrated for use with resistivity meter. See Fig. (5-9) for details.
3. No. 8 Sieve.
4. Round tin pans. 12" diameter and 2" deep.
5. 200° F. oven.
6. One balance, 5 kg. capacity, accurate to 10 g.

B. Materials

Distilled or de-ionized water.

C. Recording Data

Record data on Form T-619 or in notebook.

D. Preparation of Soil Samples

After thorough mixing of sample, screen it through a No. 8 sieve. If the sample is too moist to be sieved, it may be dried and crushed. Do not crush rocks. Only the natural material that passes the No. 8 sieve is to be used for the test.

E. Measuring the Resistivity of Soil Sample

1. Quarter or split out about 1300 grams of the passing No. 8 material.

2. If the sample was dried, add about 150 grams of distilled water to the 1300 grams of soil and thoroughly mix.

3. After the soil sample is thoroughly mixed, place and compact it (moderate compaction with the fingers is sufficient) in the soil box.

4. Measure the resistivity of the soil in accordance with the instructions furnished with the meter.

5. Remove the soil from the soil box and add about 100 additional grams of distilled water and again thoroughly mix.

6. Again place and compact the soil in the soil box and measure its resistivity.

7. Repeat this procedure once more.

8. If the resistivity of the soil has not followed a trend of high resistivity, low resistivity, and then an increase in resistivity for the preceding additions of distilled water, continue to add water in about 50 gram increments to the soil; mixing, placing, compacting, and measuring resistivity for each increment, until the minimum resistivity is obtained.

9. If the sample was not dried, begin the test procedure by adding 50 gram of water in lieu of 150 grams specified above in 1. Continue to add 50 gram increments of water followed by mixing, placing, compacting, and measuring until a minimum value of resistivity is measured.

10. Record the test value that is the minimum value of soil resistivity at any moisture content.

F. Measuring the Resistivity of a Water Sample

1. Thoroughly clean the soil box of all soil particles and rinse the soil box a minimum of three times with distilled or de-ionized water.

2. Fill the soil box with distilled water and measure its resistivity.

3. If the distilled water in the soil box measures infinite resistivity, empty the soil box of distilled water, fill with the test water, measure its resistivity, then record the measured value.

4. If the distilled water in the soil box did not measure infinite resistivity, continue to rinse the box with distilled or de-ionized water until the box is thoroughly clean, which is indicated by an infinite resistivity measurement.

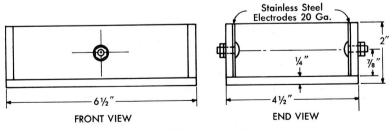

FRONT VIEW   END VIEW

Fig. 5-9. Soil box for laboratory resistivity determination.

Material for Soil Box
Bottom—1 pc. 6½" x 4½" x ¼" plastic
Ends—2 pcs. 4½" x 1¾" x ¼" plastic
Sides—2 pcs. 6" x 1¾" x ¼" plastic
Electrodes—2 pcs. 20 ga. stainless steel 6" x 1¾"
2 ea. No. 8-32 x ¾" round-head stainless steel machine screws with rubber washer and stainless steel washer and nut.

Fig. 6-1. Pipe and flume spillway of structural plate steel. Edges of flume are covered and braced with steel angles.

224

CHAPTER 6

Special Design Problems

Section A—EROSION PREVENTION

Proper design can eliminate much of the problem of maintenance caused by soil erosion. Products commonly used for this purpose include corrugated steel flumes, pipe spillways, pipe stream enclosures, ditch checks, steel sheeting and retaining walls. See Part I *APPLICATIONS, Section C Special Drainage Problems.*

CORRUGATED STEEL FLUMES

Steel flumes are essentially part-circle or half-circle channels used to convey surface storm water. They should preferably be imbedded for their full depth in the natural ground. They should not run full, but be designed with a liberal factor of safety or "freeboard." They should discharge into a catchbasin, culvert or stream in a manner to avoid undermining. Fig. 6-1.

Edges of the flume may be reinforced with a steel angle. Horizontal steel struts at intervals will help maintain the designed shape. Steel or concrete anchorages at 10 to 25 ft intervals may be needed to resist frost heaving and other loads. Flume sections are generally connected by field bolting.

Fig. 6-2. Shoulder spillway with steel end section for an inlet.

Fig. 6-3. Cantilevered steel culvert can spill water beyond the slope without undermining the pipe.

PIPE SPILLWAYS

The pipe spillway conveys surface storm water down the face of a cut slope or embankment, Fig. 6-2, on a steep approach to a culvert inlet, or a sharp drop at the outlet. See also Fig. C-3, page 23.

As an alternate means of conducting water down a steep slope, the pipe spillway may be placed on a flat slope with its end cantilevered, Fig. 6-3, to discharge the water into an "armored" stilling basin of riprap or other suitable material. A drop inlet may be used at the head of the spillway.

STREAM ENCLOSURES

Enclosing intermittent open streams or other storm water in a steel pipe sewer is a sure way of avoiding progressive erosion troubles. Not only is the maintenance decreased but eliminating an open ditch also increases safety, and makes available additional usable land. These last points hold particular merit in real estate developments and valuable land uses along streets or roadways.

Particularly on open ditch grades in excess of 5 percent, stream enclosures will be found more satisfactory than ditch checks or other erosion remedies. Corrugated steel pipe, with its continuous, flexible construction and minimum bedding requirement is most often specified as it resists disjointing and also conforms to shifting or subsiding foundation soils. Suitable grating inlets can readily be provided if necessary.

DITCH CHECKS

Ditch checks or weirs once were used extensively to control erosion in roadside ditches. Today, they are considered not only a hazard to traffic leaving the roadway, but also a handicap to power mowing. However, in rural areas

Fig. 6-4. Large structural plate pipe-arch stream enclosure serves to eliminate unsightly eroded ditch banks besides providing a needed storm sewer and unobstructed land area.

Table 6-1   Discharge for Weir Notches in Erosion Check Dams[1]*

(H) Depth of Weir Notch in Feet	Length of Weir Notch in Feet (L)				
	2	4	6	8	10
0.5	2.4	4.8	7.2	9.6	12.0
1.0	6.8	13.6	20.3	27.1	33.9
1.5	12.5	24.9	37.4	49.8	62.3
2.0	19.2	38.3	57.5	76.7	95.9
2.5	26.8	53.6	80.4	107.2	134.0
3.0	35.2	70.5	105.7	140.9	176.1
3.5	44.4	88.8	133.2	177.6	222.0
4.0	54.2	108.5	162.7	217.0	271.2
4.5	64.7	129.4	194.2	258.9	323.6
5.0	75.8	151.6	227.4	303.2	379.0

*Expressed as cu ft/sec as computed from formula $Q = 3.39LH^{3/2}$

of low traffic volume, where a ditch gradient makes the ditch check adequate and economical, it should be designed with capacity ample to prevent possible washout. To accomplish this, the drop at successive weirs should generally not exceed 3 ft.

The ditch check may consist of a corrugated steel-sheeting weir with wings sloped to fit the channel, Fig. 6-5, or a series of sodded earth dams with "pipe drops." For large channels and cross streams above and below a roadway, employ large ditch checks built of corrugated structural pipe or retaining walls.

For a sharp-crested weir on ditch spillways, Table 6-1 gives discharge rates in cu ft/sec for various depths and lengths of the weir notch.

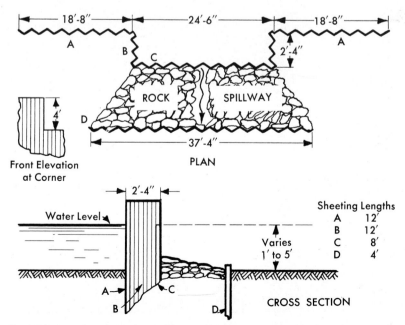

Fig. 6-5. Ditch check of corrugated steel sheeting with rock spillway apron and sheeting cutoff wall (D), as built by a reclamation district.

Fig. 6-6. Levee culverts must resist the load of high embankments plus possible unstable foundation soils and hydraulic traffic.

Section B—DAM AND LEVEE DRAINAGE

INTRODUCTION

Numerous soil and water conservation projects require building dams and levees. Included are:
small dams—for water and soil conservation; mosquito elimination
large dams—for water supply, power, recreation, navigation
levees—for flood control, and in connection with dams—Fig. 6-6
In the control of water flow as well as in general construction, several drainage and related construction projects are required, such as: culverts, diaphragms, end sections, water control gates, toe drains; large intakes and outfall lines for thermal power plants; aggregates bins and air pipes for cooling aggregates; temporary bypass tunnels; pedestrian and vehicular underpasses; shore protection, retaining walls and guardrail.

SOIL-SAVING DAMS

Thousands of small dams are built each year on farms, ranches and other rural areas. Beyond reducing erosion and saving valuable top soil, these small dams also help restore the ground water level and supply water for livestock, fishing and recreational purposes.

The size of the dam can vary from a small ditch check, to one large enough to impound a farm pond of several acres, or to an artificial lake of a hundred acres or more. The bigger the dam, the more thorough should be the precautions for handling seepage and overflow. A local or regional Soil Conservation Service office can be helpful in suggesting details based on successful local practice. Fig 6-7.[2]

DRAIN PIPE SPILLWAYS

Even for the smallest of dams, some means such as a drain pipe spillway should be provided to handle normal overflow to prevent overtopping and possible washout. For emergency overflow, a turf covered ditch or one lined with a corrugated steel flume or chute, is usually satisfactory.

A drain pipe spillway generally consists of the following elements: (1) a drop

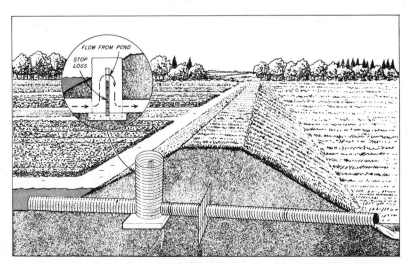

Fig. 6-7. Small earth dam with corrugated metal pipe drop-inlet spillway. Water level control is by use of stoplogs in the riser. Courtesy of U. S. Soil Conservation Service.

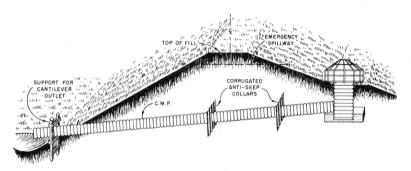

Fig. 6-8. Corrugated metal drain-pipe spillway with trash rack on riser pipe.[2]

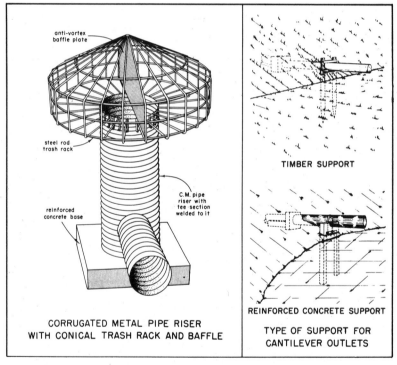

Fig. 6-9. Detail of corrugated steel pipe riser with conical trash rack and baffle.[2]
Fig. 6-10. Types of supports for cantilever outlets.[2]

inlet or manhole with a baffle board or trash rack, Figs 6-8 and 6-9; (2) a culvert with watertight seams, joints and anti-seep diaphragms; and (3) in some cases a slide headgate to control the water level or outflow, or permit draining the pond for cleaning or for other purposes. Other variations are possible. The outlet may require special end treatment to prevent erosion.

1. Drop-inlet. Size required to handle excess runoff is determined by the methods given in Chapter 4, *Estimating Runoff from Small Areas, Hydraulics of Open Channels,* or *Hydraulic Design of Culverts.* See Table 6-2.

Table 6-2   Cross-Sectional Areas for Drop-Inlet Culverts[1]

Watershed Area in Acres	Cross-Sectional Area of Culvert in Square Feet					
	Rolling Land			Hilly Land		
	Cultivated C=1.0	Pasture 0.6	Woods 0.3	Cultivated 1.4	Pasture 0.8	Woods 0.4
1	1.9	1.1	0.6	2.7	1.5	0.8
2	2.1	1.3	0.6	2.9	1.7	0.8
4	2.5	1.5	0.8	3.5	2.0	1.0
6	2.9	1.7	0.9	4.1	2.3	1.2
8	3.4	2.0	1.0	4.8	2.7	1.4
10	3.8	2.3	1.1	5.3	3.0	1.5
15	4.8	2.9	1.4	6.7	3.8	1.9
20	5.8	3.5	1.7	8.1	4.6	2.3
30	7.8	4.7	2.3	10.9	6.2	3.1
40	9.7	5.8	2.9	13.6	7.8	3.9
50	11.5	6.9	3.5	16.1	9.2	4.6
75	15.9	9.5	4.8	22.3	12.7	6.4
100	20.0	12.0	6.0	28.0	16.0	8.0
125	23.8	14.3	7.1	33.3	19.0	9.5
150	27.3	16.4	8.2	38.2	21.9	10.9
200	33.7	20.2	10.1	47.2	27.0	13.5
250	39.4	23.6	11.8	55.2	31.5	15.8
300	44.4	26.6	13.3	62.2	35.5	17.8
350	48.9	29.3	14.7	68.5	39.1	19.6
400	53.0	31.8	15.9	74.2	42.4	21.2
500	60.0	36.0	18.0	84.0	48.0	24.0
600	65.8	39.5	19.7	92.1	52.6	26.3
700	70.8	42.5	21.2	99.1	56.6	28.3
800	75.0	45.0	22.5	105.0	60.0	30.0

Values computed by Ramser Formula, $a = c \left(130 - \dfrac{77,000}{A+600} \right)$ ....(1)

Where a = cross-sectional area of culvert in sq ft.
A = watershed area in acres, c = coefficient depending on nature and type of watershed.
Formula not recommended for areas larger than given in table.
Use above values for vertical drop through culvert up to 5 ft.
Multiply above values by 0.71 for drop through culvert = 10 ft. and 0.58 for drop = 15 ft.
For fan or square shaped watersheds multiply above values by 1.25.
If side spillway of appreciable capacity is provided, reduction of culvert area may be made accordingly.

Example: A dam with a culvert having an inlet drop of 12 ft of corrugated steel pipe is to serve an ordinary watershed of 25 acres of rolling cultivated land. Interpolating in the second column of Table 6-2, between 20 and 30 acres, the cross-sectional area is 6.8 sq ft. From the footnotes of the same table, a value of 0.66 is obtained for a 12-ft drop through interpolation between values 0.71 and 0.58 for 10 and 15-ft drops. Multiply: 6.8 by 0.66 = 4.49 sq ft as the proper cross-sectional area. The nearest commercial size is a 30-in. diameter pipe with an area of 4.91 sq ft.

Size of the drop-inlet is generally larger than the culvert portion. See Fig. 6-8. The top should be at least 1 ft below the emergency spillway level and 3 or 4 ft below the top of the dam.

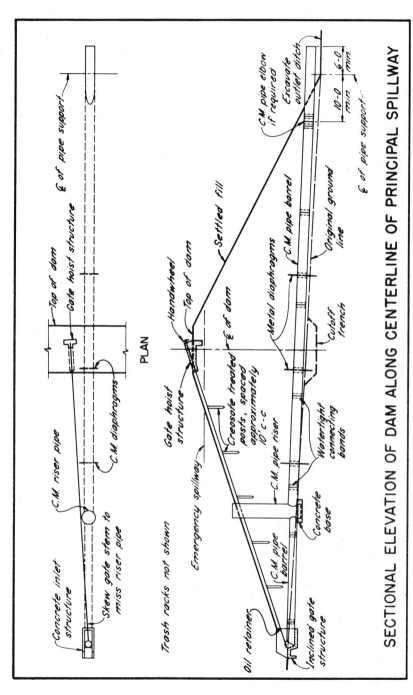

SECTIONAL ELEVATION OF DAM ALONG CENTERLINE OF PRINCIPAL SPILLWAY

Fig. 6-11. Plan and sectional elevation of dam along centerline of principal spillway, designed by Soil Conservation Service.[2]

Fig. 6-12. Levee construction showing (1) diaphragms, (2) riser or manhole, (3) corrugated steel pipe outfall, and (4) flap gate for preventing backflow.

A baffle board is recommended to stop vortex action. This should be a corrugated steel sheet or a solid timber wall, with a length of three times the diameter of the inlet pipe. This may be supplemented by a coarse steel wire screen to prevent debris from entering the drop-inlet.

2. The Culvert. The size of the horizontal culvert should be capable of accommodating practically any flood flow of the stream above the dam. Size will also control the rapidity of draining the pond for cleaning.

Steel pipe with close-riveted, welded, or lock seams and with tight joints should be employed. See Chapter 1 for details of seams and joints. Corrugated steel diaphragms should be included to intercept possible seepage caused by burrowing along the pipe by rodents.

3. Control Gate. Ordinarily the water control gate is situated at the pond end of the culvert and will consist of a hand-operated slide gate, made accessible by means of a walkway from the dam.[3]

LEVEE CULVERTS

The building of levees generally calls for blocking the natural drainage channels. To permit normal flow from these tributaries requires levee culverts. These differ from ordinary culverts in that they may be submerged during floods, or longer periods if they continue to serve as equalizers for lakes or reservoirs

To prevent a stream from backing up through a culvert, a gate is provided to open and close automatically or mechanically.

Design of the levee culvert depends on the size of opening required which is predicated on stream-flow.

Saturated and often unstable soil conditions common to levees require that corrugated steel pipe for this service be fabricated differently than ordinary culverts. Seams are made watertight and the coupling bands are selected for both watertightness and extra strength. See Chapt. 1.

Steel end sections are used on levee culverts to minimize erosion.

DIAPHRAGMS

Diaphragms are usually required as cutoff walls to retard leakage alongside the pipe. Such diaphragms or bulkheads should project no less than 2 ft beyond the outside of the pipe, regardless of pipe size, when the diaphragms are spaced 20 ft apart. Spacing greater than 20 ft calls for even larger diaphragms so that the distance the water must travel is at least 20 percent greater than without the diaphragms. See Fig. 6-11.

Locate diaphragms midway between circumferential riveted seams and at least 4 ft from a field joint. In multiple lines of pipe, space the diaphragms to provide at least 12 in. face-to-face clearance between one another on adjacent pipes.

DRAINAGE GATES[3]

Flap and screw lift operated steel water control gates are two designs used on levees. Screw lift operated gates are used where special control is desired, but they require timely opening and closing. Figs. 6-11, 6-12, 6-13.

Both flap and slide gates are available with round or rectangular openings. Flap gates are available from 4-in. diam. to 120 in. Slide gates can be specified from 6 in. by 6 in. through 120 in. by 120 in. and 6 in. to 120 in. diameter. Radial and roller type gates are also available.

Fig. 6-13. Slide gate in 48-in. corrugated steel riser on levee culvert.

Fig. 6-14. Levee culverts and their control gates are subject to periodic inspections because they are expected to be dependable over many years. Most levee culverts are of corrugated steel pipe.

LARGE DAMS

Large earth-fill and rock-fill dams often require several years to construct. Various steel products are required in temporary construction and on the completed job. Temporary construction uses include by-pass tunnels, culverts, underpasses under service roads, steel retaining walls, corrugated pipes for cooling towers, aggregate reclaim tunnels, and conveyor covers.

Permanently installed steel drainage products include culverts under relocated highways and railroads; relief wells and collector pipes (Fig. B-7, page 19); toe subdrains to control seepage through the dam and to relieve ground water pressure behind the dam; retaining walls, steel guardrail, and steel sheeting for shore protection.

Design of these products is described and illustrated under the various products listed. See Index.

ADVANTAGES OF CORRUGATED STEEL PIPE

Service records of corrugated steel pipe culverts and sewers along the Mississippi, Missouri and many other rivers indicate that even under flood conditions, they particularly resist disjoining, settlement and infiltration of the surrounding soil. Fig. 6-14. Even under flood conditions, they retain their watertightness.

REFERENCES

Sect. A. EROSION PREVENTION
1. From Iowa Engineering Experiment Station Bulletin 121, Iowa State University, Ames, Iowa.
Sect. B. DAM AND LEVEE DRAINAGE
2. Beauchamp, Keith H., *Engineering Field Manual*, Structures for Soil and Water Conservation Purposes. Soil Conservation Service, Lincoln, Nebr., 90 pp.
3. Water Control Gates, Metal Products Division, Armco Steel Corp., Middletown, Ohio, Catalog G 3268, 1968, 200 pp.

Fig. 7-1. Reasonable care in locating and installing drainage structures pays dividends in long, satisfactory service.

PART III

Installation

CHAPTER 7 **Installation Instructions**

IMPORTANCE OF GOOD INSTALLATION[2]

A well situated, properly bedded, accurately assembled and carefully back-filled galvanized steel drainage structure will function properly and efficiently for a long period of time. Smaller structures demand less care in the details of proper installation than larger ones. But in both instances, reasonable precautions in handling, base preparation, assembling and backfilling, will pay handsome dividends in satisfactory service. Fig. 7-2.

It is assumed here that the "principles of culvert location" (see page 79) have been followed in establishing the best hydraulic conditions as well as taking advantage of best foundation conditions.

Corrugated steel structures because of their strength with light weight and their resistance to fracture can be installed quickly, easily and with least expensive equipment. The flexible steel shell is designed to distribute external loads around its structure and into the backfill. Such flexibility permits unequal settlement and dimensional changes that would—and sometimes do—cause failure in rigid structures. This clear advantage of corrugated steel structures is further strengthened by a well prepared foundation and a well tamped backfill of stable material, for these best satisfy the design assumptions and insure the most satisfactory installation. Reasonable care during installation is assumed, and selection of steel gages and associated design criteria are based on that assumption. Just as with drainage structures of concrete or other materials, careless installation of corrugated steel structures can quickly undo the work of the designer.

Fig. 7-2. Installing multiple corrugated steel culvert under a Missouri River levee. Beveled ends were protected with a slope pavement.

Section A—BASE PREPARATION

BEDDING

Bedding is that portion of the foundation which is shaped to contact the bottom of the conduit. A flat surface makes compaction difficult at the very bottom of large structures. Foundation shaping to fit the entire bottom interferes with assembly of field-bolted structures and is costly and unnecessary. Bedding or shaping should therefore be wide enough to permit efficiently compacting the remainder of the backfill under the haunches of the structure, but not so wide as to interfere with bolting procedures.

A uniform blanket of loose material should cover the shaped bedding to a depth sufficient to allow the corrugations to become filled with the material.

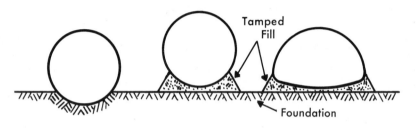

Fig. 7-3. Methods of bedding corrugated steel structures on wide, flat base.

In trench installation, keep the trench as narrow as possible but sufficiently wide to permit tamping under the haunches. Generally, trench width will range from 12 to 24 in. greater than the outside diameter of the galvanized pipe structure. Above 60-in. diameter or where mechanical tamping equipment is used, adequate trench width is required. Wide trenches require more excavation, more backfill, and also tend to increase the load on the structure. Side walls should be as vertical as practical, at least to an elevation above the top of the pipe.

DEWATERING TRENCH

Seepage or storm water standing or flowing in a trench or foundation area should be ditched to a sump and pumped out. Otherwise the pipe foundation becomes soft or interferes with making clean tight joints.

If seepage is a major problem, it may be necessary to use well points to dry up the trench. Another measure is to excavate the trench 6 or 8 in. below grade and backfill with sand or gravel which aids the drainage and pumping.

FOUNDATION SOILS

Evaluation of the conduit site may require subsurface exploration to detect undesirable foundation material, such as muck or rock ledges. Either of these gives uneven support, and in muck the conduit can shift after the embankment is constructed. Any large structure, and any size structure under high fill, is especially sensitive to inferior foundation material. Materials of poor or nonuniform bearing capacity should be removed and replaced with suitable fill to provide uniform continuous support. Large rocks or ledge rock should be replaced with suitable material, such as sand.

Fig. 7-4. Use of granular base to overcome wet soft foundation.

Unstable Foundation Soils

Especially when the excavated grade line for the structure traverses both soft and hard spots, the foundation should be made as uniform as practical. Hard spots can be excavated below grade and replaced with softer material. In any case, abrupt changes from hard to soft foundation should be avoided.

Frequently a relatively thin mat (6 to 12 in.) of granular material, well graded, will provide satisfactory support, but it may be necessary to replace very soft foundations to a greater depth. Diameter of pipe and height of fill will be controlling factors. Figs. 7-4, 7-5.

In swampy locations, especially along shore lines or adjacent to large rivers, deep unstable foundations are frequent problems. If they cannot be readily stabilized with granular material, brush or timber mats may be used to spread the load.

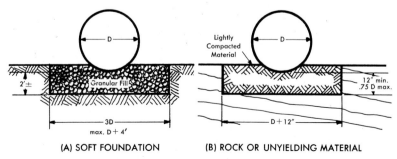

Fig. 7-5. Foundation preparation in unstable and in unyielding materials. After Bureau of Public Roads' standards.[5]

When placing large diameter culverts, particularly beneath high fill, it is generally good practice to install galvanized steel perforated pipe subdrainage on each side, parallel to the culvert, to prevent subsequent saturation of the foundation and of the fill around the pipe. In hilly country, foundation damage from seepage zones in the slopes adjacent to the fill can be similarly controlled. Details concerning proper installation of subdrains are given on page 16.

Rock Foundations

Rock encountered in the foundation should be removed to at least 12 in. below the bottom of the structure; excavate wide enough to avoid any possibility of the pipe resting on the rock. The excavated area is backfilled with compacted earth to cushion the pipe. (See Fig. 7-5.)

Camber

An embankment exerts more load on the foundation at the center of the embankment than at the toe of slope, so more settlement will occur in the center area. A corresponding settlement of the conduit will occur. Hence, the bedding profile should be cambered longitudinally. The upstream half of the pipe may be laid on almost a flat grade and the downstream half on a steeper grade. Fig. 7-6. The mid-ordinate of the curve should be determined by the soils engineer.

Fig. 7-6. Cambering or arching long lines of pipe under a high fill is a means of providing a grade line without low, pocket areas.

Fig. 7-7. "Dimpled" band connection—a more recent type of coupling for either helical or annular corrugations.

Section B—INSTALLATION OF SHOP-FABRICATED PIPE AND PIPE-ARCH

Unloading and Handling

Corrugated steel drainage products will withstand rough handling without cracking or breaking, but should be unloaded and handled with reasonable care. Lifting or rolling will protect the galvanized or bituminous coating—avoid dragging over gravel or rocky surfaces. Paved pipe sections stockpiled in hot climates should be placed to prevent flow of the asphaltic pavements.

Corrugated metal structures can be lowered down embankments or into deep trenches with the aid of ropes or slings. Lifting lugs with hookhole can be attached at the fabricating plant to avoid damaging any bituminous coating or lining.

Annularly-Corrugated Pipe

Longitudinal laps of riveted or welded corrugated steel pipe should be located at the sides.

Riveted or spot welded pipe is normally supplied in multiples of 2 ft or 4 ft, with maximum individual lengths governed by shop, transportation or field handling facilities. Culverts 20 to 30 ft long are generally supplied in a single section. Single lengths up to 50 ft have been supplied.

Helically Corrugated Pipe

Helically corrugated pipe is installed in the same manner as riveted or spot welded corrugated steel pipe. Various types of connecting bands are illustrated in Fig. 7-7 and pages 68–69, Ch. 1. To assemble, place the band (or first half, if not of one-piece construction) around or under the first pipe section. Then lay the second pipe section with the corrugations matching. Complete the band around the pipe and fasten tightly.

Bituminous Coated and Paved Pipe

Asphalt pavement is employed to protect the corrugated steel pipe against erosion from abrasive materials, and so prolong the drainage structure life. With invert paved pipe, asphalt covers about 25 percent of the circumference and fills the corrugations in the flow line. To be effective, paved pipe must be installed with the smooth, thick pavement placed and centered on the bottom.

On coated pipe, the surface between coupler and pipe may need lubrication with fuel oil or soapstone solution. This will allow the band to slip around the pipe more easily and to draw into place more firmly, particularly in cold weather. Lubricating and tapping the bands so they can be drawn to proper register will assure a strong joint.

Where damage to the bituminous coating exposes the metal, repair by patching before the structure is backfilled. Suitable materials include asphalt mastic with asbestos fibers and coal tar cutback.

Connecting Bands

Connecting bands of galvanized steel are used to join sections of corrugated steel pipe. "Standard" bands are used for most installations on all sizes of pipe. "Two-piece" bands are used on the larger sizes under difficult installation conditions. "Rod and lug" bands are used on special work where maximum watertightness is essential—as in levees, aerial sewers and similar installations. (For various types of couplings, see Chapt. 1, Sec. B.)

Width of the connecting band varies with the pipe diameter, ranging from 7 to 24 in.

For helically corrugated and spun-lined pipe, the adjacent ends may butt together.

In installing corrugated bands on riveted and spot welded pipe, first slip the band into position over the end of one pipe section with the band open to receive the next section. The adjoining length is brought to within about 1 in. of the first section, and the band is tightened with the corrugations of the band matching the corrugations of the pipe sections. For every band used, the rated length of pipe will increase $2\frac{2}{3}$ or 3 in.—equal to the width of one corrugation.

Keep dirt and gravel out of the joint, so that corrugations fit snugly. As the plain galvanized band is tightened, tap it with a mallet or hammer to take up slack and to insure a tight joint. Mere torqueing of bolts will not produce a tight joint on large diameter culverts.

To speed the coupling operation, especially for large diameter structures, a chain or cable-cinching device will help draw the band tight.

Fittings

Steel fittings can be specified and installed to the same strength and tightness values as the remainder of the lines. The couplings described on preceding pages are generally suitable for this purpose.

With smaller fittings, the sleeve joint or stab joint is integral with the fittings. No bolting is necessary but gaskets may be added as required.

Medium size fittings usually require bolted couplings of adequate strength, with or without gaskets for watertightness and to keep out surrounding soil.

Aerial sewers demand a little extra care to insure adequate strength and tightness. Structural plate fittings are assembled and bolted together on the job. Where watertightness is needed, seam sealants or possibly welding may be specified.

Diaphragms

Steel diaphragms or cutoff walls reduce danger of water seepage that might cause a washout along the outside of the structure. Typical of such installa-

Fig. 7-8. Use of square, steel diaphragms on levees discourages seepage.

tions are pipes through levees or dams where the pipe may be subjected to a hydraulic head. Fig. 7-8.

Diaphragms should be located midway between two adjacent riveted circumferential seams, as near the center of a pipe length as possible, and at least 4 ft from a field joint. In multiple line installations, space the diaphragms to assure at least 12-in. clearance between the faces of diaphragms on adjacent pipes for working room in backfilling.

The bottom half of the diaphragm is placed after excavating for the pipe and before laying and joining the pipe. Generally a narrow trench is excavated for the diaphragm, although it may be driven or jetted into place under some soil conditions. The diaphragm must be lined up to mesh with the corrugations of the pipe. The top half of the diaphragm is placed as soon as the pipe has been placed. The cross trench for the lower half should be backfilled with good fill material and tamped to give maximum compaction.

Multiple Installations

Two or more structures laid parallel in the same trench or streambed should be separated (as indicated in Fig. 7-14) sufficiently for mechanical equipment to operate between them. Such tamping and compaction helps prevent washouts during high water or flood stage.

Fig. 7-9. Using a minimum number of bolts until the structure is assembled makes for greater flexibility in erecting.

Section C—STRUCTURAL PLATE PIPE, PIPE-ARCHES UNDERPASSES AND ARCHES

UNLOADING AND HANDLING

Plates for structural plate pipes, pipe-arches and arches are ordinarily shipped nested in packs. These are usually of such size that cranes, towmotors or other construction equipment on the job are needed for unloading purposes. Ordinary care in handling is required to keep the plates clean and free from damage by rough treatment.

BOLTING PROCEDURE

Structures are shipped complete with all plates, bolts and nuts necessary for erection. Inside one package or keg of bolts, clearly marked, are detailed erection instructions showing the order of assembly and position of each plate. Bolt heads are color coded for different lengths.

Structures should initially be assembled with as few bolts as possible. Three or four untightened bolts near the center of each plate, along longitudinal and circumferential seams, are sufficient. This procedure gives maximum flexibility until all plates are fitted into place. See Figs. 7-9 and 7-10.

After part of the structure has been assembled into shape by partial bolting, the remaining bolts can be inserted and hand tightened. Always work from the center of a seam toward the plate corner. Do not insert corner bolts until all others are in place and tightened.

Alignment of bolt holes is easiest when bolts are loose. Drifting with a drift pin is best done when adjacent bolts are tight.

Progressively and uniformly tighten nuts, starting at one end of the structure, *after all plates* are in place. See Fig. 7-9. The operation should be repeated to be sure all bolts are tight.

If the plates are well aligned, the torque applied with a power wrench need not be excessive. A setting of 300 ft-lb, plus or minus 50, is ordinarily satisfactory. A good fit of the plates is better than high torque. Bolts should not be overtightened.[1]

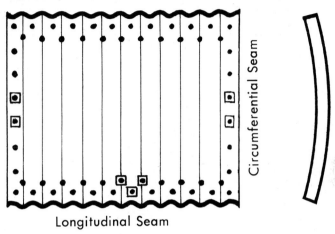

Longitudinal Seam

Fig. 7-10. Details of curved corrugated structural plate. Squares indicate preferred sequence of bolting, beginning at the middle and working towards the plate corners.

Structural Plate Arches

Structural plate arches are generally erected on a masonry foundation. The arch rests in a groove or unbalanced channel, which must be accurately built to line and grade for easy assembly of the plates. When the arch is set on a skew, holes in unbalanced channels must line up with those in the plates. Layout for channel installation is shown on special plate assembly drawings furnished with each skewed structural plate arch. For straight-end arches on which headwalls are to be built, allowance should be made in design for a lip (approx. 2 in.) at each end.

Cut Ends and End Treatment

The ends of large steel plate structures may require some special protection during backfilling and tamping operations. This is especially true for beveled or skewed ends. Temporary braces or tie wires may be desirable. Backfilling equipment and mechanical tampers should not get closer than 8 to 12 inches from the ends of the structure.

In unstable soils, the use of cutoff walls at the ends of hydraulic structures is essential and should be included in the design. Due to lack of such precautions, failure of the structure and of the embankment can occur and has occurred in a limited number of cases.

Asphalt Coating—Shop or Field

Where structural plates require a protective coating in addition to the galvanizing, there is a suitable material available for applying in the field or on pre-assembled structures in the plant. Plates need to be clean and dry.

The type of coating consists of a fibrated asphalt mastic sprayed on under high pressure to a thickness of approximately $\frac{1}{16}$ in. This has been found more satisfactory than hot-dip coatings. (Coating F, Federal Spec. WW-P-405A, 1968.)

Fig. 7-11. A granular material makes the best backfill. However, cohesive materials can be used if the moisture is controlled.

Section D—SOIL BACKFILL

For the roadway conduit to support the pavement or track above it adequately and uniformly, a stable composite structure is vital. Stability in a soil-structure interaction system requires not only adequate design of the structure barrel, it also presumes a well engineered backfill. Performance of the flexible conduit in retaining its shape and structural integrity depends greatly on selection, placement and compaction of the envelope of earth surrounding the structure and distributing its pressures to the abutting soil masses.

Requirements for selecting and placing backfill material around or near the conduit are similar to those for a roadway embankment. The main difference in requirements is due to the fact that *the conduit may generate more lateral pressure than would the earth within the embankment if no structure existed.*

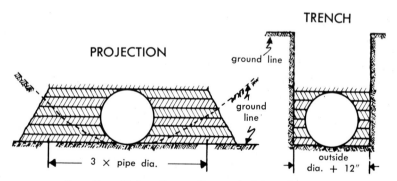

Notes: Place fill in uniform well tamped 6" layers.
Keep fill at same elevation on both sides of pipe.

Fig. 7-12. Backfill should be placed in uniform, well tamped 6-in. layers on both sides of the structure.

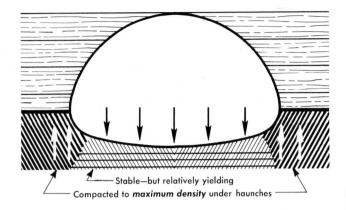

Fig. 7-13. Compaction under the corners of pipe-arches is important.

Choice of Material

All highway and railroad engineering departments have adequately detailed specifications for selecting and placing material in embankments. These specifications provide for wide variations in terrain and for available local materials, and so can generally apply to backfill material around conduits for normal installations. If abnormal conditions exist at a specific site or if unusual performance is expected of a conduit and embankment, a competent soils engineer should be consulted for designing the backfill.

Backfill material should preferably be granular to provide good structural performance. Cohesive type material can also be used if careful attention is given to compaction at optimum moisture content. Very fine granular material may infiltrate into the structure and should be avoided when high ground water table is anticipated. A plastic cover or a filter layer may be placed between fine soil and the pipe. Bank run gravel or similar material compacted to 90 to 95 percent standard density is ideal.

Experience and research have shown the "critical density" of backfill to be below 85% standard AASHO density. Backfill must be compacted to a greater density than "critical" to assure good performance. Compaction to over 85% is recommended as a minimum allowable under any circumstances.

Placing Backfill Around Structure

Fill material under haunches and around the structure should be placed alternately in 6-in. layers on both sides of the pipe to permit thorough tamping. The fill is placed alternately to keep it at the same elevation on both sides of the structure at all times. Figs. 7-12 and 7-13 show how pipe and pipe-arch structures should be backfilled. Pipe-arches require that the backfill at the corners (sides) be of the best material and be especially well tamped.

Tamping can be done with hand or mechanical equipment, tamping rollers or vibrating compactors, depending upon field conditions. More important than method is that it be done carefully to insure a thoroughly tamped backfill.

Compaction of fills by puddling or jetting is not recommended. These methods usually do not produce reliable backfills for corrugated steel structures, except where supervised by a qualified soils engineer.

Fig. 7-14. Proper use of vibratory tamper alongside a large pipe-arch structure.

Tamping Equipment

1. *Hand Equipment.* For tamping under the haunches of a structure, a pole or 2 x 4 in. timber is generally needed to work in the small areas. Hand tampers for compacting horizontal layers should weigh not less than 20 lb and have a tamping face not larger than 6 x 6 in. Ordinary "sidewalk" tampers are generally too light.
2. *Mechanical Tampers.* Most types of power tampers are satisfactory and can be used in all save the most confined areas. However, they must be used carefully and completely over the entire area of each layer to obtain the desired compaction. Avoid striking the structure with power tamping tools. Fig. 7-14.
3. *Tamping Rollers.* Where space permits, sheepsfoot, rubber-tired and other types of tamping rollers can be used to compact backfill around the structure. If rollers are used, fill adjacent to the structure should be tamped with hand or hand-held power equipment. Be sure to keep the rollers from hitting the structure. Smooth rollers are generally not satisfactory for compacting fills. Particular attention should be given to keeping the fill at the same elevation on both sides of the pipe.
4. *Vibrating Compactors.* Vibrating equipment can be used to compact the granular backfills but generally is unsatisfactory for clay or other plastic soils.

Backfill on Arches

Care must be taken in backfilling arches, especially half-circle arches, because they have a tendency to shift sideways or to "peak up" under backfilling loads. The ideal way is to cover an arch in layers—each layer conforming to the shape of the arch. *If one side is backfilled more than the other, the arch will move away from the larger load.* If both sides are backfilled equally and tamped thoroughly, the top of the arch may peak up unless enough fill has been placed over it to resist the upward thrust. These precautions apply also to other corrugated steel structures, but to a lesser degree. See Fig. 7-15.

Filling on only one side causes arch to shift. If fill is not placed on top as backfilling proceeds, arch may raise, thereby flattening side radius.

COMMON MISTAKES IN BACKFILLING ARCHES (above)

Place fill on arch by distributing material around and over the structure in uniform layers, tamping thoroughly. Place material from top of arch.

RECOMMENDED BACKFILLING PRACTICE

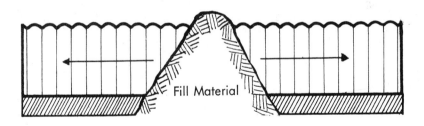

Fill Material

SIDE VIEWS—Without and With Headwalls

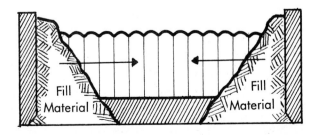

Fill Material

Fill Material

Fig. 7-15. Recommended and poor backfilling practice for corrugated steel arches.

Arches Without Headwalls

When backfilling arches without headwalls, or with headwalls not sufficiently strong to maintain the shape of the arch, place the first fill midway between the ends of the arch. This fill should be kept in as narrow a strip as possible until the top of the arch is reached. The remainder of the backfill should be placed from the top of the arch, starting at the center and working both ways to the ends. By this means, illustrated in Fig. 7-15, least side pressure is developed until the top is loaded.

Arches With Headwalls

In backfilling arches with headwalls heavy enough to maintain the shape of the arch, it is advisable to place the fill against one head wall until the top of the arch is reached. Continue dumping in layers toward the opposite headwall.

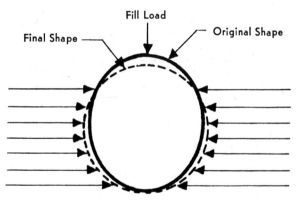

Fig. 7-16. Proper side support enables a flexible steel structure to resist tremendous fill loads.

Vertical Elongation

As a corrugated steel pipe structure deflects under load, its vertical diameter shortens and the horizontal diameter increases. This spreading in the horizontal dimension compresses the backfill and builds up an increasing side support for the structure. Fig. 7-16, exaggerated for clarity, demonstrates this action. Magnitude of deflection is a measure of backfill compaction, since the better the backfilling, the less the deflection.

Corrugated Steel Pipe. When required, riveted, spot welded or helically corrugated steel pipe is provided by the fabricating plant formed to the specified vertical elongation.

Structural Plate Pipe. Structural plate pipe can be preformed at the fabricating plant to elliptical shape by the use of short and long radius plates.

Completing the Fill Over Structure

Complete the fill over a corrugated steel structure using materials essentially the same as those used for the backfill and placed and compacted in the same manner. Distribute and compact the fill evenly to a depth equal to the height of the structure, or the entire fill, if it is shallow.

In trenches, fill material should be tamped in layers from the top of the structure to the original ground level. This assures thorough compaction and eliminates settlement.

Protection of Structure During Construction

It is important to protect drainage structures during construction because maximum strength does not develop until fill consolidates. To avoid imposing concentrated loads far in excess of those the structure would normally carry, heavy construction equipment should not cross the structure prematurely. Also, heavy vehicles moving too close to the wall of the structure can create an eccentric loading with harmful results.

More than normal fill is a frequent need to protect the structure during construction, especially if heavy equipment is used. The minimum cover required has been tentatively established as one eighth of the barrel diameter (or span) for highway conduits and one quarter diameter for railway conduits, with a minimum as specified in the fill height tables. How much excess protective fill is needed depends upon the wheel loads of equipment used as well as frequency of loading.

Cut Ends

By cutting the ends of corrugated metal structures, need for additional end finish can often be eliminated. Ends cut to specified embankment slopes are furnished by the culvert fabricator. They can be beveled (limit 2:1), skewed or a combination of skew and bevel. Ends cut as skews or bevels (or both) are not as strong as square ends, and in the case of large structures may require temporary bracing. Skew angles less than 70° or greater than 110° when combined with bevels, require the addition of full headwalls or ring beams.

The embankment slope around the structure can be protected against erosion by a cutoff wall and by riprapping around the structure end with stone, bags filled with dry sand-cement mixture, or by use of a slope pavement. Cut ends should be reinforced with masonry or concrete headwalls, when the bevel exceeds 2:1 and the skew is greater than 15 degrees.

Fig. 7-17. Beveled end and low cutoff wall provide a neat end finish.

Fig. 7-18. Jacking an 84-in. diameter steel pipe under a highway embankment. Earth is removed at the heading in a wheelbarrow or cart.

Section E—JACKING

New openings for culverts, sewers, conduits, underpasses, etc., are frequently required under existing railroads, highways, runways, levees and other engineering works. Four methods of placing such openings are: open trenching, jacking, tunneling and boring.[2]

Open trenching, most commonly used, is well adapted to new construction and to replacements under shallow fills and areas of light traffic. This method is detailed on preceding pages.

The *jacking method* of installation, in use for the past four decades, offers important advantages. These include protection of the general public, and fast, uninterrupted movement of traffic. In various parts of the country, experienced subcontractors will do this kind of work at predetermined prices. Fig. 7-18.

Acceptance of Jacking

This method of installing new openings has today become standard procedure for most railroads and for numerous highway departments. It saves time, money and material, and supplies a factor of safety all-important to present day movement of traffic. Jacking also avoids the cost and nuisance of repeated maintenance of the fill (due to settlement) usually necessary when open trench installation is used. For levee or dike installations, jacking avoids sacrificing valuable land and the building of new setback levees.

Testing of Soil

Jacking should not be attempted (1) in dry sand, (2) in gravelly soil known to contain large boulders, (3) through fills where logs or stumps are known to exist or (4) where it is impractical or uneconomical to lower the water table below the excavation.

In all questionable soil conditions, test the soil by boring or sampling before deciding upon jacking. Such testing is neither costly nor time-consuming. Effective chemical means now exist to stabilize soils ahead of the jacking face.

Diameters

Pipes from 30 to 96-in. diameter have been installed by jacking with no settlement of surface structures and no interruption of traffic. However, 36 to 60-in. are sizes most commonly jacked today. One essential working condition: the structure must be large enough to allow a man to excavate ahead of the pipe without being too cramped. For the average size man, minimum working space seems to be 36-in. diameter. Maximum pipe diameter capable of being jacked depends on several factors; the main ones are: ground conditions, height of cover and safety.

Lengths

Maximum length of pipe capable of being jacked is variable; it depends on the pipe diameter, ground conditions and the pressures required to push the pipe.

Lengths greater than 400 ft have been installed by jacking. In such installations, ground conditions must approach the ideal, and the pipe must be kept in motion continuously to keep it from "freezing" tight.

Where pipe does "freeze up" it is possible, under most conditions, to jack the balance of the pipe from the opposite side of the fill to meet the end already in place. Proper junction of these two pipes is a matter not only of engineering calculation, but also careful control of field crew work to assure that line and grade are accurately met and maintained.

Depth of Cover

Overburden on pipe to be jacked beneath operating railroads should be at least one pipe diameter below base of rail—no less than 3 ft—to get below the ballast line and into stable material. Under reinforced highway slabs, the cover can be the least needed for a cushion between slab bottom and pipe top. Under bituminous type pavements, the cover should equal that beneath railroads.

JACKING PROCEDURE[3]

Approach Trench

Pipe to be jacked through fills higher than the diameter of the pipe, plus required minimum cover, need no working pit. However, an open jacking face is desirable. Excavate an approach trench into the fill far enough to provide a jacking face of 3 ft or more above the pipe. This open face should be shored securely to prevent slipping or raveling of the embankment. Make provision for a sump in one corner of the approach trench or pit.

Backstop and Guides

A substantial backstop is necessary to take the thrust of the jack. A 60 to 80-ft length jacking job in reasonably good soil often develops 150 to 300 tons of jacking resistance.[4] The backstop is of heavy timbers or steel framing.

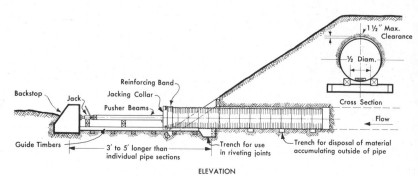

ELEVATION

Fig. 7-19. Set-up for typical jacking operation. There is no interference at traffic level.

Steel rails or timbers that support the pipe as it enters the bore must be accurately placed on line and grade. Both line and grade should be checked at least once per shift as work progresses. Fig. 7-19.

Pipe for Jacking

To jack corrugated pipe, sections are especially prepared for field jointing by riveting or bolting. A jacking band is recommended to reinforce the end receiving the thrust—especially for long lines or large diameters. When jacking through loose or gravelly soils, smooth steel sheets of light gage should be bolted to top and bottom of the pipe sections.

Equipment

Necessary equipment for jacking includes an electric power plant for lights, pumps, excavating tools, muck handling equipment and jacks. A wheelbarrow is economical for pipe 48 in. and larger. For smaller pipe, some type of skip or dolly-mounted dirt box is required.

Jacking Operation

As material is excavated ahead of the pipe, the pipe is jacked in to follow this excavation. The distance dug ahead of the pipe rarely exceeds 12 to 18 in. Some loose soils may reduce this to 3 or 4 in.

Section F—BORING

Boring is another means of installing conduits and culverts without disturbing surface structures or traffic. This method is generally confined to pipe diameters from 10¾ in. through 36 in. Various types of machines on the market are built to perform this operation.

Two basic boring methods exist. In the first, conduit pipe is pushed into the fill as the boring auger drills out the ground. Fig. 7-20. The second method consists of drilling the hole through the fill and pushing the conduit pipe into the hole after the drill auger has completed the bore. Both methods have their advantages. But if there is any doubt concerning ground conditions, the first method is the safer of the two; it offers greater protection to the surface structure under which the conduit is placed.

Location of Holes

Boring installations are generally small diameters, so the prospect of being stopped by boulders, rocks—even utility lines—should be considered and alternate locations provided for the conduit. Rocks and boulders are prevalent in some locations. In other areas, the possibility of encountering such obstacles is remote. The engineer and the contractor must guide their thinking accordingly.

Where obstacles are encountered in fills, it may be necessary to abandon that exact location.

Some machines will bore through rock and coal but it is not often economically practical to adapt these rock cutters to earth augers. Most earth boring augers will penetrate soft rock, wood or brick, but experience and "feel" are required to judge the practicability of going ahead when such obstacles are met. Line and grade may suffer because of these obstacles and even though it is possible to complete the bore, it may not be satisfactory for the purpose intended. Under such circumstances it may be wiser to abandon the bore when the obstacle is encountered and move a few feet to try again.

Fig. 7-20. Boring under an express highway to provide conduit for a sewer or water line. Smooth-wall steel pipe is used for this purpose.

Fig. 7-21. Lining and extending a failing twin masonry arch under a mainline railroad using elliptical shaped 22-ft diameter structural plate pipe. Space between old and new structure was backfilled. New structure has step-beveled ends and a 3-ft deep toe-wall.

Section G—LINING

There comes a time when tunnels, stone arches, conduits and culverts begin to deteriorate and lose strength. The decision to rehabilitate or replace is usually based on available methods, safety and economics. Also, due to changing conditions, some old structures must be strengthened to accommodate present and future loads greater than those for which the structures were originally designed.

Discussion here is confined to some of the economical methods used to rehabilitate and strengthen drainage openings, small bridges, sewers, etc.

Masonry and Concrete Arches: These structures begin to deteriorate from natural causes after being in service for a limited period of years. Mortar comes out of the joints, the stones loosen; alternate freezing and thawing causes trouble. Concrete begins to crack and spall off or heavy loads cause foundation settlement, resulting in cracking and spalling. Consequently, the structure needs to be strengthened or must be replaced. Rehabilitation in numerous cases is the most economical and can be accomplished with least effort.

Lining such a structure with a structural steel plate or steel liner plate arch takes little space, and conserves a maximum amount of the original waterway capacity. These steel arches can be supported on new concrete side walls or on original bench walls where feasible. Fig. 7-21. Small arches, 6 ft or less, can be lined with riveted corrugated steel sections.

Over the past 30 years, many hundreds of lineal feet of masonry arches have been given renewed life by this lining method. Results have been very satisfactory.

Pressure Grouting

Pressure grouting the space between the old and new structures, prevents further collapse of the old structure and avoids concentrated pressures on the new lining. Two-inch grout couplings welded into the liner plates can be furnished at proper intervals for convenience in grouting. A mixture of 1 part cement to 3 parts sand, plus an additive for lubrication, has been found satisfactory.

Grouting should be carefully done. Inspect frequently to see that voids are being thoroughly filled. In fact, due to shrinkage of the grout after "set up", the top row of grout holes should be "check grouted" after grout placement is completed to be sure any voids due to shrinkage have been filled.

Other Shapes of Structures

This same relining method can be applied to full round, elliptical or other structural shapes that have begun to show signs of deterioration or collapse. New corrugated steel pipe, structural steel plate or liner plate can be threaded inside an old structure to give it new life for long trouble-free service. Frequently, due to excessive deflection or joint settlement, the diameter of the new lining will necessarily be much smaller in order to have clearance for threading. In such cases it sometimes is necessary to jack or tunnel a supplementary opening alongside the present structure to restore the waterway capacity lost from the old culvert. See Chapter 8 *Tunnel Liner*.

It also happens that changes in runoff conditions may no longer require as large an opening as originally. In these cases, any reduction in waterway area due to "threading" is not serious. These changing conditions should be investigated before the engineer defines his requirements.

Rehabilitation through relining can also be applied to storm or sanitary sewers which are beginning to show signs of weakening. Fig. 7-22. Methods of installation of liners for sewers will vary with sewer size and the liner type, but the basic principles here would be the same as those used in "threading" or lining any relatively short culvert open at both ends.

Fig. 7-22. Lining a failing sewer by threading with corrugated steel pipe, asphalt coated and paved.

Section H—BRIDGE AND TRESTLE REPLACEMENT

On railroads and highways are innumerable small bridges—built of timber, concrete and steel, or a combination of these materials—larger than the drainage area truly demands. Maintenance on these bridges becomes quite costly as the structure ages. Eventually, arrangements must be made for major repairs or complete replacement. At that time a complete investigation should be made of the actual waterway opening required, the importance of the structure from a traffic standpoint, consideration of fire hazard, elimination of maintenance and the most economical material to be used.

Economics of materials does not necessarily mean low first cost. Reduced maintenance cost, long trouble-free life, ease of installation without traffic interruptions and capital investment should be considered along with the cost of retiring the old structure and/or rerouting traffic.

Structural plate and corrugated steel pipe have been used quite extensively over the past 30 years for filling and replacing timber trestles on railroads, and small steel, wood or concrete spans on county and state highway systems. The success of these metal structures is evidenced by the growing acceptance of their use. In some instances one opening will take care of the waterway; while in other cases a whole battery of pipes may be necessary. Drainage area and available headroom will determine the size and number of pipes required. Fig. 7-23.

Fig. 7-23. Providing a creek crossing with eight 14-ft diameter structural plate pipes with the beveled ends pre-assembled and lifted into place.

Backfill Method Important

Proper foundation and tamping of the backfill are very significant and these operations are of sufficient importance to warrant repeating. At those spots where the pipe or pipes are close to existing pile bents and cross bracing, a good job of backfilling and tamping is mandatory. Preferably, surround the pipe with pit run gravel or other types of pervious material (except cinders or slag) rather than clay. Precautions should be taken to seal the upstream end against seepage under and alongside the pipe—a cause of failures.

Impervious materials can be used on top of the pervious material to build up the fill; but since water will follow the line of piling and cross bracing (and could cause soft spots around the pipes), it would be better for such water to collect on the outside and seep into the culvert before it can do harm to the fill. This is particularly true where structural plate is used. After the fill has consolidated, this pervious material will gradually cease to function as a water collector. However, it should be there at the time of installation to help eliminate soft spots alongside the pipe that tend to form from rainfall during the fill build up.

In case of replacement of railroad trestles, the caps and stringers should remain in place to handle traffic until the fill has become consolidated. Otherwise the railroad should be willing to raise track that settles with the fill. In case of highway bridge replacements, a temporary surface should be placed on the new fill until consolidation is final.

REFERENCES AND BIBLIOGRAPHY

1. Arrand, C.O.D., *"Study of the Properties of Corr. Metal Pipe Joints Subjected to Compression and Bending."* Ohio Dept. of Highways and FPWA, Report No. EES-279-1, Ohio State Univ. Eng. Experiment Sta., Columbus, Ohio, 1968, 123 pp. (unpublished)
2. National Corr. Steel Pipe Assn., *"Installation Manual for Corrugated Metal Structures"*, Manual CMPA-1165, Chicago, Ill., 1965, 54 pp.
3. Colvin, C. M., *"Jacking Culverts Through Fills"*, Western Construction, San Francisco, Calif., April, 1953.
4. Feld, Jacob, Highway Research Board, Bulletin No. 14, 1948.
5. *"Corrugated Metal Pipe Culverts"*—Recommended Installation Practices, Bureau of Public Roads, 26 pp., 1966.

Fig. 8-1. Access shaft for tunnel, 16 ft in diameter, 30 ft deep, completed in three working days. Four-flange steel tunnel liner plates were used for the shaft and the tunnel.

CHAPTER 8 Tunnel Liner Plates

INTRODUCTION

The "open-trench" method of placing underground conduits has in the past been commonly used on new construction of culverts, sewers and underpasses. Interference with traffic, as well as inconvenience to and disruption of business or industry is an undesirable and costly consequence of "open-trench" emplacement. Tunneling is a safe and practical alternative. Fig. 8-1.

More than forty years of field experience with strong, lightweight pressed steel liner plates has popularized the tunneling method of construction. These plates, plus modern excavating and material handling equipment, and increasing knowledge of effective soil stabilization techniques, have led to many thousands of feet of small tunnel jobs completed each year.

Tunneling with steel liner plates means less excavation and less backfilling. Expensive pavements and utilities need not be destroyed and replaced. Future expense caused by street or track settlement can be avoided.

GENERAL APPLICATIONS

Uses of steel liner plates include conduits under railways, highways and streets—for culverts, storm drains, sanitary sewers, and as underpasses for pedestrians, livestock, aggregate conveyors, utility lines, (Fig. 8-2), and freight. Other applications are: lining failing masonry structures such as culverts, sewers (Fig. 8-7); and highway and railway tunnels; mine and sewer entry shafts; steam and utility tunnels and foundation caissons for bridges, buildings, and towers.

Liner plates may act as a temporary conduit or skin to be lined by other materials. They also serve alone as the permanent lining or conduit itself. Installation, including bolting, is necessarily from the inside.

Non-tunneling uses of steel liner plates include storage bins and surge tanks.

Fig. 8-2. Corrugated liner plate tunnel driven under railroad track serves as a conduit to protect a large steel water line.

AASHO DESIGN SPECIFICATIONS*[4]

DESIGN: LOADING CONSIDERATIONS

The supporting capacity of a non-rigid tunnel lining such as a steel liner plate results from its ability to deflect under load so that side restraint developed by the lateral resistance of the soil constrains further deflection. Deflection thus tends to equalize radial pressures and to load the tunnel liner as a compression ring.

The load carried by the tunnel liner is a function of the type of soil. In a granular soil, with little or no cohesion, the load is a function of the angle of internal friction of the soil and the diameter of the tunnel. In cohesive soils such as clays and silty clays the load carried by the tunnel liner is dependent on the shearing strength of the soil above the roof of the tunnel.

A subsurface exploration program and appropriate soil tests should be performed at each installation before undertaking a design.

LOAD PREDICTIONS

External load on a circular tunnel liner made up of tunnel liner plates may be predicted by various methods including actual tests. In cases where more precise methods of analysis are not employed, the external load P can be predicted by the following:

1. If the grouting pressure is greater than the computed external load, the external load P on the tunnel liner should be the grouting pressure.

2. The external load can be computed by the formula $P = P_1 + P_d$ .....(1)

where: P = the external load on the tunnel liner

P_1 = the vertical load at the level of the top of the tunnel liner due to live loads

P_d = the vertical load at the level of the top of the tunnel liner due to dead load.

For an H20 load on an unsurfaced fill, values of P_1 are approximately the following:

H (ft)	4	5	6	7	8	9	10
P_1 (lb per sq ft)	375	260	190	140	110	90	75

For E 80 Railway Live Load Plus Impact, values of P_1 are approximately the following:

H (ft)	2	5	8	10	12	15	20	30
P_1 (lb per sq ft)	3800	2400	1600	1100	800	600	300	100

H is the height of soil fill above the top of the tunnel liner.

---

*The design information presented here is from the AASHO "Design Specifications for Tunnel Liner Plates" and is reprinted with permission.

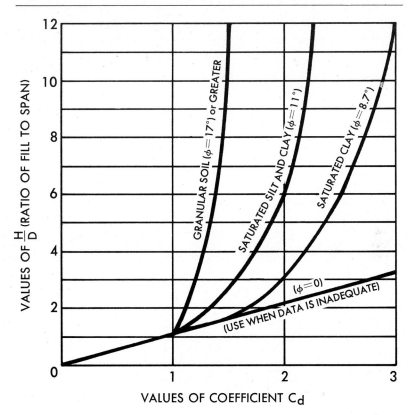

Fig. 8-3. Coefficients for tunnels in various soils.

In the absence of adequate borings and soil tests, the full overfill height should be the basis for P_d in the tunnel liner plate design.

Values of P_d may be calculated using Marston's formula,

$$P_d = C_d\ WD \dots\dots\dots\dots\dots\dots\dots\dots\dots\dots\dots\dots\dots(2)$$

where: C_d = coefficient for tunnel liner, Fig. 8-3

W = total (moist) unit weight of soil

D = horizontal diameter or span of the tunnel

DESIGN CRITERIA

The following criteria must be considered in the design of liner plates:

    (A) Joint strength

    (B) Critical buckling of liner plate wall

    (C) Handling and installation strength

    (D) Deflection or flattening of tunnel section

A. JOINT STRENGTH

Seam strength for two-flange liner plates should be sufficient to withstand the thrust developed from the total load supported by the liner plate. This thrust, T, in pounds per lineal foot is

$$T=\frac{PD}{2} \dots\dots\dots\dots\dots\dots\dots\dots\dots\dots\dots\dots\dots(3)$$

where P = load as defined on page 262

D = diameter or span, in feet

Thrust, T, multiplied by the safety factor, FS, ($FS = 3$, recommended) should not exceed the ultimate seam strength shown in Table 8-1.

Table 8-1   Ultimate Longitudinal Seam Strength of Tunnel Liner Plates

Plate Thickness in Inches	Ultimate Strength in kips/ft	
	2-flange	4-flange
0.075	20.0	
0.105	30.0	26.4
0.135	47.0	43.5
0.164	55.0	50.2
0.179	62.0	54.5
0.209	87.0	67.1
0.239	92.0	81.5
0.250		84.1
0.313		115.1
0.375		119.1

Bolts and nuts used with lapped seams shall be not less than ⅝ inch in diameter. The bolts shall conform to the specifications of ASTM A 449 for plate thickness equal to or greater than 0.209 inch and A 307 for plate thickness less than 0.209 inch. The nuts shall conform to ASTM Designation A 307.

Bolts and nuts used with four-flanged plates shall be not less than ½ inch in diameter for plate thicknesses to and including 0.179 inch and not less than ⅝ inch in diameter for plates of greater thickness. The bolts and nuts shall be quick-acting coarse thread and shall conform to ASTM Specification A 307, Grade A.

B. CRITICAL BUCKLING OF LINER PLATE WALL

Wall buckling stresses are determined from the following formulae:

For diameters less than $\dfrac{r}{K}\sqrt{\dfrac{24E}{f_u}}$ $\dots\dots\dots\dots\dots\dots\dots\dots\dots\dots\dots\dots(4)$

$$f_c = f_u - \frac{f_u^2}{48E}\left(\frac{KD}{r}\right)^2 \text{ in psi}$$

For diameters greater than $\dfrac{r}{K}\sqrt{\dfrac{24E}{f_u}}$ $\dots\dots\dots\dots\dots\dots\dots\dots\dots(5)$

$$f_c = \frac{12E}{\left(\dfrac{KD}{r}\right)^2} \text{ in psi}$$

where: f_u = minimum specified tensile strength, psi

f_c = buckling stress, psi, not to exceed specified yield strength

K = soil stiffness factor, 0.22

D = pipe diameter, inches

r = radius of gyration of section

E = modulus of elasticity, psi

Design for buckling is accomplished by limiting the ring compression thrust T to the buckling stress multiplied by the cross-sectional area of the liner plate, A, divided by the factor of safety:

$$T = \frac{f_c A}{FS} \dots\dots\dots\dots\dots\dots\dots\dots\dots\dots\dots\dots\dots\dots\dots\dots\dots\dots\dots (6)$$

where: T = thrust per lineal foot from Equation (3)

A = cross sectional area of liner plate, sq in. per ft

FS = factor of safety for buckling

Recommended $FS = 2$

C. HANDLING AND INSTALLATION STRENGTH

The liner plate ring should have enough rigidity to resist the unbalanced loadings of normal construction: grouting pressures, local slough-ins and miscellaneous concentrated loads. This rigidity is measured by a Flexibility Factor, *FF*, determined by the formula:

$$FF = \frac{D^2}{EI} \dots\dots\dots\dots\dots\dots\dots\dots\dots\dots\dots\dots\dots\dots\dots\dots\dots\dots\dots\dots (7)$$

where: FF = flexibility factor

D = diameter, inches

E = modulus of elasticity, psi

I = moment of inertia, inches to the 4th power per inch

For ordinary installations:

$FF = 2.0 \times 10^{-2} = 0.020$ (2-flange)

$FF = 0.9 \times 10^{-2} = .009$ (4-flange)

D. DEFLECTION OR FLATTENING

Deflection of a tunnel depends significantly on the amount of over excavation of the bore and is affected by delay in backpacking or inadequate backpacking. The magnitude of deflection is not primarily a function of soil modulus or the liner plate properties, so it cannot be computed with usual deflection formulae.

Where the tunnel clearances are important, the designer should over-size the structure to provide for a normal deflection. Good construction methods should result in deflections of not more than 3 percent of the normal diameter.

PRODUCT DETAILS

Steel liner plates are produced in two general designs: (1) four-flange type with abutting end joints, and (2) two-flange type with lapped offset end joints.

The two-flange plates are supplied with deep corrugations running through lapped end joints. See Fig. 8-4. Four-flange plates are normally supplied with various types of corrugated backs by individual manufacturers, but with no important differences in physical properties or strength. Dimensions, physical properties and gages are given in the accompanying tables as supplied by the manufacturers. Tables 8-2, 8-3 and 8-4. Section properties are reproduced from the manufacturers' data.

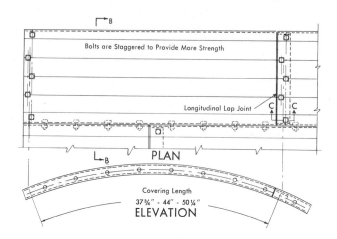

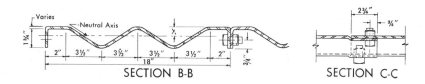

SECTION B-B   SECTION C-C

Fig. 8-4. Details of 2-flange liner plate.

Table 8-2. Sectional Properties and Weights of 2-Flange, Lap-Joint Steel Liner Plates[1]
For 18-inch wide section

Thickness T in In.	Area of Section A in In.²	Moment of Inertia I in In.⁴	Section Modulus S in In.³	Radius of Gyration r in In.	N. A. to Outer Face x in In.	Approx. Plate Weights Including Bolts, in Pounds		
						12 Pi Plate	14 Pi Plate	16 Pi Plate
0.0747	1.7237	0.6202	0.5809	0.5998	0.7571	25	28	31
0.1046	2.4266	0.8847	0.8229	0.6038	0.7795	33	37	42
0.1345	3.1292	1.1528	1.0624	0.6070	0.7994	41	47	52
0.1644	3.8382	1.4306	1.3064	0.6105	0.8193	49	56	63
0.1793	4.1947	1.5788	1.4372	0.6135	0.9308	53	61	68
0.2092	4.8949	1.8558	1.6707	0.6157	0.8485	61	70	79
0.2391	5.6104	2.1470	1.9166	0.6186	0.8689	70	80	90

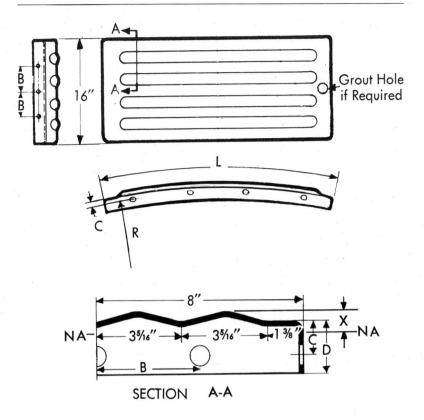

Fig. 8-5. Details of 4-flange liner plate—Type 1.

**Table 8-3 Sectional Properties and Weights of
4-Flange Tunnel Liner Plate—Type 1[2]**

For 16-inch-wide Section

Thickness T in Inches	Area of Section A in In.²	Moment of Inertia I in In.⁴	Radius of Gyration r in Inches	N.A. to Outer Fiber x in Inches	Approximate Plate Weights Including Bolts in Pounds	
					Full Plate	Half Pl.
.1046	2.1008	.6364	.55	.577	24.2	12.9
.1196	2.4306	.7492	.55	.578	27.7	14.7
.1345	2.7212	.8270	.55	.578	31.2	16.5
.1644	3.3390	1.1346	.58	.620	38.2	20.8
.1793	3.6564	1.2336	.58	.624	40.9	21.7
.2092	4.1752	1.4460	.59	.629	48.6	26.2
.2391	4.8174	1.8920	.62	.656	54.9	28.9
.3125	6.1714	2.5894	.65	.744	68.6	36.1
.375	7.4062	3.5234	.69	.786	82.3	43.3

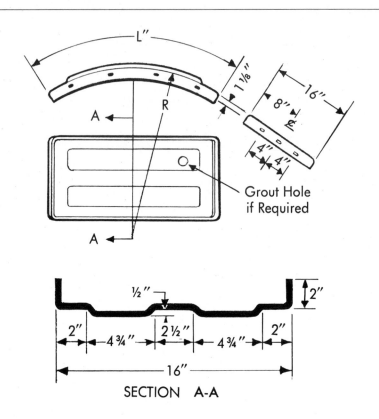

Fig. 8-6. Details of 4-flange liner plate—Type 2.

**Table 8-4 Sectional Properties and Weights of
4-Flange Liner Plate—Type 2[3]**

For 16-inch-wide Section

Thickness T in In.	Area of Section A in In.²	Moment of Inertia I in In.⁴	Section Modulus S in In.³	Radius of Gyration r in In.	N. A. to Outer Fiber x in In.	Approx. Plate Weights Including Bolts, in Pounds		
						Full* Plate	Half Plate	Quarter Plate
0.1046	2.1472	0.7347	0.3716	0.5850	0.5231	24.5	13.3	7.7
0.1345	2.7469	0.9283	0.4728	0.5813	0.5367	31.3	17.0	9.8
0.1644	3.3408	1.1156	0.5722	0.5779	0.5502	38.0	20.6	11.9
0.1793	3.6347	1.2066	0.6210	0.5762	0.5569	41.3	22.4	12.9
0.2092	4.2203	1.3849	0.7177	0.5729	0.5702	48.0	25.9	14.9
0.2500	5.0106	1.6196	0.8472	0.5685	0.5834	55.5	29.9	17.1
0.3125	6.2026	1.9616	1.0412	0.5624	0.6160	68.5	36.8	21.0
0.3750	7.3724	2.2855	1.2310	0.5568	0.6434	81.3	43.5	24.6

*Full Plate 16″ wide x 37¹¹⁄₁₆″ long.

INSTALLATION NOTES

Steel liner plates are installed to support the ground exposed by the mining operations. The excavated opening should fit closely the outside shape of the liner plates.

Where too much ground is removed, the annular space between plates and ground should be backfilled promptly or temporarily packed with hay and later grouted. Backfill may consist of pneumatically placed pea gravel, lean grout, sand or other suitable material.

Some of the liner plates should be provided with grout holes, and a sufficient number of these installed so that grouting can be effectively done at various levels. Grout or backfill should be kept as close to the heading as possible, using grout stops behind the plates where necessary. When grout is used for backfill, it should be injected in lower holes first, moving up as the back space is filled. Plugs, preferably threaded, should be installed in holes after filling at each one.

With extremely heavy loads or a tunnel too large for practical use of liner plates alone, reinforcing rings of I-beam or T-section may be used. In unstable soils—where ground will not remain in place long enough to excavate for a liner plate—the ground can be held with steel poling plates, wood spiling boards, or a shield and breast boards in the face. Chemical stabilization of the soil is also practicable in some cases. Tunneling machines are useful for long lines and in uniform soils.

Fig. 8-7. Lining a failed pipe with 72-in. diameter steel liner plate.

Fig. 8-8. Renewing an arch culvert over a canal by means of steel liner plates. Space between the structures was filled by grouting.

CAISSON DESIGN

The load to be carried by a caisson may be computed by known methods of determining horizontal pressure at a specified depth and multiplying this by one-half the caisson diameter. Unit pressures of some soils at various depths, assuming that pressure increases uniformly with depth, are shown in Fig. 8-9. The required thickness of liner plates may be selected from safe load tables for the type liner plate used.

Example

Soil: Damp plastic clay
Depth of caisson: 40 ft
Diameter of caisson: 20 ft
From the graph (Fig. 8-8):
    Load per 18-in. ring per ft of diameter = 3500 lb

$$3500 \times \frac{20 \text{ ft}}{2} = 35,000 \text{ lb per 18-in. lap joint}$$
                  or 23,300 lb per ft of seam or joint.

Ultimate lap joint strength for plates of 0.239-in. thickness with ASTM A 449 high strength steel bolts = 92,000 lb per ft of seam*

$$\text{Factor of safety} = \frac{92,000}{23,300} = 3.95$$

*From Table 8-1, page 264, based on 2-flange offset-type plates.
For additional data on liner plate *underpasses*, see page 27.

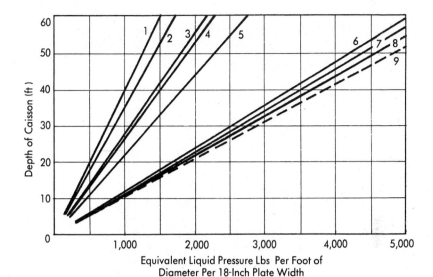

Fig. 8-9. Equivalent fluid pressure for caisson construction.

1. Clay: Lumpy & dry
   Earth: Loose & either dry or slightly moist
2. Earth: Fairly moist & packed
3. Earth: Perfectly dry & packed
4. Clay, sand and gravel mixture

5. Drained river sand
6. Earth: Soft flowing mud
7. Clay: Damp & plastic
8. Earth: Soft, packed mud
9. Hydrostatic pressure of water

REFERENCES

1. *Armco Liner Plate*, Metal Products Div., Armco Steel Corp., Middletown, Ohio, Catalog LP-7869, 1969, 20 pp.
2. *Soft Ground Tunneling*, Commercial Shearing & Stamping Co., Youngstown, Ohio, Catalog T-1, 10M-37, 34 pp.
3. *Republic Steel Tunnel Liner Plates*, Republic Steel Corp., Mfg. Div., Youngstown, Ohio, Catalog G-142.
4. AASHO Design Specifications for Steel Tunnel Liner Plates, Washington, D. C., 1970.

Fig. 9-1. Driving corrugated steel sheeting through the ice for a float-plane base.

CHAPTER 9

Sheeting, Light-Weight

Steel sheeting or sheet piling is quite commonly used where bank erosion is to be prevented or earth retained, as in the case of trenches, cofferdams, bulkheads and cutoff walls. Comparatively light-weight corrugated steel sheets are now being used for these purposes where the depths and loads do not exceed the strength limitations of the section. Fig. 9-1.

Advantages which sheeting offers are:

1. There are units to suit various service conditions
2. Because of size and weight they are easy to handle
3. Ease and speed of driving
4. Ample strength
5. Resistance to damage to the driving and leading edges
6. Ability to be salvaged readily and re-used frequently
7. Ease of storage and shipping
8. Nestability for compactness in shipping.

Because of the many uses to which steel sheeting is put, several types are needed to best meet varying conditions. Two widely used types are *interlocking* and *flange*. (See Table 9-1). The *interlocking* type is used where practical watertightness is desired, as in cutoff walls. *Flange* type is commonly used for sheeting trenches, particularly where watertightness is not essential. The flanges can butt against each other, or alternate sections can be reversed so that the flanges overlap.

Fig. 9-2. Neat appearance with minimum maintenance is an important advantage of steel sheeting along the waterfront.

DIMENSIONAL DATA

Flange type units are 16 in. wide, in thicknesses of .1046 to .1793 in. Standard lengths are multiples of 2 ft, from 6 to 20 ft and more.

Interlocking type units have a nominal covering width of 14, 15 or 18 in. Also available are 12 and 28 in. Standard lengths are multiples of 2 ft, from 6 to 20 ft.

Sheeting used for temporary purposes is generally of black (uncoated) steel. For increased durability in permanent dams and cutoff walls the sheeting may be galvanized or bituminous coated or both.

Several types of corner sections, along with a T and X section for intermediate bulkheads and junctions, are available for the interlocking type. Sectional properties of interlocking and flange sheeting panels are given in Table 9-1.

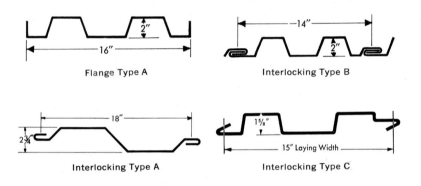

Flange Type A   Interlocking Type B

Interlocking Type A   Interlocking Type C

Fig. 9-3. Types of lightweight corrugaged steel sheeting or piling.

Table 9-1 Sectional Properties—Corrugated Steel Sheeting
Per Section Width

Type	Uncoated Thickness, in In.	0.1046	0.1345	0.1644	0.1793
Flange—A²	Area of section, in.²	2.406	3.094		4.124
	Weight per ft/length, lb	8.27	10.781	13.2	14.375
16 in. wide	Moment I—in.⁴/Sect.	1.4937	1.9207		2.5604
	Sect. mod. S—in.³/Sect.	1.185	1.526	1.87	2.030
Interlocking-A¹	Area of section, in.²	2.43	3.13	3.82	
	Weight per ft/length, lb	8.48	10.90	13.32	
18. in. wide	Moment I—in.⁴/Sect.	2.23	2.83	3.67	
	Sect. mod. S—in.³/Sect.	1.62	2.06	2.67	
Interlocking-B²	Area of section, in.²	2.406	3.094		4.124
	Weight per ft/length, lb	8.27	10.78	13.2	14.375
14 in. wide	Moment I—in⁴/Sect.	1.458	1.875		2.50
	Sect. mod S—in³/Sect.	1.190	1.531	1.87	2.040
Interlocking-C³	Area of section, in.²	2.29	3.00	3.68	4.00
	Weight per ft/length	8.16	10.5	12.8	14.0
15 in. wide	Moment I—in.⁴/Sect.	0.881	1.162	1.42	1.55
	Sect. mod. S per ft/wall	0.848	1.10	1.31	1.40

Fig. 9-4. Driving lightweight steel piling. It is easy to handle and has other advantages where heavy hot-rolled piling is not needed.

DRIVING

A hand maul or light pneumatic hammer is satisfactory for driving steel sheeting in a trench where the bottom can be excavated ahead of driving, and when the earth loads on the sheeting are light.

If the sheeting is to be driven in advance of excavation, Fig. 9-4, or the side pressures are heavy, then heavier equipment, such as a drop hammer or a pneumatic or steam pile-driver, will be needed. Under these conditions the use of heavy driving equipment will make for faster driving with less injury to the sheeting. Light equipment for this type of driving tends to batter the top edge of the sheeting and slow down the driving.

The driving equipment must be capable of supplying ample foot-pounds of energy to move the sheeting easily. A driver that strikes a heavy blow with a low velocity at impact will do the most work with least damage to the sheeting. A long, heavy sheet pile requires more energy to start it moving than a light, short section.

Soil friction on the sheeting surfaces and force required for penetration are factors hard to evaluate. Certainly, selecting the appropriate driving equipment requires knowledge of local conditions and experience with various types of equipment. Vibratory equipment has been found suitable for "driving" sheeting in some granular soils.

REFERENCES

1. *Armco Steel Sheeting*, Metal Products Div., Armco Steel Corp., Middletown, Ohio, Catalog SH-4669, 1969, 18 pp.

2. *USF Sheet Piling*, United Steel Fabricators, Inc., Wooster, Ohio,

Data sheets P1-70 and P3-70.

3. Foster Lightweight Steel Piling, L. B. Foster Co., Pittsburgh, Pa., Folder FC8-1338-R, 4 pp.; also Report, 27 pp., 1971.

Fig. 10-1. Supplementing the abutment, a bin-type steel retaining wall provides valuable roadway space under a highway bridge.

CHAPTER 10 Retaining Walls

GENERAL

Soils and other materials have their own *angle of repose*. To maintain a steeper slope, some type of wall or support is necessary to prevent sloughing. Retaining walls are widely used for this purpose.

For low walls up to 20 ft, empirical methods are usually employed to determine earth pressures. For high walls, if a major item of a construction project, a complete soil survey and more thorough analysis of loads may be justified by possible savings.

USES OF WALLS

Retaining walls have the following uses:
1. To solve problems of limited right of way and to confine ground slopes within practical limits.
2. On road-widening and grade-separation projects.
3. To stabilize steep cut and embankment slopes (but not to stop landslides).
4. To repair breaks in roadway embankment.
5. To prevent shore or bank erosion.
6. As wingwalls for abutments and headwalls.
7. As loading platforms or ramps.
8. For parking areas.
9. For cutoff walls or ditch checks in deep channels.
10. As aircraft splinter protection walls and barricades, or explosion walls in chemical plants.

Pressures which act upon a retaining wall tend to slide it forward, or to make it settle, or to overturn it. Determination of the magnitude, direction and point of application of pressure is a lengthy and involved procedure: the reader is directed to standard reference works on this subject.

Fig. 10-2. Retaining wall of corrugated steel lagging (bridge plank) behind a row of H piles.

Fig. 10-3. Bridge abutment of steel piles backed by corrugated steel sheeting.

An adequate foundation is necessary for satisfactory performance of a retaining wall. Coarse-grained soils are generally satisfactory, with foundation piling used for only unusual cases.

Backfilling with predominantly clayey soils should be avoided, particularly if seepage exists in the slopes. Pervious granular soils, supplemented with pipe subdrains, ensure the most satisfactory backfill and stability of the wall.

TYPES OF WALLS

There are several basic types of walls: gravity, cantilever, buttress, bulkhead. Steel walls are of either the gravity or bulkhead type with many different variations available.

Specific wall designs in steel are common in the bulkhead type. Figures 10-2 and 10-3 show typical examples.

BIN-WALL

Bin-wall is a gravity retaining wall in which continuously connected steel bins are filled with earth. The earth mass acts as the gravity wall with the steel members serving to hold the earth mass intact. Bin-walls thus utilize the cellular or crib wall concept, but are not merely steel crib walls.

Bin-walls are constructed of lightweight deep-corrugated sides with bolted corners. Deflection is thus available in the sides of the bins, permitting some stress relief from soil pressure while the corners are positive connections able to distribute shearing forces. Conventional crib walls with articulated corners and rigid sides do not have these characteristics.

Unit Number	Name	Description
1.	Vertical Connector	Vertical member connecting all other units
2.	Vertical Connector cap	Cover for front vertical connector
3.	Stringer Stiffener	Top flange protector
4.	Stringer	Horizontal longitudinal members in front and rear walls
5.	Connecting Channel	Connector for attaching stringers to vertical connectors
6.	Spacer	Transverse members that separate the front and rear vertical connectors
7.	Bottom Spacer	Special bottom transverse member
8.	Base Plate	Installation plate on which the vertical connector rests
9.	1¼″ x ⅝″ bolts	
10.	⅝″ nuts	
11.	⅝″ spring nuts	

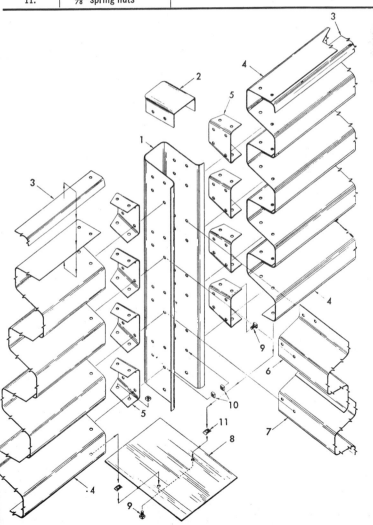

Fig. 10-4. "Exploded" view of a front panel joint of steel bin-type retaining wall, as seen from the rear.

Details of bin-wall are shown in Figure 10-4. Front and rear side members are "stringers" with a 16-in. net height module and 9.5-ft length, in 0.064 to 0.138 in. thicknesses. Transverse side members are "spacers" with 16-in. net height module in lengths of 5.2 to 14.0 ft in 0.064 to 0.109 in. thicknesses. Corner connections utilize a U-shaped vertical member and connector channels, both in 0.168 in. thickness. Base plates are provided to aid erection and are not a functional part of the bin.

Table 10-1 Thickness and Number of Steel Bin-Wall Elements Required for Walls of Various Heights*[1]

Wall Height		Quantity of Stringers				Stringer Stiffener
		Specified Thickness in In.				
Feet	Feet–In.	0.064	0.079	0.109	0.138	
4.00	4-0	4				1
5.33	5-4	6				1
6.67	6-8	8				1
8.00	8-0	10				1
9.33	9-4	12				1
10.67	10-8	14				1
12.00	12-0	14	2			1
13.33	13-4	14	4			1
14.67	14-8	14	6			1
16.00	16-0	14	8			1
17.33	17-4	14	8	2		1
18.67	18-8	14	8	4		1
20.00	20-0	14	8	6		1
21.33	21-4	14	8	8		1
22.67	22-8	14	8	10		1
24.00	24-0	14	8	12		1
25.33	25-4	14	8	14		1
26.67	26-8	14	8	14	2	1
28.00	28-0	14	8	14	4	1
29.33	29-4	14	8	14	6	1
30.67	30-8	14	8	14	8	1

*NOTE: This table gives the total number of stringers and stringer stiffeners for front and back of a single 10-ft panel or element of standard bin-wall.
Net length of stringers and stiffeners is 9.5 ft.
Thicknesses apply to 1:6 batter walls only.

Table 10-2   Thicknesses and Lengths of Spacer Elements for Steel Bin-Walls[1] (Front to Rear)

Design	A	B	C	D	E
Specified Thickness in In.	0.064	0.064	0.079	0.109	0.109
Length in Feet	5.2	7.4	9.6	11.8	14.0

For cross-sections of DESIGNS A, B, C, D and E, see Figs. 10-6 and 10-7.

DESIGN CONSIDERATIONS

Bin walls are designed as any gravity wall with the earth and steel "box" dimensioned to resist overturning and sliding forces imposed by the retained soil and other superimposed loads. The required width of major walls should be individually engineered with loads and foundation requirements investigated and calculated. The design chart for bin walls in Figure 10-5 is no substitute for this individual site design. However, it does represent a long-used gravity wall criteria for height-to-width ratio for the typical loading conditions in Table 10-3. These design standards, augmented with foundation investigations, historically have served many users very well and are presented herein as established guidelines.

As stated previously, the gravity wall is actually the confined earth mass. It is important to treat the structure as such at all times. Support for the wall is needed under the earth mass, not under the steel members. On rigid foundations, provisions must be made to allow slight settlement of the vertical corner members. Normal practice is to provide a compressible cushion under the base plates with approximately 8 in. of loose dirt.

Sliding forces may or may not be important in a specific installation. Conventional design practices can be employed to check this requirement. As a matter of practice, bin walls have been placed from 1.5 to 3.0 ft below grade to provide sliding resistance.

Where there is a limited or level surcharge, it is conservative practice to specify base width equal to about 45 percent of over-all height. With a heavily surcharged wall, base width should be increased to at least 55 percent of the height. For recommended designs, see Figs. 10-6 and 10-7, and the chart on loading conditions, Table 10-3.

To increase wall stability, a batter or inclination of 1 to 6 (or 2 in. per ft of height) has been adopted in the accompanying design charts. If the wall is to be installed without batter, additional stability can be obtained by selecting a design with a greater base width.

Table 10-3   Load Conditions for Retaining Walls

Batter	Level Surcharge	Slight Surcharge With Superimposed Load	Infinite Surcharge
Wall On 1:6 Batten	① R = .45	② R = .50	③ R = .55
Wall Vertical	③ R = .55	④ R = .60	⑤ R = .65

DESIGN WIDTHS AND HEIGHTS

In steel bin-walls, five basic design widths exist: *A, B, C, D, and E,* as shown in Fig. 10-5. Widths vary from 5.5 ft to 14.3 ft and in general are about one-half the height of the wall. (Wall height is measured over-all, not just ground level to top of wall.)

Battered walls (1:6) are recommended. When vertical walls are designed, a small batter should be required in installation to provide for slight settlement of the toe.

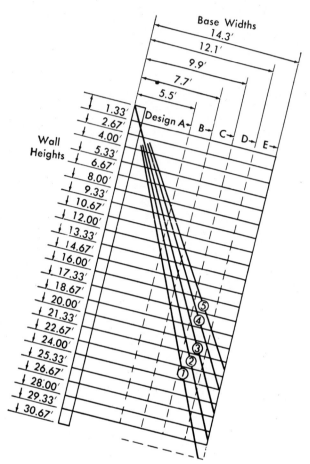

Fig. 10-5. Design chart for determining base widths for various designs and steel bin-wall heights.

Example:

Required: Find wall base width.

Assume a 20-ft high wall on a 1:6 batter. Surcharge, infinite.

Approach: In Table 10-1, these conditions are found in column 4.

In Fig. 10-5, line *3* intercepts the 20-ft height line about the midpoint of Design D, which has a base width of 12.1 ft.

The solution can also be obtained by using the formula:

$$R = base\ width \div height,\ or$$
$$base\ width = R \times height$$
$$= .55 \times 20 = 11$$
$$Nearest\ design\ is\ D,\ or\ 12.1\ ft$$

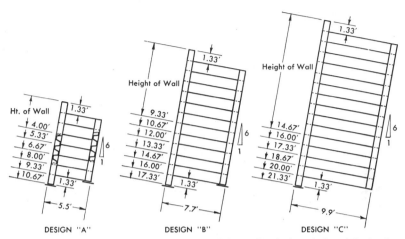

Fig. 10-6. Cross sections of bin-type steel retaining walls, designs A, B and C, showing some of the standard sizes available. Walls may be vertical as well as on a batter as shown.

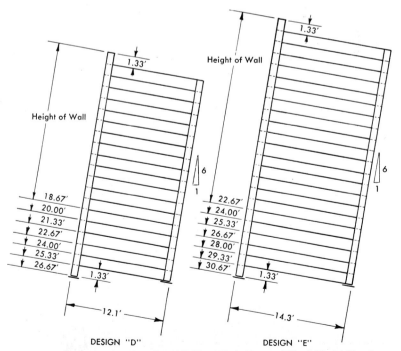

Fig. 10-7. Dimensions of designs D and E. The ratio between width and height is a function of surcharge and material behind the walls.

Fig. 10-8. How base width and height of bin-type retaining wall can be varied.

CHANGES IN ELEVATION

Stringers may be erected on a horizontal plane and stepped in multiples of 16 in. as in Fig. 10-8 to meet a change in grade. Where a change in wall height requires a change in the base width, a 'split' vertical unit is attached to the transverse spacers at an intermediate joint, as shown in the same drawing.

CURVED WALLS

Bin-type steel retaining walls can be built to almost any degree of curvature or with sharp change of direction tangentially. Four methods are illustrated in Fig. 10-10. The data applies to the five designs of walls (*A, B, C, D, and E*)

Fig. 10-9. Series of curved steel retaining walls. Purpose of this installation is to protect a micro-wave relay station on a mountain top.

Example of use of the curvature chart:

Required: Build a Design D wall 20 ft high on a 1400-ft radius curve.

Approach: Method 2 applies in this case. (Method 1 would apply only for very flat curves of 3900-ft radius. Methods 3 and 4 are required only for curves of 700 ft or less.) Use one set of short stringers for each five panel sections.

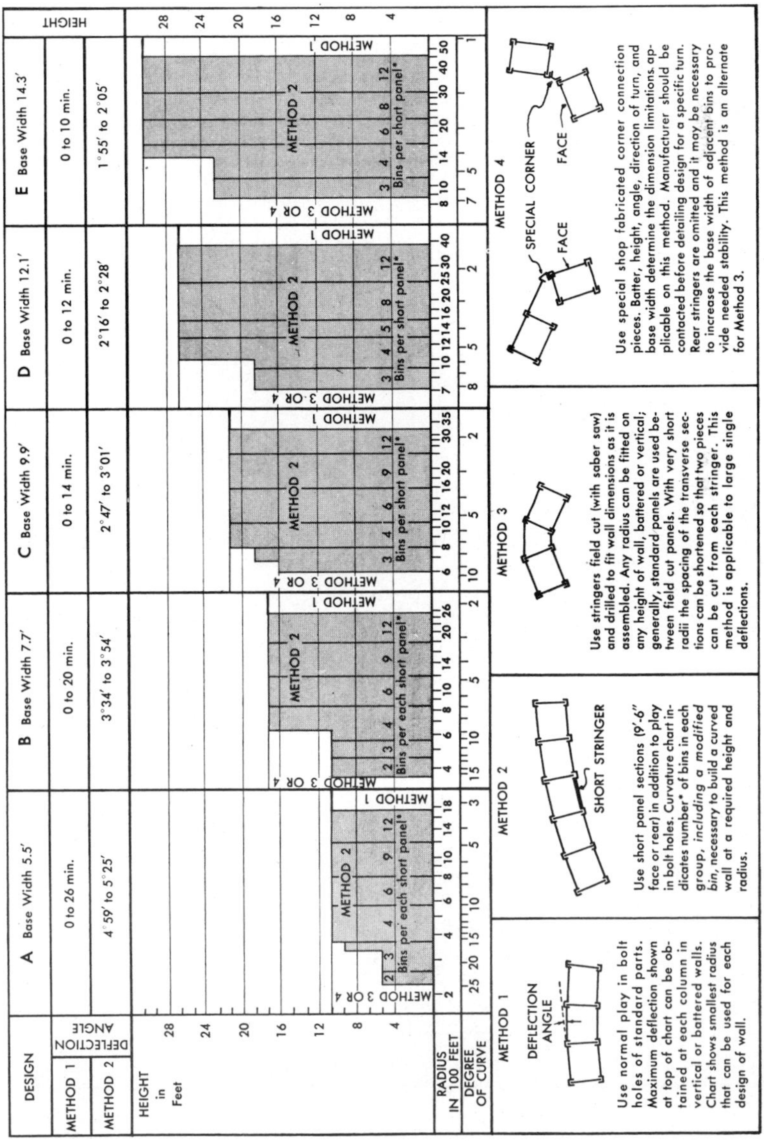

Fig. 10-10. Curvature chart for steel bin-type retaining walls on a 1 to 6 batter.

with varying base widths) in limited heights for 1:6 batter. For vertical walls, they apply without height restrictions. Consideration should be given to placing curved walls vertically instead of on a batter.

The second and third lines at the top of the chart, Fig. 10-10, show the deflection angles (between faces of adjacent stringers) that can be obtained at one vertical connector, using either Method 1 or 2. The first three methods use standard parts and are, therefore, more economical. Method 4 requires special shop drawings and fabrication.

Right angle turns in vertical walls can be made by starting a new wall at the rear of the first wall and using the end transverse section for a face panel. For battered walls, a special corner closure can be provided.

SPECIAL TREATMENT

Bin wall is normally furnished in a galvanized finish conforming to ASTM A 444. For particularly corrosive conditions, additional protective coatings are available. Units may be field coated with fibrated asphalt mastic or be constructed of bare weathering steel, provided the side exposed to soil is field coated.

When special aesthetic treatment is required, it can be achieved in several ways: Bonderized galvanizing offers a flat dark appearance; bonded asbestos provides a dull white-grey surface; weathering steel face members blend in well with surroundings; a latex cement field coating gives a rough textured finish in any color desired; and walls may be planted with vegetation in special slots or openings in the stringers.

Fig. 10-11. To widen an access road on the edge of a 100-ft cliff, a steel retaining wall was an economical solution. Careful compaction assures a sturdy installation.

Fig. 10-12. Revetments or steel retaining walls, set vertically and filled with earth, protect military planes in Vietnam against damage by mortar and rifle fire.

INSTALLATION CONSIDERATIONS

Retaining walls are more effective and less susceptible to failure if used near the top of a slope than at the bottom. Soundings or borings should be made to determine the subsoil, ground water and foundation conditions. A uniform foundation is best.

By trenching only for the walls of the bins, earth below the ground line need not be disturbed. Any earth that is excavated can be used to backfill the preceding bins.

Assembly of the wall can be handled either by building it piece by piece or by making a subassembly of the transverse section members, lifting them in place with a small crane, and then connecting with the stringers. Fig. 10-11.

Backfill inside the bin is a key part of the finished wall. As such, it must be a controlled backfill placed and properly compacted in 6 to 8-in. lifts. No mass dumping of loose soil inside the bins can be tolerated. Backfill *behind* the wall should also be properly controlled and compacted to minimize the active load on the wall and prevent settlements damaging to surface facilities.

Proper drainage of the backfill is critical to any retaining wall. The load on the wall and the capacity of the foundation can be excessive if ground water is not removed. Every wall should be well drained—either by the use of highly permeable backfill and base material or by proper subdrainage systems. (See Part I *Applications*)

REFERENCES

1. *Armco Bin-type Retaining Walls*, Metal Products Div., Armco Steel Corp., Middletown, Ohio, Catalog BW-3570, 1970, 16 pp.

Fig. 11-1. Guardrail and median barriers are essential for separating traffic in opposing lanes and preventing head-on collisions which so often are fatal.

CHAPTER 11 Guardrail and Median Barriers

The general intent of the highway engineer is to design a roadway in which the geometry creates a safe driving environment that does not require guardrail or median barriers. Unfortunately, certain limitations are placed on this objective, even in new construction. Site conditions, economics and other considerations may make the use of guardrail the best answer to the safety problem.

DESIGN PURPOSE

The purpose of guardrails and median barriers is to make highways safer by reducing accident severity. See Figs. 11-1, 11-2. To accomplish this objective, systems are designed to:

1. Prevent errant-vehicle penetration. Median barriers prevent vehicles from crossing the median and causing head-on collisions. Guardrails reduce accident severity by excluding vehicles from dangerous areas.
2. Redirect errant vehicles in a direction parallel to traffic flow, thereby minimizing the danger to following and adjacent traffic.
3. Minimize the hazard to the vehicle occupants during impact.

In addition to the basic objective, guardrail and median barrier systems should have certain desirable performance characteristics. These can be summarized as follows:

1. Minimize vehicle damage so the auto can be maneuvered after impact.
2. Be resistive to impact damage.
3. Be economical in construction, installation and maintenance.
4. Have a pleasing functional appearance.

Fig. 11-2. Steel beam guardrail along embankment clearly marks limits of safe travel.

Table 11-1 Warrants for Guardrail Placement of Roadside Obstacles and Hazards[1]

Roadside Obstacles and Hazards Within 30 ft of Traveled Way	Guardrail Required	
	Yes[a]	No
1. Sign supports:[b]		
(a) Posts of breakaway design		X
(b) Wood poles or posts with area greater than 50 sq. in.	X[c]	
(c) Sign bridge supports	X	
(d) Metal shapes with depth greater than 3½ in.	X	
(e) Concrete base extending 6 in. or more above ground	X	
2. Metal lightpoles[d]		X
3. Bridge piers and abutments at underpasses	X	
4. Retaining walls and culvert headwalls	X	
5. Trees with diameter greater than 6 in.	X	
6. Wood poles or posts with area greater than 50 sq. in.	X[c]	
7. Nontraversable hazards (see text)	X	

a Guardrail recommended only if obstacles cannot be removed from 30-ft zone.
b Breakaway design should be used exclusively, regardless of distance from traveled way.
c The cross-sectional area of large wood members can be reduced to 50 sq in. or less by boring holes or notching at about 6 in. above grade. If this is not feasible, guardrail is recommended.
d Use of breakaway bases for metal lightpoles is good practice; however, guardrail should not be placed at existing metal lightpoles of nonbreakaway design.

RESEARCH AND TECHNOLOGY

A number of states and other agencies both domestic and foreign have tested guardrail and bridge rail systems. These include components of steel, wood, concrete and aluminum. Pioneer work was done by General Motors Proving Ground, with subsequent research by the state highway departments of California, New York and Texas, the Cornell Aeronautical Laboratory, and the Southwest Research Institute.

From this continuing research and development of improved components have evolved three basic systems characterized by their *deflection* response. These are:

1. *Rigid.* These barriers do not deflect under impact. They function best at shallow impact angles. All lateral deceleration must be absorbed by the vehicle itself.

2. *Semirigid.* The semirigid systems can yield slightly under vehicle impact, thereby reducing some of the impact transmitted to the vehicle. Two examples are (a) the blocked-out W-beam rail (with or without a rubbing rail) and (b) the strong-beam, "weak post" system.
   (a) The W-beam rail spans relatively rigid closely-spaced posts. (b) The strong-beam (box beam) weak post system depends on the bending resistance of the strong, heavy beam element alone.

3. *Flexible.* These systems may be composed either of W-beam rails or of cables mounted on weak posts. The flexible systems absorb the impact energy, redirect the vehicle in the direction of traffic, and are "kindest" to the vehicle and driver.
   The semirigid systems offer perhaps the best overall solution to the design problem.

The National Cooperative Highway Research Program Report 54[1] relates the different systems in line with the deflection criteria. Recommendations are shown in Table 11-1.

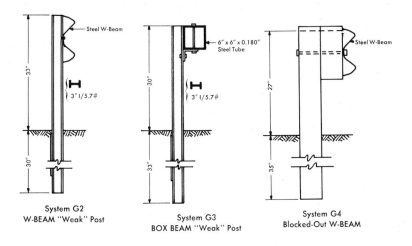

Fig. 11-3. Guardrail systems using W-Beam and box beam rails, with "weak posts" and with blocked-out strong posts.

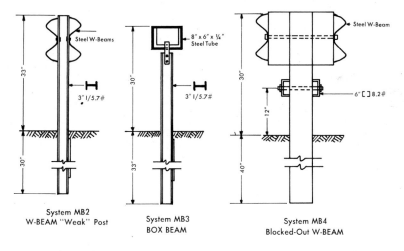

Fig. 11-4. Median barriers, double-faced, and comparable to the guardrails above. Note the rub-rail at right.

Table 11-2   Sectional Properties of W-Beam Guardrail per Unit Section*

Uncoated Thickness in Inches	Area of Section in Inches²	Moment of Inertia in Inches⁴	Section Modulus in Inches³	Radius of Gyration in Inches	Approximate Weight in Pounds	
					12½-ft Length	25-ft. Length
.1046	1.9874	2.2960	1.3640	1.0748	97	186
.1345	2.5555	2.9190	1.7322	1.0687	123	238

*Bolt holes not considered. Dimensions are nominal, subject to manufacturing tolerances.

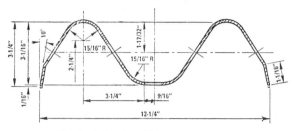

Fig. 11-5. Details of W-beam guardrail.

DESCRIPTION OF SEMI-RIGID GUARDRAIL SYSTEMS

A. W-BEAM

1. *Rail*—Rail elements are cold-formed standard W Sections of 0.109 in. specified thickness steel as shown in the drawings and conforming to the requirements of AASHO Designation M 180. Standard laying lengths are 12 ft-6 in. and 25 ft-0 in.

2. *Posts*—Wooden posts including blocks are of construction grade Douglas Fir, pressure treated. Steel posts are standard 6 in. I 8.5 lb hot rolled structural shapes conforming to ASTM A 36 or A 588.

3. *Rail Coatings* (painted, galvanized, or weathering)—Standard coating is galvanizing before or after fabrication with 2 oz per sq ft of double-exposed surface, according to ASTM A 525 or ASTM A 123. Bolts are galvanized per ASTM A 153. Special weathering steel is available in which rail elements conform to (ASTM 375) AASHO Designation M 180 and nuts and bolts to ASTM A 242.

4. *Splices* (bolts, back-up plates)—All splices and post bolts are flat rounded, headed with oval shoulders to prevent turning. Bolts are ⅝ in. ASTM A 307 and galvanized to ASTM A 153.

Fig. 11-6. Details of offset mounting of W-beam on strong steel post.

5. *Terminals, Transitions*—Terminal sections are 0.108 in. specified thickness steel and galvanized similar to the rail. Transition connectors are 0.138 in. thickness steel and capable of transmitting the full tensile strength of the rail.

B. BOX BEAM

1. *Rail*—Rail elements consist of box sections cold formed from steel tubes and fabricated as shown on the drawings. The steel is ASTM A 500 or A 501; or, for weathering steel, ASTM A 618.

2. *Posts*—Posts are of structural steel conforming to ASTM A 36, or special weathering steel conforming to ASTM A 588.

3. *Coatings*—Standard coating of entire rail system is galvanized conforming to ASTM A 123. Special weathering steel conforming to ASTM A 618 is available.

4. *Splices*—Splice plates are of steel meeting ASTM A 36. All bolts and nuts meet requirements of ASTM A 307 (except that splice bolts and nuts shall conform to ASTM A 325) and be galvanized per ASTM A 153.

Fig. 11-7. Terminal sections of guardrail, flared, and anchored at ground level.

C. CURVING

W-Beam—Rail elements for curved sections from 20 ft to 150 ft radius are shop curved. Curves beyond 150 ft radius may be accomplished in field erection of straight elements.

Box Beam Guide Rail (6 x 6)—Elements are shop curved for radii less than 720 ft.

Box Beam Median Rail (6 x 8)—Elements are shop curved for radii less than 1500 ft.

INSTALLATION PRACTICE

The following Installation Layout Practices are taken from NCHRP* Report 54.

Installation Length. Installations should be extended upstream from warranted limits to prevent vehicle access behind the protective system. Short sections should be avoided as they are often more hazardous than none. Isolated sections of unanchored guardrail should not be less than 100 ft long. To eliminate short lengths, flattening of critical portions of embankment should be considered. Short gaps between installations should be avoided. Ends of guardrail should be anchored in accordance with Figs. C-5, C-6.*

Transition Between Systems. Transition from one type to another should be smooth, with a graduated stiffness. Flexible systems should not be directly connected to rigid systems. A length of semirigid section with graduated post spacing will produce an effective stiffness transition. Recommended transitions are shown in Appendix A, Figs. B-1, B-2 of the reference.*

Shoulder Requirements. AASHO recommends increasing overall shoulder width by 2 ft on fills where guardrails are necessary. Ideally, any curb should be put in the preferred position behind the installation. If the curb must be in front of the installation, the curb should be of the low mountable type.

Uniform Clearance. A desirable feature of highway design is its uniform clearance to all roadside elements. These basic elements—parapet, retaining wall, abutment, guardrail—should be in line to prevent vehicle snagging. Shoulder width should be constant whether the highway is in cut, on fill, or on structure.

General Treatment at Structures. The installation should be attached to the structure so that adequate strength of the system is developed.** Recom-

*National Cooperative Highway Research Program, Report 54, Appendix B, 1968.
**See Chapt. 12 *Bridge Railing*

Fig. 11-8. Box beam median barrier across a bridge.

Fig. 11-9. Assembling and bolting the joints of steel guardrail proceeds rapidly,

mended methods are shown in drawings. Roadway narrowing transition should be gradual—15 to 20 ft longitudinally per foot of width reduction. To effect a smooth transition in rigidity, the post spacing should be graduated from the structure end, as shown in the standards.

Treatment at Highway Appurtenances. Short installations around light standards, signs, and gore areas are not recommended because they increase accident frequency, seldom decrease accident severity, and frequently cost more than modification or relocation of the appurtenance.* Serious consideration should be given to relocating the appurtenance or utilizing break-away construction with no barrier. For large signs, bridge abutments, large trees, and other roadside obstacles, examples are shown.

---

*See Chapts. 13 and 14 *Sign and Luminaire Supports*

REFERENCES AND BIBLIOGRAPHY

1. Michie, J.D., and Calcote, L.R., *Location, Selection and Maintenance of Highway Guardrails and Median Barriers*, Southwest Research Institute, San Antonio, Texas, Highway Research Board/National Cooperative Highway Research Program Report No. 54.

2. *Beam-Type Guard Rail*, Bethlehem Steel Corporation, Bethlehem, Pa., Booklet No. 1977.

3. *Highway and Bridge Guard Rail—Deep Beam Type*, Granco Steel Products Co., St. Louis, Mo., Cat. G-571, 8 pp.

4. *Armco FLEX-BEAM Guardrail for Safer Highways*, Metal Products Div., Armco Steel Corp., Middletown, Ohio, Cat. FB-3469, 1969, 14 pp.

5. Kress, R.W., *Guardrail Maintenance*, Illinois State Toll Road Commission, Public Works Mag., New York, N.Y., Nov. 1964, p. 120.

Fig. 12 1. Steel bridge railing in urban area consisting of three tubular rails on steel posts with brick ornamentation at every third post.

CHAPTER 12 Bridge Railing

INTRODUCTION

Safety and minimal damage are the objectives of railings on bridges and over-passes—for errant vehicles and others on the bridge and for the traffic on the roadways, railroads, or waterways below. A bridge rail must *restrain* a colliding vehicle, *prevent* it from vaulting, and at the same time, *slow* it to a safe speed without severe redirection, pocketing, or snagging. Furthermore, the stiffer bridge rail must be coordinated with the softer off-deck guardrail system.

During the past two decades, progress toward more reliable bridge rail systems has resulted from the efforts of engineers involved in design and full-scale research. The trend is towards integrating roadway and bridge rails into one cohesive system.

BRIDGE RAIL RESEARCH

Following are some observations based on a recent research project of the Southwest Research Institute for United States Steel Corporation.[1] The guidelines for selecting appropriate bridge rail configurations were based on AASHO design criteria.[2] Two guardrail systems considered amenable to bridge rail purposes, and therefore included in the study, were:

(1) Steel box beam (Standard G3 in Report 54).[3]

(2) Blocked-out W-beam (Standard G4 in Report 54).

Fig. 12-2. Tubular steel bridge railing on highway overpass structure.

BOX BEAM

The box beam guardrail, developed by New York, consists basically of a 6x6x³⁄₁₆-in. wall steel tube supported by 3-I-5.7 lb steel posts at 6-ft centers. Fig. 12-2. The top of the beam was raised from a minimum of 2 ft 3 in. to 30 in. The beam is mounted to "weak" posts. A rub rail was added to prevent wheel snagging on (strong) posts under high-angle impact conditions, unless the rail is blocked out from the posts for a considerable distance.

A second type of box beam test, an innovation in bridge rail design, included a frangible tube energy absorber which fragments as it is forced over a die attached to the bridge rail post. Fig. 12-3.

BLOCKED-OUT W-BEAM

The blocked-out W-beam was tested with steel posts (as an alternate to the timber posts and block-outs shown in Report 54). The steel posts were 6 in.-B-8.5 lb post, on 6 ft 3 in. spacing, similar to many current state standards.

A channel rub rail was centered 12 in. above grade, and the top of the W-beam was 30 in. above grade.

For the bridge rail system, a design quite similar to a current Texas Highway Department standard was selected. However, the design was changed to take advantage of the block-out and rub rail concepts to minimize post snagging. This system on the bridge consisted of an 8 in.-11.5 lb section serving as the bridge rail.

The 8 ft 4 in. post spacing was selected based on the 25-ft module of the standard W-beam. By maintaining the top of the channel at the minimum 27-in. requirements of the bridge specification, the 6WF-25 lb. post could be used and a beveled block-out bracket clears the channel and yet permits the top of the W-beam to be at the desired 30 in. above grade.

The posts immediately off the structure are again set in concrete to (develop the post strength and) provide the stiffness graduation desired.

Fig. 12-3. Typical transition from box beam guardrail to bridge rail.

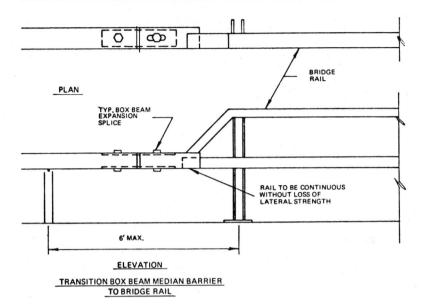

PLAN

TYP. BOX BEAM
EXPANSION
SPLICE

BRIDGE
RAIL

RAIL TO BE CONTINUOUS
WITHOUT LOSS OF
LATERAL STRENGTH

6' MAX.

ELEVATION

TRANSITION BOX BEAM MEDIAN BARRIER
TO BRIDGE RAIL

Fig. 12-4. Transition box beam median barrier to bridge rail. Developed by New York.

REFERENCES AND BIBLIOGRAPHY

1. Bronstad, M.E., *Bridge Rail Concepts Utilizing Standard Guardrail Components*, Report of Southwest Research Institute, San Antonio, Texas, for U.S. Steel Corp., SwRI Project 03-2761, June 1970.

2. AASHO *Standard Specifications for Highway Bridges*. Tenth Edition, 1969.

3. NCHRP Report 54—1968. National Cooperative Highway Research Program.

4. *Safer Roadside Structures*, Report of Texas Transportation Institute, Texas A & M Univ., College Station, Texas, for U.S. Steel Corp., 1970, Part C, 22 pp.

Fig. 13-1. Bottom-lighted overhead steel signs at an exit on an Interstate highway.

CHAPTER 13 Steel Signs and Supports

INTRODUCTION

Well-designed, well-placed signs are essential for motorist convenience, assurance and safety on all highways. Such signs are for three general purposes—(1) *regulatory* as to safe and legal speeds, (2) *warning* as to unusual grades, alignment, possible obstructions or hazards, unfavorable weather or roadway conditions, and (3) *guide* as to destinations, exits, available services, rest areas and others.[1]

Size, location and character of signs depend on the type of thoroughfare, roadway or street; the amount of traffic and the ability to carry that traffic at reasonable speeds. Signs erected for construction or maintenance differ essentially as to size, frequency, illumination and as to mobility.

SAFETY CONSIDERATIONS

Signs are intended to aid in making a road safer to travel. Yet, by their very size and the closeness of the supports to the traveled way, these signs may be a hazard in case an errant vehicle leaves the pavement at high speeds and under limited control. Hazard can be reduced by placing the sign supports at a greater distance from the roadway. A second means of reducing hazard is to replace the rigid sign support with a "break-away" post that disengages from its foundation upon impact from the vehicle. A third means is to protect the support with guardrail if within 30 ft of the roadway, and not of break-away design.

Fig. 13-2. Back of steel highway sign comprised of bolted panels and supported on steel posts.

SIGN PANELS

Most small sign panels commonly used on local roads, are square, rectangular, diamond, triangular or octagonal in shape and usually consist of stamped blanks. Expressway guide signs on the other hand are usually large, rectangular and made up of bolted vertical or horizontal flanged panels. These may be bolted or welded to vertical steel posts.

SURFACE MATERIAL AND FINISH

ASSHO Standard Specification for Highway Bridges covers materials and methods for painting sign faces and supports.[1]

Steel provides an excellent flat sheet material for embossed signs. Steel sheets available include galvanized, galvannealed, aluminum coated, and stainless. For best paint adhesion, the sign should be suitably phosphatized. Hot-dip galvanizing (ASTM: A 525), although slightly higher in first cost, is a more durable and economical coating.

Galvanized steel signs can cost 30 percent less than signs made of competitive materials of equal quality. They are also more salvable and adaptable to reuse.

Reflectorized sheeting can be applied easily to such sign blanks.

Large Sign Faces. The difficulty of maintaining large signs is ample justification for using A 374 or A 375 high strength steel or a steel suitable for vitreous enameling such as the very low carbon steels or aluminum-coated steel. Chief advantage of this last is its resistance to corrosion if the porcelain coating is damaged and the base exposed to air and moisture.

SIGN SUPPORTS, GROUND-MOUNTED

Regulatory and warning signs range from 12 x 18 in. to 4 x 6 ft. These, plus route markers and comparable signs are small enough in horizontal dimension to mount on single steel supports without excessive deflection under wind loads. Sheet signs more than 4 ft wide are usually supported by two or three posts. See Fig. 13-3.

Post selection data are given in Table 13-1 for single and double standard pipe posts of A 53 steel, for wind pressures of 50, 40 and 30 psf. More recent research on wind loads on roadside signs indicate that wind pressure criteria have been unconservative and sign structures built to the criteria specifications would be underdesigned.[2]

Table 13-1 Allowable Sign Area for Single or Double Post Highway Signs

ALLOWABLE SIGN AREA PER POST		
Wind Pressure	50 p.s.f.	40 p.s.f.	30 p.s.f.
h, h₁ or h₂ (in feet)	15 14 13 12 11 10 9 8	15 14 13 12 11 10 9 8	15 14 13 12 11 10 9 8

Standard Pipe Posts* A 53	50 p.s.f.	40 p.s.f.	30 p.s.f.
2½(5.79)	5 5 6	6 7 7	8 9 10
3(7.58)	5 6 6 7 8 9 10	7 8 8 9 10 11 12	9 10 11 12 13 15 17
3½(9.11)	7 8 8 9 10 11 12 14	9 10 11 12 12 14 15 17	12 13 14 15 17 19 21 23
4(10.79)	10 11 11 12 14 15 17 19	12 13 14 16 17 19 21 24	17 18 19 21 23 25 28 32
5(14.62)	17 18 20 21 24 26 29 32	21 23 25 27 29 32 35	28 31 33 36 39
6(18.97)	27 29 31 33	33 36	

*Standard pipe size is designated by nominal diameter in inches and weight per linear foot in pounds in parentheses.

OVERHEAD SIGN BRIDGES

Overhead signs are mounted on sign bridges (usually of welded tubular construction) that span the roadway, (see Fig. 13-1), or in some cases are attached directly to overhead grade separation structures. (Cantilevering of signs over the roadway or adjacent areas is no longer considered desirable practice.)

New developments include the application of the break-away principle to these large structures. Hinged supports are placed far enough apart on each side of the roadway that only one can be hit by an errant vehicle. The remaining supports can keep the sign truss from falling.

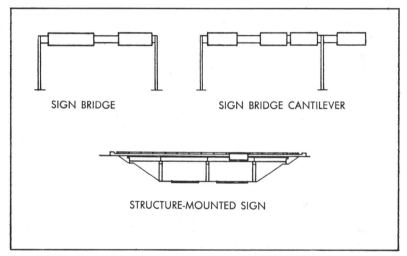

Fig. 13-3. Typical supporting structures for overhead signs—AASHO Standards.

Fig. 13-4. Informational sign of steel panels on steel posts outside the traveled way.

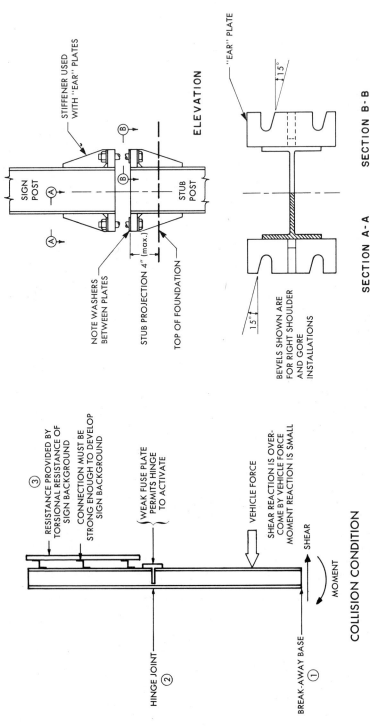

STIFFENER USED
WITH "EAR" PLATES

SIGN
POST

STUB
POST

NOTE WASHERS
BETWEEN PLATES

STUB PROJECTION 4" (max.)

TOP OF FOUNDATION

ELEVATION

"EAR" PLATE

15°

15°

BEVELS SHOWN ARE
FOR RIGHT SHOULDER
AND GORE
INSTALLATIONS

SECTION A-A   SECTION B-B

③ RESISTANCE PROVIDED BY
TORSIONAL RESISTANCE OF
SIGN BACKGROUND

CONNECTION MUST BE
STRONG ENOUGH TO DEVELOP
SIGN BACKGROUND

WEAK FUSE PLATE
PERMITS HINGE
TO ACTIVATE

VEHICLE FORCE

SHEAR REACTION IS OVER-
COME BY VEHICLE FORCE
MOMENT REACTION IS SMALL

SHEAR

MOMENT

HINGE JOINT

②

BREAK-AWAY BASE

①

COLLISION CONDITION

Fig. 13-5. Left: Break-away sign collision condition, and, right: horizontal base plate for large sign supports. Small sign supports require an inclined base plate to permit sign to be catapulted over the crash vehicle.

BREAK-AWAY POSTS

Posts of "break-away" design have been extensively researched[3] and suitable designs established. See Fig. 13-5.

The break-away feature consists primarily of a bolted fuse-type or slip-base connection between the buried or foundation portion of the post and that above the ground. Also included is a weak fuse plate just below the sign which permits a hinge to activate.

DESIGN RECOMMENDATIONS

1. *Post Sizes*
   A standard structural section weighing less than 45 lb per ft selected to resist the maximum wind load moment.
2. *Base Plate and Base Connection*
   The base plate should be designed for the maximum wind loads and not weigh more than the maximum values shown below. The base bolts should be designed to resist the maximum wind load assuming no pretension. The initial bolt forces given below are recommended:

Table 13-2   Details of Break-away Supports

Post Size Lb per Ft	Bolt Diam. in In.	Bolt Force in Lb	Torque (A325, galv.)		Base Plate Weight in Pounds
			Lb per In.	Lb per Ft	
0–8	½	920–1380	200–300	16.7– 25.0	8.0
9–20	⅝	1740–2660	460–680	37.5– 56.5	12.0
21–30	¾	2400–2660	750–1060	67.5– 88.3	21.0
30+	⅞	2400–3600	350–1280	70.8–106.8	21.0
30+	1	2400–3600	450–1470	77.1–118.2	21.0

3. *Fuse Connection*
   The moment capacity for the fuse connection is determined by the maximum wind load moment (M) at the base. (Details of design for slotted plates and for torque wrench tightening are available).[3]
4. *Background-to-Post Connection*
   The maximum connection force anticipated is 10,000 lb.
5. *Rotational Stiffness of Sign Background*
   A minimum stiffness of 100 ft lb per degree (5730 ft lb per radian).

Design recommendations based on research by the Texas Highway Department and Texas A & M University[3] are given in the above listing. Their recommendation is "With a thorough understanding of the conceptual principles of the break-away support and the prudent application of these recommendations, a satisfactory design can be obtained."[3] The break-away designs are now considered standard throughout the United States by AASHO as well as the Federal Highway Administration.

REFERENCES AND BIBLIOGRAPHY

1. Specifications for the Design and Construction of Structural Supports for Highway Signs. AASHO, 1961.
2. *An Investigation of Wind Loads on Roadside Signs*, Highway Research Record No. 222, Highway Research Board, Washington, D.C., 1968.
3. *Design Criteria for Break-Away Sign Supports*, Highway Research Record No. 222, Highway Research Board, Washington, D.C., 1968, 7 pp. (Based on research with models by Texas Highway Department and Texas A & M University.)
4. *Safer Roadside Structures*, Report of Texas Transportation Institute, College Sta., Texas, for U.S. Steel Corp., 1970, Part D, 31 pp.

Fig. 14-1. Simple light standard of galvanized steel pipe serving economically under coastal conditions.

Fig. 14-2. Double light standard approximately 30 ft high. Luminaire arm is 15 ft and single arm 35 ft long.

CHAPTER 14 Luminaire Supports

INTRODUCTION

Lighting of streets and principal highways is increasing and improving as new products and techniques are developed. This is true for the roadways in heavy traffic areas and for important road signs. Improvements include such factors as intensity, uniformity, reduction of glare, and economy.

Earlier practice has been to place the luminaires at 25 to 32½ ft height, depending on location and types of luminaires. These heights are currently being increased to 40 to 50 ft for roadway lighting, and as high as 100 to 175 ft for interchanges and toll plazas. This permits using fewer supports with larger luminaires, thereby also reducing the number of traffic hazards.

SAFETY

As a source of numerous and severe collisions when errant vehicles leave the highways, luminaire supports are in a class comparable to sign supports (Chapter 13). Preliminary full scale crash tests[5] of steel and aluminum supports establish the fact that to insure low-impact resistance, it is necessary to incorporate a base that will allow the pole to break away in a collision, but which possesses sufficient strength to resist static and wind-induced loads.

Fig. 14-3. Attractive steel light standard at a highway interchange.

The four basic concepts tested, from the least severe to the most severe, were: (1) a triangular slip joint or base, (2) frangible (brittle) insert (cast aluminum transformer base), (3) steel progressive shear base, and (4) cast aluminum shoe base. A multi-directional slip base (1) resulted in minimum damage. A frangible insert (2) is considered satisfactory for remedial designs of existing systems but apparently not for new designs.

Placing the luminaire support at least 30 ft from the roadway is another method of reducing collisions.

DESIGN CONSIDERATIONS

The AASHO Committee on Bridges and Structures has published structural design specifications for lighting standards. The structural design is based on dead weight, wind load and ice load on the standard and luminaire; also on loads imposed by overhead electrical wiring. Luminaires in common use weigh from 15 to 150 pounds. Projected areas for luminaires range from 1.3 sq ft for filament units to 8 sq ft for large fluorescent fixtures.

Wind speed values (converted to pressure) are obtainable from maps from the U. S. Weather Bureau in cooperation with the Bureau of Public Roads. These pressures are expressed as "isotachs of extreme mile" at various heights above ground and at recurrence intervals. At heights of 15 to 30 ft above ground, and at speeds from 60 to 120 mph, pressures will vary from 16 to 62 psf (for a 50-year mean recurrence interval). The basic formula is $P = 0.00256 (1.3V)$, where $V =$ wind speed. Gust speeds may reach $1.3V$.

Pole manufacturers are able to advise on shape factors for various cross sections of poles, brackets and luminaires not shown in the AASHO specifications.

Mounting heights for standard roadway lighting units range from 40 to 50 ft for various locations and types of luminaires; for toll plazas, much higher. To achieve these heights, pole shafts usually range from 35 to 45 ft in length. Upsweep of the bracket arm achieves the desired luminaire height. Steel brackets range from 4 to 15 ft in length. Traffic signal arms range to 40 ft in length.

Traffic signals may be hung from independent poles or share the light standards with luminaires.

Most steel lightpoles are mounted either to a shoe or a transformer base fastened through a break-away base to a concrete foundation. Concrete foundations normally are drilled caissons whose depth depends on most height and soil conditions.

TYPES

Steel shafts or poles are generally circular, square or octagonal in cross section. These shapes afford high resistance to torsion from wind load on the luminaire. Most shafts taper, usually at about 0.14 in. per ft, to provide greater resistance to bending at the base of the pole.

Table 14-1   Characteristics of Steel Lightpole Shafts

Maker	Thickness in Inches	Shape	Hot-Rolled Steel	Treatment	Yield Strength psi
A	.1196 .1793 .2391	Round	Mild	Cold rolled	48,000
B	.1345 .1793 .2391	Round	Mild	Cold rolled	33,000
C	.1196 .2391	Octagonal	High strength, low-alloy	Cold rolled	50,000
D	.1196 .1793 .2391	Octagonal	High strength, low-alloy	Press brake	50,000
E		Octagonal	High strength, nickel stainless		75,000

SPECIFICATIONS

Many agencies accept the specifications of lightpole manufacturers whereas others develop their own detailed designs and specifications. The latter procedure simplifies competitive bidding and permits describing any desired custom features.

Steel, mild or high strength, is preferred for lightpoles and brackets because of its superior resistance to torsion due to wind loads. Galvanized coatings minimize the need for maintenance; painting is highly satisfactory with proper surface preparation. Where stainless steel is used, maintenance of standards is virtually eliminated. Weathering steel is also available.

Steel light supports are thoroughly cleaned at the factory and then dip-prime coated with red oxide or red oxide chromate primer, or hot-dip galvanized for maximum durability. Paint-primed poles are finish-painted either prior to shipping or (more generally) after erection. Hot-dip galvanized and weathering steel supports are normally not painted.

REFERENCES AND BIBLIOGRAPHY

1. *American Standard Practice for Street and Highway Lighting,* D 12-1, Illum. Eng. Soc., N.Y., 1953.
2. AASHO, *An Informational Guide for Lighting Controlled Access Highways,* Washington, D.C., 1960.
3. *Light Standards,* Sect. III, Technical Notebook, Vol. 2, U.S. Steel Corp., Pittsburgh, Pa., 1962.
4. *Designer's and Buyer's Guide to Preferred Lighting,* General Electric Co., Schenectady, N.Y., 1960.
5. *Development of Design Criteria for Safer Luminaire Supports,* Highway Research Board, National Cooperative Highway Research Program Report 77, 82 pp., 1969.

Fig. 15-1. Reflooring an old bridge on a secondary school bus route. Top: The old timber floor was in poor condition. Center: Steel bridge flooring welded in place—awaiting asphalt pavement. Bottom: Completed, resurfaced bridge showing improvements.

CHAPTER 15 Steel Bridge Plank

INTRODUCTION

Steel bridge flooring or planking is used as a structural support or deck and is normally surfaced with a bituminous pavement. It is frequently used to replace worn wood plank flooring on older bridges and overpasses as well as in new short-span bridge construction. Steel bridge flooring can be used to replace obsolete concrete decks and to increase live load capacity of bridges.

Reflooring old truss or trestle-type bridges, whose decks are in poor condition but where supports are adequate, is readily done at low cost with steel bridge flooring. After the bridge flooring has been secured, a bituminous concrete surface is applied. This system will often add lateral stiffness to the entire bridge and may contribute less dead load than the deck system which it replaces. Successful use of steel bridge flooring in its present form has been a matter of record since 1946.[1]

DESCRIPTION

Steel bridge flooring in sheet and plate gages has trapezoidal corrugations, 6-in. pitch by 2-in. depth, with a 24-in. or an 18-in. net laying width. See Fig. 15-2. It is usually furnished in 6 to 18-ft maximum lengths for 10 and 12 gage, and shorter lengths for 7 gage and heavier. These lengths may be welded end-

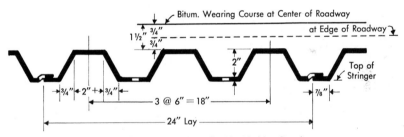

Fig. 15-2. Cross section of typical bridge flooring.

Table 15-1 Sectional Properties of Steel Bridge Flooring

Specified Thickness T	Section* Modulus In. ³/Ft	Weight of Steel Bridge Floor		Resisting Moment and Max. Allowable Span for 20,000 PSI Fiber Stress	
		Pounds Per Lineal Foot of Section	Pounds Per Square Foot of Section	‡Resisting Moment Inch-Lb.	†Maximum Allowable Span L In.
⁷⁄₆₄ "	1.176	12.4	6.2	39,300	22
⁹⁄₆₄ "	1.488	16.0	8.0	49,800	25
³⁄₁₆ "	1.944	21.4	10.7	64,900	30
⁵⁄₁₆ "	3.036	35.9	18.0	101,200	41

Formed steel bridge floor and end dam painted one shop coat of rust-inhibitive primer immediately after fabricating. Before paint is applied the steel is thoroughly cleaned.
†Based on H15 and on H20 loading for steel grid and timber floors. Assumed distribution of wheel load is 20 in. longitudinally and transversely.
‡Based on 20-in. width of floor section. References 2 through 5.
*Per foot of width. To obtain approximate value per unit, multiply by 2.

to-end to form continuous sections across the bridge floor. Physical properties and maximum allowable spans are shown in Table 15-1. Also, 9-in. pitch by 3-in. depth, 18-in. wide is available.

One coat of rust-inhibitive primer paint is applied before the steel bridge flooring leaves the shop; or the steel may be ordered with galvanized coating. Galvanized minimizes need for maintenance of the underside of the floor, and often eliminates it altogether.

Welded end dams retain the road surfacing material at the floor edges.

LOADS AND STRESSES

Each corrugation in the flooring transmits some of the superimposed load to adjacent corrugations as well as to its own supports. Wheel loads are distributed over an area 20 in. x 20 in. at the center of the flooring span and for stringer design, the load may be considered applied evenly over a 20-in. length of stringer.

Steel bridge flooring is designed to carry the live load plus 30 percent for impact with a maximum allowable working stress of 20,000 psi for steels conforming to ASTM A 245, grade C, for sheet gages and ASTM A 283, grade D, for plate thicknesses. Maximum positive bending moments are computed as for a continuous beam with a uniform load symmetrically placed over a portion of one interior span.

INSTALLATION SUGGESTIONS

An A-frame derrick on a winch truck is a convenient way of removing the old flooring and carrying the new units from stockpile to bridge. Uniform support of the steel flooring over the old stringers is desirable to prevent excessive deflection and rupturing of the pavement. Steel shims are used to attain this support. If necessary, the old stringers should be strengthened or replaced.

Fig. 15-3. Tack welding the seams, end dams and bridge plank units to the understructure of a steel bridge.

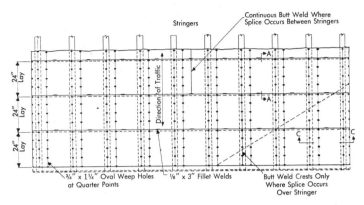

PLAN OF BRIDGE FLOOR

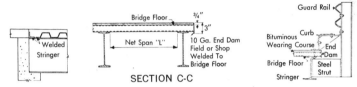

SECTION AT ABUTMENT   CURB AND GUARDRAIL DETAILS

Fig. 15-4. Plan view showing method of attaching flooring to bridge stringers, and cross sections showing method of attaching steel curb and guard rail.

After proper positioning, the steel flooring is anchored to the stringers by a few scattered welds. When all flooring is in place, welding is completed by placing ⅛ in. x 1 in. fillet welds on each side of the slotted welding holes in the valley of each corrugation. Fig. 15-4. Adjacent plates are joined at the edges by overlapping and welding with a ⅛-in. x 3-in.-long fillet weld at approximately 24 in. center to center spacing.

When steel bridge flooring is applied over wood stringers, the plates are attached with lag screws and washers, and adjacent plates are welded together.

BITUMINOUS PAVEMENT

Bituminous pavements have been used successfully with steel bridge flooring. The only precautions necessary are to make the pavement smooth and of such consistency that it will not shove under the action of traffic. Densely graded mixes which are not too rich in bitumen and which are compacted in place, should provide trouble-free service. The best guide to proper pavement construction is the experience of the local highway department.

REFERENCES AND BIBLIOGRAPHY

1. American Road Builders' Association, *Formed Steel Structural Plate Bridge Plank*, Tech. Bull. No. 221, Washington, D. C., 1956, 32 pp.
2. *Bethlehem Formed Steel Bridge Flooring*, Bethlehem Steel Co., Bethlehem, Pa. Folder 781-A, 1963, 4 pp.
3. *USF Structural Plate Bridge Flooring*, United Steel Fabricators, Inc., Wooster, Ohio. Folder BF4, 1960.
4. Unpublished investigation, 1965. *Sectional Properties of Steel Bridge Plank*, Research & Technology, Armco Steel Corp., Middletown, Ohio.
5. *Armco Bridge Plank*, Metal Products Div., Armco Steel Corp., Middletown, Ohio. Manual BP-8469, 1969, 8 pp.

Fig. 16-1. Installing permanent steel bridge deck forms on bridge. Aligning the forms and fastening to supports is quickly done.

Fig. 16-2. Permanent steel bridge deck forms, with steel reinforcing bars installed, ready for pouring of concrete slab.

CHAPTER 16 Permanent Steel Bridge Deck Forms

Unprecedented expansion of highway construction during the 1960's has resulted in the demand for a better, faster, safer and more economical system for forming concrete bridge decks. The versatility and strength of fabricated sheet steel has been utilized in the development of the present remain-in-place galvanized steel bridge form system. The choice of sheet thicknesses permits economical design to meet varying stringer spacings. Pitch variations of the flute patterns permit placement of most positive reinforcing steel over the flutes to obtain the required concrete cover around the reinforcing bars. Varying slab elevations are easily accommodated by varying support angle elevations. See Figs. 16-1, -2 and -3.

A system of curved corrugated arches, placed between bottom flanges of structural steel stringers, has been in service at least five decades. While uneconomical in current structural steel design loads, these early remain-in-place galvanized steel bridge deck forms are examples of bridge design engineers' and bridge contractors' never-ceasing search for a faster, safer and more economical way of forming concrete bridge decks.

Installation of permanent steel bridge deck forms is completed from the top of the stringers. Topside erection can be used on all types of stringers, on new decks or for replacement of concrete decks. It is ideally suited for projects over existing rail or vehicular traffic, over water (see Fig. 16-6) or over power transmission lines. The cost of form removal and touching up the bottom of deck slabs is eliminated. Saddle assemblies can be used to avoid welding to top tension flanges where required.

DESIGN AND MATERIALS

Permanent steel forms are designed in accordance with established engineering principles of flexural analysis and the requirements of the AISI "Specification for the Design of Light Gage Cold-formed Steel Structural Members."[1] The forms are designed to carry a 50 psf construction live load plus the dead load of freshly poured concrete at 150 pcf (see AASHO Standard Specifications for Highway Bridges). The thickness and corrugation pitch of the form

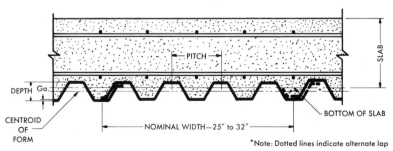

Fig. 16-3. Cross section of steel-form slab vs. conventional slab. Dotted lines indicate alternate type of lap.

315

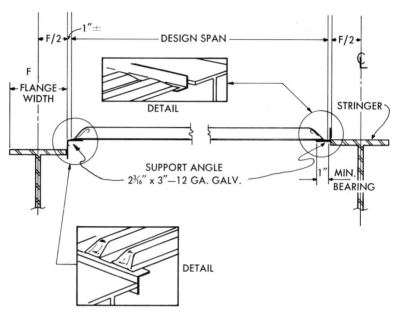

Fig. 16-4. Permanent steel bridge deck forms showing angle supports turned up, at left, and down in "detail." Bottom of slab is above top of stringers in both cases.

sheets are selected by considering: design span, design loads, limiting deflections, stresses, and reinforcing bar spacing of the slab. The form sheets are proportioned for a maximum bending stress under design load not to exceed 29,000 psi for steel conforming to ASTM A 446 Grade C, or 36,000 psi for steel conforming to ASTM A 446 Grade E. The maximum mid-span deflection of the form under uniform dead load of freshly poured concrete is usually limited to clear span divided by 180, or not more than approximately ½ inch. If deflection exceeds these limits, pre-camber may be used.

Form supports angles, usually 10, 12, or 14 gage, are welded to the stringer

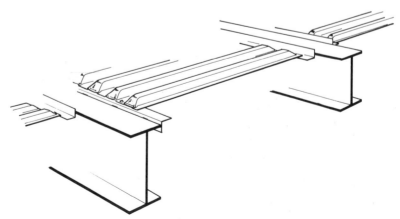

Fig. 16-5. Perspective view of swaged-end steel bridge deck forms in erected position. Angle supports are shown turned up and turned down.

Fig. 16-6. Placing steel bridge deck forms on a high bridge, fast and safely.

flanges, or attached to saddle assemblies. Stringer details will usually determine the type of support to be used. Figs. 16-4 and 16-5 show typical support positions.

All form sheets and exposed accessories are manufactured of galvanized steel conforming to ASTM Specification A 525, coating class 2.00 ounces. Form sheets are made from 22 through 14 gage steel. Supports may be formed from steel conforming to ASTM A 446, Grade A or C.

ERECTION

Permanent steel bridge forms are installed by the form erector in accordance with erection drawings, instructions and approved details provided for the structure. The drawings will clearly indicate locations where the forms are supported by steel beam flanges subject to tensile stresses. Form supports are placed against the stringer top flange, adjusted to grade, and either are welded to the stringer at intervals not to exceed 15 in., or fastened by other approved details.

Steel forms are furnished with closed end flutes or with channel closures to provide a grout-tight form. Each form sheet is securely welded or screw fastened in place after alignment in at least one place on each end of each sheet prior to laying succeeding sheets. Final fastening will include one center and two side fasteners to *minimize* concrete leakage. Field cutting may be necessary to fit the forms at expansion joints, floor beams, diaphragms and skewed end abutments. Cutting may be done with a steel cutting saw, cutting torch, electric arc welder or shears.

Normal construction practices are used in placement of reinforcing bars and concrete and in vibration of the freshly poured concrete to assure a structurally sound slab.

REFERENCES AND BIBLIOGRAPHY

1. *Bethlehem Bridgform*, Bethlehem Steel Corporation, Bethlehem, Pa., Booklet 2739.
2. *Stay-in-Place Forms*, Granco Steel Products Division, St. Louis, Mo.
3. *Wheeling Bridge Form*, Wheeling Corrugating Company, a Division of Wheeling-Pittsburgh Steel Corporation, Wheeling, W. Va., WC-357R-1.

Glossary

Definition of Terms:

Many terms in this handbook are common to drainage, highway, and other related design and construction disciplines. Most of these are defined, described or illustrated where they appear in the book. However, to aid the engineering student and to clear up unfamiliar words for the professional engineer, a number of terms are here defined even though they may be elementary. For other unfamiliar terms, many are keyed in the index of this book, particularly where the definitions already appear in the text.

Sources:

(1) Brown, V. J. and Runner, D. G. **Engineering Terminology,** Gillette Publishing Co., Chicago, Ill. 439 pp.

(2) American Society of Civil Engineers, **Nomenclature for Hydraulics,** Abbreviations, Units of Measurement, Symbols and Glossary. Task Force Report. New York, N. Y. 1962, 501 pp.

(3) American Society for Testing and Materials, **Standard Specifications.** Philadelphia, Pa. Current.

(4) Manufacturers' literature.

A

abrasion—Wear or scour by hydraulic traffic.

abutment—A wall supporting the end of a bridge or span, and sustaining the pressure of the abutting earth.

aerial sewer—An unburied sewer (generally sanitary type), supported on pedestals or bents to provide a suitable grade line.

angle of repose—The angle which the sloping face of a bank of loose earth, or gravel, or other material makes with the horizontal.

asbestos protection—Fibers of asbestos felt embedded in the galvanized coating of sheet steel to enable bituminous coatings to adhere more tenaciously, and to provide greater corrosion resistance.

B

backfill—Earth or other material used to replace material removed during construction, such as in culvert, sewer and pipeline trenches; and behind bridge abutments and retaining walls. Also refers to material placed in bin-walls or between an old structure and a new lining.

backfill density—Percent compaction for pipe backfill (required or expected).

base (course)—A layer of specified or selected material of planned thickness, constructed on the subgrade (natural foundation) or subbase for the purpose of distributing load, providing drainage, or upon which a wearing surface or a drainage structure is placed.

batter—The slope or inclination from a vertical plane—as the face or back of a wall.

bedding—The earth or other material on which a pipe or conduit is supported.

berm—The space between the toe of a slope and excavation made for intercepting ditches or borrow pits.

—An approximately horizontal space introduced in a slope.

—Often used for word "shoulder" in road work.

bin-wall—A series of connected bins, generally filled with earth or gravel to serve as a retaining wall, abutment, pier, or as protection against explosions or gunfire. (See Chapt. 10)

bituminous (coating)—Of or containing bitumen; as asphalt or tar.

boring—An earth-drilling process used for installing conduits or pipelines.

bridge—A structure for carrying traffic over a stream or gulley, including the pavement directly on the floor of the structure. (A structure measuring 10 ft or more in clear span.)

bridge plank (deck or flooring)—A corrugated steel sub-floor on a bridge to support a wearing surface.

buoyancy—The power of supporting a floating body, including the tendency to float an empty pipe (by exterior hydraulic pressure).

buckling strength—see Chapt. 3 *Structural Design*, Equations (4), (5), (6).

C

caisson—A watertight box or cylinder used in excavating for foundations or tunnel pits—to hold out water so concreting or other construction can be carried on.

camber—Rise or crown of the center of a bridge, or flowline through a culvert, above a straight line through its ends. See *Index*.

cantilever—The part of a structure that extends beyond its support.

cathodic protection—Preventing corrosion of a pipeline by using special cathodes (and anodes) to circumvent corrosive damage by electric current. —Also a function of zinc coatings on iron and steel drainage products— galvanic action.

cofferdam—A barrier built in the water so as to form an enclosure from which the water is pumped to permit free access to the area within.

cohesive soil—A soil that when unconfined has considerable strength when air-dried, and that has significant cohesion when submerged.

combined sewer—A sewer that carries both storm water and sanitary or industrial wastes.

compaction—The densification of a soil by means of mechanical manipulation.

conduit—A pipe or other opening, buried or above ground, for conveying hydraulic traffic, pipelines, cables or other utilities.

consolidation—The gradual reduction in the volume of a soil mass resulting from an increase in compressive stress.

critical density—Zone separating the levels of backfill compaction that will and will not prevent deflection failure of a pipe. (Between 70% and 80% standard AASHO density). See page 135.

critical depth, flow, etc.—See Chapt. 4 *Hydraulics*.

culvert—see *Culverts* in *Index*.

cutoff wall—A wall, collar or apron intended to prevent seepage or undermining. See *diaphragm*.

D

deadman—Buried anchorage for a guy, cable, etc.

deflection—Change in shape or decrease in diameter of a conduit, produced without fracture of the material.

diaphragm—A metal collar at right angles to a drain pipe for the purpose of retarding seepage or the burrowing of rodents.

design life—The length of time for which it is economically sound to require a structure to serve without major repairs.

discharge (Q)—Flow from a culvert, sewer, channel, etc.

ditch check—Barrier placed in a ditch to decrease the slope of the flowline and thereby decrease the velocity of the water.

drainage—Interception and removal of ground water or surface water, by artificial or natural means.

E

effluent—Outflow or discharge from a sewer or sewage treatment equipment.

embankment (or fill)—A bank of earth, rock or other material constructed above the natural ground surface.

end section—Flared metal attachment on inlet and outlet of a culvert to prevent erosion of the roadbed, improve hydraulic efficiency, and improve appearance. See *Index.*

energy gradient—Slope of a line joining the elevations of the energy head of a stream. (See Chapt. 4 *Hydraulics*)

energy head—The elevation of the hydraulic gradient at any section, plus the velocity head.

equalizer—A culvert placed where there is no channel but where it is desirable to have standing water at equal elevations on both sides of a fill.

erosion—Wear or scouring caused by hydraulic traffic or by wind.

F

filter—Granular material placed around a subdrain pipe to facilitate drainage and at the same time strain or prevent the admission of silt or sediment.

flexibility factor (*FF*)—Relative elastic deflection of a conduit. See Chapt. 3 *Structural Design.* Equation (9).

flume—An open channel or conduit of metal, concrete or wood, on a prepared grade, trestle or bridge.

ford—A shallow place where a stream may be crossed by traffic.

foundation—That portion of a structure (usually below the surface of the ground) which distributes the pressure to the soil or to artificial supports. *Footing* has similar meaning.

free outlet—(as pertaining to critical flow)—Exists when the backwater does not diminish the discharge of a conduit.

free water—Water (in soil) free to move by gravity (in contrast to capillary or hygroscopic moisture).

G

gage—Standard measurement of the thickness of metal sheets or wire (and bearing a relation to the weight of the metal).

—Also a term for the distance measured between railroad rails; (standard is 4 ft 8½ in).

gradation—Sieve analysis of aggregates.

grade—Profile of the center of a roadway, or the invert of a culvert or sewer. Also refers to slope, or ratio of rise or fall of the grade line to its length. (Various other meanings)

gradient—see *grade.*

granular—Technical term referring to (the uniform size of) grains or crystals in rock. See *granular backfill* in *Index.*

groin—A jetty built at an angle to the shore line, to control the waterflow and currents, or to protect a harbor or beach.

ground water table (or level)—Upper surface of the zone of saturation in permeable rock or soil. (When the upper surface is confined by impermeable rock, the water table is absent.)

grout—A fluid mixture of cement, sand, and water that can be poured or pumped easily.

H

head—(static)—The height of water above any plane or point of reference. (The energy possessed by each unit of weight of a liquid, expressed as the vertical height through which a unit of weight would have to fall to release the average energy possessed.) See Chapt. 4 *Hydraulics.*
Standard unit of measure shall be the foot. Relation between pressure expressed in psi and psf of head is

$$\text{Head in feet} = \frac{\text{lb/sq in. x 144}}{\text{Density in lb/cu ft}}$$

for water at 68°F
1 lb/sq in. = 2.310 ft

headwall—A wall (of any material) at the end of a culvert or drain to serve one or more of the following purposes: protect fill from scour or undermining; increase hydraulic efficiency, divert direction of flow, and serve as a retaining wall. See *Index.*

height of cover (*HC*)—Distance from crown of a culvert or conduit to the finished road surface or the base of rail.

hydraulic radius—The cross-sectional area of a stream of water divided by the length of that part of its periphery in contact with its containing conduit; the ratio of area to wetted perimeter.

hydraulics—That branch of science or engineering which treats of water or other fluid in motion.

hydrogen ion (*pH*)—Refers to acidity or alkalinity of water or soil. An ion is a charged atom or group of atoms in solution or in a gas. Solutions contain equivalent numbers of positive and negative ions.

I

impact—Stress in a structure caused by the force of a vibratory, dropping, or moving load. This is generally a percentage of the live load.

impervious—Impenetrable. Completely resisting entrance of liquids.

inlet control—See Chapt. 4 *Hydraulics.*

interaction (soil-steel)—The division of load carrying between pipe and backfill and the relationship of one to the other.

intercepting drain—A ditch or trench filled with a pervious filter material around a subdrainage pipe.

invert—That part of a pipe or sewer below the springing line—generally the lowest point of the internal cross section.

J

jacking (for conduits)—A method of providing an opening for drainage or other purposes underground, by cutting an opening ahead of the pipe and forcing the pipe into the opening by means of horizontal jacks.

K

kip—A stress unit equal to 1000 lb.

L

liner plate—Formed steel unit used to line or reinforce a tunnel or other opening. See Chapt. 8 *Tunnel Liner Plates.*

lock seam—Longitudinal seam in a pipe, formed by overlapping or fold-ing the adjacent edges. Seam may be helical.

luminaire—In highway lighting, a complete lighting device consisting of a light source, plus a globe, reflector, refractor, housing, and such support as is integral with the housing. The light standard (bracket or pole) is not considered a part of the luminaire.

M

Manning's Formula—An equation for the value of coefficient *C* in the Chezy Formula, the factors of which are the hydraulic radius and a coefficient of roughness.

median barrier—A double-faced guardrail in the median or island dividing two adjacent roadways.

modulus of elasticity (*E*)—The stress required to produce unit strain, which may be a change of length (Young's modulus); a twist or shear (modulus of rigidity), or a change of volume (bulk modulus), expressed in dynes per square centimeter.

moment, bending—The moment which produces bending in a beam or other structure. It is measured by the algebraic sum of the products of all the forces multiplied by their respective lever arms.

moment of inertia—Function of some property of a body or figure—such as weight, mass, volume, area, length, or position, equal to the summation of the products of the elementary portions by the squares of their distances from a given axis.

N

neutral axis—An axis of no stress.

O

outfall (or outlet)—In hydraulics, the discharge end of drains and sewers.

outlet control—See Chapt. 4 *Hydraulics.*

P

parapet—Wall or rampart, breast high. Also, the wall on top of an abutment extending from the bridge seat to the underside of the bridge floor and designed to hold the backfill.

Pascal's Law—Pressure exerted at any point upon a confined liquid is transmitted undiminished in all directions.

pavement, invert—Lower segment of a corrugated metal pipe provided with a smooth bituminous material that completely fills the corrugations, intended to give resistance to scour and erosion, and to improve flow.

perched water table—In hydrology, the upper surface of a body of free ground water in a zone of saturation, separated by unsaturated material ·from an underlying body of ground water in a differing zone of saturation.

periphery—Circumference or perimeter of a circle, ellipse, pipe-arch, or other closed curvilinear figure.

permeability—Penetrability.

pile, bearing—A member driven or jetted into the ground and deriving its support from the underlying strata and/or by the friction of the ground on its surface. (See also *Sheeting*)

plate—A flat-rolled iron or steel product. See *structural plate*.

ponding—Jetting or the use of water to hasten the settlement of an embankment—requires the judgment of a soils engineer. In hydraulics, *ponding* refers to water backed up in a channel or ditch as the result of a culvert of inadequate capacity or design to permit the water to flow unrestricted.

precipitation—Process by which water in liquid or solid state (rain, sleet, snow) is discharged out of the atmosphere upon a land or water surface.

R

radian—An arc of a circle equal in length to the radius; or the angle at the center measured by the arc.

radius of gyration—The distance from the reference at which all of the area can be considered concentrated that still produces the same moment of inertia. Numerically it is equal to the square root of the moment of inertia, divided by the area. (See Chapt. 1 *Product Details*).

rainfall (*R*)—Precipitation in the form of water (usage includes snow and hail)—generally expressed in inches per hour.

retaining wall—A wall for sustaining the pressure of earth or filling deposited behind it. See Chapter 10 *Retaining Walls*.

revetment—A wall or a facing of wood, willow mattresses, steel units, stone, or concrete placed on stream banks to prevent erosion.

Reynolds number (aeronautic)—A non-dimensional coefficient used as a measure of the dynamic scale of a flow.

right bank—That bank of a stream which is on the right when one looks *downstream*.

ring compression—The principal stress in a confined thin circular ring subjected to external pressure.

riprap—Rough stone of various sizes placed compactly or irregularly to prevent scour by water or debris.

roadway—(highway)—Portion of the highway included between the outside lines of gutters or side ditches, including all slopes, ditches, channels and appurtenances necessary to proper drainage, protection and use.

—(railway)—That part of the right of way prepared to receive the track. (During construction the roadway is often referred to as the "grade.")

roughness coefficient (*n*)—A factor in the Kutter, Manning, and other flow formulas representing the effect of channel (or conduit) roughness upon energy losses in the flowing water.

runoff—That part of precipitation carried off from the area upon which it falls. Also, the rate of surface discharge of the above. That part of precipitation reaching a stream, drain or sewer. Ratio of runoff to precipitation is a "coefficient" expressed decimally.

S

safety factor (or factor of safety)—See Chapt. 3 *Structural Design;* Chapt. 4 *Hydraulics*.

sectional properties—End area per unit of width, moment of inertia, section modulus, and radius of gyration. See Chapt. 1 *Product Details*.

section modulus—The moment of inertia of the area of a section of a member divided by the distance from the center of gravity to the outermost fiber. See *Index.*

seepage—Water escaping through or emerging from the ground along some rather extensive line or surface, as contrasted with a spring, the water of which emerges from a single spot.

shaft—A pit or well sunk from the ground surface into a tunnel for the purpose of furnishing ventilation or access to the tunnel.

sheeting—A wall of metal plates or wood planking to keep out water, or soft or runny materials. See Chapt. 9 *Sheeting, Lightweight.*

siphon—(inverted)—A conduit or culvert with a U or V shaped grade line to permit it to pass under an intersecting roadway, stream or other obstruction.

skew (or skew angle)—The acute angle formed by the intersection of the line normal to the centerline of the road improvement with the centerline of a culvert or other structure.

slide—Movement of a part of the earth under force of gravity.

span—Horizontal distance between supports, or maximum inside distance between the sidewalls of culverts.

spelter—Zinc or galvanized coating on steel products.

spillway—A low-level passage serving a dam or reservoir through which surplus water may be discharged; usually an open ditch around the end of a dam, or a gateway or a pipe in a dam.

—An outlet pipe, flume or channel serving to discharge water from a ditch, ditch check, gutter or embankment protector.

springing line—Line of intersection between the intrados and the supports of an arch. Also the maximum horizontal dimension of a culvert or conduit.

spun lining—A bituminous lining in a pipe, made smooth or uniform by spinning the pipe around its axis.

structural plate—Deeply corrugated steel plates or sheets, bolted together to form large pipes, pipe-arches, arches and other structures. See Chapt. 1 *Product Details.*

subdrain—A pervious backfilled trench containing a pipe with perforations or open joints for the purpose of intercepting ground water or seepage.

subgrade—The surface of a portion of the roadbed on which paving, or railroad track ballast, or other structure is placed.

T

tailwater—The water just downstream from a structure.

threading—The process of installing a slightly smaller pipe or arch within a failing drainage structure. See Chapt. 7 *Installation.*

time of concentration—See Chapt. 4 *Hydraulics.*

toe drain—A subdrain installed near the downstream toe of a dam or levee to intercept seepage.

U

underdrain—See *subdrain*

V

velocity head (symbol H_v)—For water moving at a given velocity, the equivalent head through which it would have to fall by gravity to acquire the same velocity.

W

wale—Guide or brace of steel or timber, used in trenches and other construction.

water table—The upper limit of the portion of ground wholly saturated with water.

watershed—Region or area contributing to the supply of a stream or lake; drainage area, drainage basin, catchment area.

wetted perimeter—The length of the wetted contact between the water prism and the containing conduit, (measured along a plane at right angles to the conduit).

Symbols

Various disciplines of engineering, hydraulics, physics, chemistry, etc., have established standard symbols or letters to denote various factors or dimensions in formulas, tables, drawings and texts. Some of these are found in dictionaries; others have been published by technical associations. Some of the symbols used in this handbook are listed here. For others, reference should be made to sources such as are listed for the foregoing Glossary.

Symbol	Definition or Use	Where Used in Handbook	
a	area, cross-sectional, culvert	Ramser formula	Table 6-2
A	area, cross-sectional, of waterway, sq ft	Chezy formula	Ch. 4
A	drainage area, acres	Rational formula; subdrainage; Ramser (above)	
A	area of section, sq in	Cross-section of corrugated plate	Ch. 1, 3, 8, 9
B	invert to spring line	pipe-arch	Ch. 1
c	coefficient of roughness drainage area	Chezy	Ch. 4
C	coefficient, runoff	Rational; subdrainage	
℄	centerline		Ch. 2
C	ring compression, thrust, lb/ft		Ch. 3
C_d	soil coefficient for tunnel liner		Ch. 8
d	depth of channel		Ch. 4
d_c	critical depth		Ch. 4
D	diameter of conduit, inside—or maximum span		Ch. 1, 3
		Ring compression formula (3)	Ch. 3
$\triangle$	delta, tangent angle, corrugation		Ch. 1
DL	dead load		Ch. 3
E	modulus of elasticity, psi		Ch. 1, 3, 8
E	railroad live load, Cooper		Ch. 3
f	friction factor	Darcy-Weisbach formula	p. 32
F	force		
FF	flexibility factor	Formula (9)	Ch. 3, 8
f_b	buckling stress	(4) (5) (6)	Ch. 3, 8
f_c	compressive stress	(7)	Ch. 3, 8
f_u	maximum tensile strength		Ch. 8
FS	factor of safety	(7)	Ch. 3, 8
g	gravitational acceleration		Ch. 4
H	height of cover		Ch. 3, 8
H	drop of water surface, inlet to outlet, in ft		Ch. 4

Symbol	Definition or Use	Where Used in Handbook	
H	depth of weir notch, in ft		Table 6-1
h_o	tailwater depth (HW)		Ch. 4
H	head, total	Bernoulli formula, etc.	Ch. 4
H_e	head, entrance loss		Ch. 4
H	height of remote point above outlet of drain	(charts)	Ch. 4
H_f	head, friction loss		Ch. 4
H_v	head, velocity		Ch. 4
HC	height of cover	Strength design	Ch. 3
HW	headwater depth		Ch. 4
i	intensity, rainfall, in. per hr	Rational formula	Ch. 4
I	imperviousness, relative	(see C)	
I	moment of inertia, in^4/unit of width		Ch. 1, 3, 8, 11
k	coefficient for filter (backfill materials)		Ch. 3, 4
K	soil stiffness factor; load factor		Ch. 3, 8
k_e	coefficient of head loss at entrance		Table 4-9
L	length of channel or travel		Ch. 4
L	length of weir notch in ft		Table 6-1
L	length of tunnel liner plate		Ch. 8
LL	live load		Ch. 3
N	circumferential rivet space ($= 3\pi$ or 9.6 in.)	Periphery measure	Ch. 1
n	roughness factor	Manning	Ch. 4
P	pressure, external load		Ch. 3, 8
P	pressure, wind, psf	Light standard	Ch. 14
P_v	design pressure, ring compression		Ch. 3
P_d	design pressure, liner plate		Ch. 8
pH	hydrogen ion concentration		Ch. 5
pi	$\pi = 3.1416$		
Q	discharge (peak volume rate of flow) cfs—(or quantity reaching a drain)	Rational; Chezy	Ch. 4
r	radius of gyration		Ch. 1, 3, 8, 11
R	resistivity, electrical	Calif. corrosion test (Fig. 5-6)	Ch. 5
R	hydraulic radius	Chezy formula	Ch. 4
R	rainfall, rate in. per hr	(also runoff)	Ch. 4
R	ratio of base width to height	Bin-wall	Ch. 10
R	ratio of rise to span	Arch or pipe-arch	Ch. 1
R	rise of pipe-arch	Invert to crown	Ch. 1
R_b	radius of bottom (plates)	Pipe-arch	Ch. 1

Symbol	Definition or Use	Where Used in Handbook	
R_c	radius of corner (plates)	Pipe-arch	Ch. 1
R_s	radius of side (plates)	Pipe-arch	Ch. 1
R_t	radius of top (plates)	Pipe-arch	Ch. 1
S	span of arch or pipe-arch		
	(or max. horiz. diameter of any shaped structure)		
S	slope (of ground, channel, invert)		
	ft/ft	Chezy, etc.	Ch. 4
S_c	slope, critical		Ch. 4
S_o	slope, bed (at outlet)		Ch. 4
S	section modulus, in.³		Ch. 1, 8, 11, 15
SF	safety factor (or FS)		Ch. 3
T	thrust, ring compression lb/ft		Ch. 3
T, t	thickness of sheet or plate, in.		Ch. 1
T_c	time of concentration of flow		Ch. 4
TL	tangent length		Ch. 1
t	time		
T	temperature		
TW	tailwater depth		Ch. 4
V	velocity, wind, mph		Ch. 14
V	velocity, mean, fps	Chezy	Ch. 4
W	width, bottom of channel		Ch. 4
W	wetted perimeter		Ch. 4
W	weight of moist soil		Ch. 8
X	distance from neutral axis to outer fiber		Ch. 8
x	horizontal coordinate	(in direction of flow)	
y	vertical coordinate	(normal to flow)	
z	horizontal coordinate	(normal to flow)	

Conversion Tables

Table C-1   Length

Ordinary Units

1 foot = 12 inches
1 yard = 3 feet
1 mile = 5280 feet
1 nautical mi = 1.1516 statute mi
1° of latitude at the equator = 69.16 statute mi
                              = 60 nautical mi
1 acre = 208.71 ft on one side of square

Metric Units

10 millimeters (mm) = 1 centimeter (cm)
100 cm = 1 meter (m)
1000 m = 1 kilometer (km) (about ⅝ mi)

Equivalents

1 inch   = 2.5400 centimeters
1 foot   = 0.3048 meter
1 statute mi = 1.60935 kilometers
1 nautical mi = 1.853 kilometers
1 centimeter = 0.39370 inch
1 meter   = 3.28 feet
1 kilometer   = 3280.83 feet = 0.62137 mile

Table C-2   Area

Ordinary Units

1 square foot = 144 square inches
1 square yard = 9 sq ft
              = 1296 sq in.
1 acre   = 43,560 sq ft
              = 4840 sq yds
1 sq mile   = 640 acres
              = 1 section of land (U.S.)

Equivalents

1 square centimeter = 0.155 square inch
1 square meter   = 10.76 square feet
                    = 1.196 square yards
1 square kilometer = 0.386 square mile
1 square inch   = 6.45 square centimeters
1 square foot   = 0.0929 square meter
1 square yard   = 0.836 square meter
1 square mile   = 2.59 square kilometers

Table C-3 Volume and Capacity

Ordinary Units

1 cu ft of water at 39.1° F = 62.425 lbs
1 United States gallon = 231 cu in.
1 imperial gallon = 277.274 cu in.
1 cubic foot of water = 1728 cu in.
                     = 7.480519 U. S. gallons
                     = 6.232103 imperial gallons
1 cubic yard   = 27 cu ft = 46,656 cu in.
1 quart   = 2 pints
1 gallon   = 4 quarts
1 U. S. gallon = 231 cu in.
               = 0.133681 cu ft
               = 0.83311, imperial gallon
               = 8.345 lbs
1 barrel = 31.5 gallons = 4.21 cu ft
1 U. S. bushel = 1.2445 cu ft
1 fluid ounce = 1.8047 cu in.
1 acre foot = 43,560 cu ft
            = 1,613.3 cu yds
1 acre inch = 3,630 cu ft
1 million U. S. gallons = 133,681 cu ft
                       = 3.0689 acre-ft
1 ft depth on 1 sq mi = 27,878, 400 cu ft
                      = 640 acre-ft

Equivalents

1 cu in. = 16.387 cu cm
1 cu ft = 0.0283 cu m
1 cu yd = 0.765 cu m
1 cu cm = 0.0610 cu in.
1 cu m = 35.3 cu ft
         = 1.308 cu yds
1 liter = 61.023378 cu in. (about 1 quart)
         = 0.264170 U. S. liquid gallon
         = 0.2201 imperial gallon
1 U. S. liquid quart = 0.946 liter
1 U. S. liquid gallon = 3.785 liters

Table C-4 Weight

Ordinary Units

1 pound   = 16 ounces (avoirdupois)
1 ton   = 2000 lbs
1 long ton = 2240 lbs
1 lb of water (39.1° F) = 27.681217 cu in.
                        = 0.016019 cu ft
                        = 0.119832 U. S. gallon
                        = 0.453617 liter

Equivalents
1 kilogram   = 2.205 avoirdupois pounds
1 metric ton   = 0.984 gross or long ton
                   = 1.102 net or short tons
1 avoirdupois ounce = 28.35 grams
1 avoirdupois pound = 0.4536 kilogram

Table C-5   Pressure

Comparison of Heads of Water in Feet with Pressures in Various Units

One foot of water at 39.1° F =   62.425 pounds per square foot (psf)
                                 = 0.4335 pound per square inch
                                 = 0.0295 atmosphere
                                 = 0.8826 inch of mercury at 30° F
                                 = 773.3 feet of air at 32° F and atmospheric pressure
One foot of water at 62° F = 62.355 pounds per square foot
                           = 0.43302 pound per square inch
One pound of water on the square inch at 62° F = 2.3094 feet of water
One ounce of water on the square inch at 62° F = 1.732 inches of water
1 atmosphere at sea level (32° F) = 14.697 lbs per sq in.
                                = 29.921 in. of mercury
1 inch of mercury (32° F) = 0.49119 lb per sq in.

Table C-6   Flowing Water

cfs   = cubic feet per second, or second feet
gpm = gallons per minute
1 cfs = 60 cu ft per min
     = 86,400 cu ft per 24 hrs
     = 448.83 U. S. gals per min
     = 646,317 U. S. gals per 24 hrs
     = 1.9835 acre-foot per 24 hrs (usually taken as 2)
     = 1 acre-inch per hour (approximate)
     = .028317 cu meter per second
1 U. S. gpm = 1440 U. S. gals per 24 hrs
            = 0.00442 acre-foot per 24 hrs
            = 0.0891 Miners inches, Ariz., Calif.
1 million U. S. gal per day = 1.5472 cfs
                         = 3.07 acre-feet
                         = 2.629 cu meters per min

Table C-7   Miscellaneous

Temperature

Freezing point of water = 32° Fahrenheit
                          = 0° Centigrade
Boiling point of water (at normal air pressure) = 212° Fahrenheit
                                                 = 100° Centigrade
1 degree Fahrenheit = 0.5556 degree (Centigrade)
1 degree Centigrade = 1.8 degrees Fahrenheit

Circular Measure

1 minute (')   = 60 seconds (")
1 degree (°)   = 60 minutes
1 right angle   = 90 degrees
1 circumference = 360 degrees

Time Measure

1 minute = 60 seconds
1 hour   = 60 minutes = 3600 seconds
1 day   = 24 hours = 1440 minutes
1 week   = 7 days
1 year   = 365 days, 5 hr, 48 min, 48 sec

Ice and Snow

1 cubic foot of ice at 32° F weighs 57.50 pounds; 1 pound of ice at 32° F has a volume of 0.0174 cubic foot = 30.067 cubic inches (Clark).

1 cubic foot of fresh snow, according to humidity of atmosphere, weighs 5 pounds to 12 pounds. 1 cubic foot of snow moistened and compacted by rain weighs 15 pounds to 50 pounds (Trautwine).

Table C-8 Inches and Fractions Expressed in Decimals of a Foot

Inches	Fractions of Inches							
	0	⅛	¼	⅜	½	⅝	¾	⅞
0	.0000	.0104	.0208	.0313	.0417	.0521	.0625	.0729
1	.0833	.0937	.1042	.1146	.1250	.1354	.1458	.1562
2	.1667	.1771	.1875	.1979	.2083	.2188	.2292	.2396
3	.2500	.2604	.2708	.2813	.2917	.3021	.3125	.3229
4	.3333	.3437	.3542	.3646	.3750	.3854	.3958	.4062
5	.4167	.4271	.4375	.4479	.4583	.4688	.4792	.4896
6	.5000	.5104	.5208	.5313	.5417	.5521	.5625	.5729
7	.5833	.5937	.6042	.6146	.6250	.6354	.6458	.6562
8	.6667	.6771	.6875	.6979	.7083	.7188	.7292	.7396
9	.7500	.7604	.7708	.7813	.7917	.8021	.8125	.8229
10	.8333	.8437	.8542	.8646	.8750	.8854	.8958	.9062
11	.9167	.9271	.9375	.9479	.9583	.9688	.9792	.9896
12	1.0000	....	....	....	....	....	....	....

From King's "Handbook of Hydraulics."

Table C-9 Slope in Inches Reduced to Feet

In. per 100 Ft	Ft per 100 Ft	Ft per Mile	In. per 100 Ft	Ft per 100 Ft	Ft per Mile
¼	.0208	1.098	¼	.5208	27.498
½	.0417	2.202	½	.5417	28.602
¾	.0625	3.300	¾	.5625	29.700
1	.0833	4.398	7	.5833	30.798
¼	.1042	5.502	¼	.6042	31.902
½	.1250	6.600	½	.6250	33.000
¾	.1458	7.698	¾	.6458	34.098
2	.1667	8.802	8	.6667	35.202
¼	.1875	9.900	¼	.6875	36.300
½	.2083	10.998	½	.7083	37.398
¾	.2292	12.102	¾	.7292	38.502
3	.2500	13.200	9	.7500	39.600
¼	.2708	14.298	¼	.7708	40.698
½	.2917	15.402	½	.7917	41.802
¾	.3125	16.500	¾	.8125	42.900
4	.3333	17.598	10	.8333	43.998
¼	.3542	18.702	¼	.8542	45.102
½	.3750	19.800	½	.8750	46.200
¾	.3958	20.898	¾	.8958	47.298
5	.4167	22.002	11	.9167	48.402
¼	.4375	23.100	¼	.9375	49.500
½	.4583	24.198	½	.9583	50.598
¾	.4792	25.302	¾	.9792	51.702
6	.5000	26.400	12	1.0000	52.800

General Tables

Table G-1   Areas of Plane Figures

Triangle: Base $\times$ $\frac{1}{2}$ perpendicular height

$$\sqrt{s(s-a)\ (s-b)\ (s-c)}$$
$s = \frac{1}{2}$ sum of the three sides a, b and c

Trapezium: Sum of areas of the two triangles

Trapezoid: $\frac{1}{2}$ sum of parallel sides $\times$ perpendicular height

Parallelogram: Base $\times$ perpendicular height

Regular Polygon: $\frac{1}{2}$ sum of sides $\times$ inside radius

Circle: πr^2 $= 0.78540 \times$ dia^2 $= 0.07958 \times$ circumference^2

Sector of Circle: $\dfrac{\pi r^2\, A^\circ}{360} = 0.0087266\ r^2 A^\circ = $ arc $\times$ $\frac{1}{2}$ radius

Segment of Circle: $\dfrac{r^2}{2}\left(\dfrac{\pi A^\circ}{180} - \sin A^\circ \right)$

Circle of same area as square: diameter $=$ side $\times$ 1.12838

Square of same area as circle: side $=$ diameter $\times$ 0.88623

Ellipse: Long diameter $\times$ short diameter $\times$ 0.78540

Parabola: Base $\times$ $\frac{2}{3}$ perpendicular height

Table G-2   Trigonometric Formulas

Radius, $1 = \sin^2 A + \cos^2 A$
$$= \sin A \operatorname{cosec} A = \cos A \sec A$$
$$= \tan A \cot A$$

Sine $A = \dfrac{\cos A}{\cot A} = \dfrac{1}{\operatorname{cosec} A} = \cos A \tan A$
$$= \sqrt{1 - \cos^2 A}$$

Cosine $A = \dfrac{\sin A}{\tan A} = \dfrac{1}{\sec A} = \sin A \cot A$
$$= \sqrt{1 - \sin^2 A}$$

Tangent $A = \dfrac{\sin A}{\cos A} = \dfrac{1}{\cot A} = \sin A \sec A$

Cotangent $A = \dfrac{\cos A}{\sin A} = \dfrac{1}{\tan A} = \cos A \operatorname{cosec} A$

Secant $A = \dfrac{\tan A}{\sin A} = \dfrac{1}{\cos A}$

Cosecant $A = \dfrac{\cot A}{\cos A} = \dfrac{1}{\sin A}$

Table G-3 Natural Trigonometric Functions

Angle	Sin	Cosec	Tan	Cotan	Sec	Cos	
0°	0.000	......	0.000	......	1.000	1.000	90°
1°	0.017	57.30	0.017	57.29	1.000	1.000	89°
2°	0.035	28.65	0.035	28.64	1.001	0.999	88°
3°	0.052	19.11	0.052	19.08	1.001	0.999	87°
4°	0.070	14.34	0.070	14.30	1.002	0.998	86°
5°	0.087	11.47	0.087	11.43	1.004	0.996	85°
6°	0.105	9.567	0.105	9.514	1.006	0.995	84°
7°	0.122	8.206	0.123	8.144	1.008	0.993	83°
8°	0.139	7.185	0.141	7.115	1.010	0.990	82°
9°	0.156	6.392	0.158	6.314	1.012	0.988	81°
10°	0.174	5.759	0.176	5.671	1.015	0.985	80°
11°	0.191	5.241	0.194	5.145	1.019	0.982	79°
12°	0.208	4.810	0.213	4.705	1.022	0.978	78°
13°	0.225	4.445	0.231	4.331	1.026	0.974	77°
14°	0.242	4.134	0.249	4.011	1.031	0.970	76°
15°	0.259	3.864	0.268	3.732	1.035	0.966	75°
16°	0.276	3.628	0.287	3.487	1.040	0.961	74°
17°	0.292	3.420	0.306	3.271	1.046	0.956	73°
18°	0.309	3.236	0.325	3.078	1.051	0.951	72°
19°	0.326	3.072	0.344	2.904	1.058	0.946	71°
20°	0.342	2.924	0.364	2.747	1.064	0.940	70°
21°	0.358	2.790	0.384	2.605	1.071	0.934	69°
22°	0.375	2.669	0.404	2.475	1.079	0.927	68°
23°	0.391	2.559	0.424	2.356	1.086	0.921	67°
24°	0.407	2.459	0.445	2.246	1.095	0.914	66°
25°	0.423	2.366	0.466	2.145	1.103	0.906	65°
26°	0.438	2.281	0.488	2.050	1.113	0.899	64°
27°	0.454	2.203	0.510	1.963	1.122	0.891	63°
28°	0.469	2.130	0.532	1.881	1.133	0.883	62°
29°	0.485	2.063	0.554	1.804	1.143	0.875	61°
30°	0.500	2.000	0.577	1.732	1.155	0.866	60°
31°	0.515	1.942	0.601	1.664	1.167	0.857	59°
32°	0.530	1.887	0.625	1.600	1.179	0.848	58°
33°	0.545	1.836	0.649	1.540	1.192	0.839	57°
34°	0.559	1.788	0.675	1.483	1.206	0.829	56°
35°	0.574	1.743	0.700	1.428	1.221	0.819	55°
36°	0.588	1.701	0.727	1.376	1.236	0.809	54°
37°	0.602	1.662	0.754	1.327	1.252	0.799	53°
38°	0.616	1.624	0.781	1.280	1.269	0.788	52°
39°	0.629	1.589	0.810	1.235	1.287	0.777	51°
40°	0.643	1.556	0.839	1.192	1.305	0.766	50°
41°	0.656	1.524	0.869	1.150	1.325	0.755	49°
42°	0.669	1.494	0.900	1.111	1.346	0.743	48°
43°	0.682	1.466	0.933	1.072	1.367	0.731	47°
44°	0.695	1.440	0.966	1.036	1.390	0.719	46°
45°	0.707	1.414	1.000	1.000	1.414	0.707	45°
	Cos	Sec	Cotan	Tan	Cosec	Sin	Angle

Table G-4   Properties of the Circle*

Circumference of Circle of Dia 1 $= \pi = 3.14159265$

Circumference of Circle $= 2\,\pi\,r$

Dia of Circle $=$ Circumference $\times 0.31831$

Diameter of Circle of equal periphery as square $=$ side $\times 1.27324$

Side of Square of equal periphery as circle $=$ diameter $\times 0.78540$

Diameter of Circle circumscribed about square $=$ side $\times 1.41421$

Side of Square inscribed in Circle $=$ diameter $\times 0.70711$

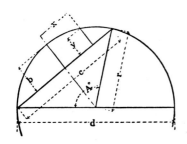

Arc, $a = \dfrac{\pi\,r\,A°}{180} = 0.017453\,r\,A°$

Angle, $A = \dfrac{180°\,a}{\pi\,r} = 57.29578\,\dfrac{a}{r}$

Radius, $r = \dfrac{4\,b^2+c^2}{8\,b}$ Diameter, $d = \dfrac{4\,b^2+c^2}{4\,b}$

Chord, $c = 2\sqrt{2\,b\,r-b^2} = 2\,r\,\sin\dfrac{A°}{2}$

Rise, $b = r - \tfrac{1}{2}\sqrt{4\,r^2-c^2} = \dfrac{c}{2}\tan\dfrac{A°}{4} = 2\,r\,\sin^2\dfrac{A}{4}$

Rise, $b = r + y - \sqrt{r^2-x^2}$ $y = b - r + \sqrt{r^2-x^2}$ $x = \sqrt{r^2-(r+y-b)^2}$

$\pi = 3.14159265, \log = 0.4971499$

$\dfrac{1}{\pi} = 0.3183099, \log = \overline{1}.5028501$

$\pi^2 = 9.8696044, \log = 0.9942997$

$\dfrac{1}{\pi^2} = 0.1013212, \log = \overline{1}.0057003$

$\sqrt{\pi} = 1.7724539, \log = 0.2485749$

$\sqrt{\dfrac{1}{\pi}} = 0.5641896, \log = \overline{1}.7514251$

$\dfrac{\pi}{180} = 0.0174533, \log = \overline{2}.2418774$

$\dfrac{180}{\pi} = 57.2957795, \log = 1.7581226$

*From Carnegie's "Pocket Companion."

Table G-5   Areas of Circles

Diameter in Inches	Area Square Inches	Area Square Feet	Diameter in Inches	Area Square Inches	Area Square Feet	Diameter in Inches	Area Square Inches	Area Square Feet
1.0	0.7854	.005454	4.0	12.5664	.087266	7.0	38.4845	.267254
.1	0.9503	.006599	.1	13.2025	.091684	.1	39.5919	.274944
.2	1.1310	.007854	.2	13.8544	.096211	.2	40.7150	.282743
.25	1.2272	.008522	.25	14.1863	.098516	.25	41.2825	.286684
.3	1.3273	.009218	.3	14.5220	.100847	.3	41.8539	.290652
.4	1.5394	.010690	.4	15.2053	.105592	.4	43.0084	.298669
.5	1.7671	.012272	.5	15.9043	.110446	.5	44.1786	.306796
.6	2.0106	.013963	.6	16.6190	.115410	.6	45.3646	.315032
.7	2.2698	.015763	.7	17.3494	.120482	.7	46.5663	.323377
.75	2.4053	.016703	.75	17.7205	.123059	.75	47.1730	.327590
.8	2.5447	.017671	.8	18.0956	.125664	.8	47.7836	.331831
.9	2.8353	.019689	.9	18.8574	.130954	.9	49.0167	.340394
2.0	3.1416	.021816	5.0	19.6350	.136354	8.0	50.2655	.349066
.1	3.4636	.024053	.1	20.4282	.141863	.1	51.5300	.357847
.2	3.8013	.026398	.2	21.2372	.147480	.2	52.8102	.366737
.25	3.9761	.027612	.25	21.6475	.150330	.25	53.4562	.371223
.3	4.1548	.028852	.3	22.0618	.153207	.3	54.1061	.375736
.4	4.5239	.031416	.4	22.9022	.159043	.4	55.4177	.384845
.5	4.9087	.034088	.5	23.7583	.164988	.5	56.7450	.394063
.6	5.3093	.036870	.6	24.6301	.171042	.6	58.0880	.403389
.7	5.7256	.039760	.7	25.5176	.177205	.7	59.4468	.412825
.75	5.9396	.041247	.75	25.9672	.180328	.75	60.1320	.417584
.8	6.1575	.042760	.8	26.4208	.183477	.8	60.8212	.422370
.9	6.6052	.045869	.9	27.3397	.189859	.9	62.2114	.432024
3.0	7.0686	.049087	6.0	28.2743	.196350	9.0	63.6173	.441786
.1	7.5477	.052414	.1	29.2247	.202949	.1	65.0388	.451658
.2	8.0425	.055851	.2	30.1907	.209658	.2	66.4761	.461640
.25	8.2958	.057609	.25	30.6796	.213053	.25	67.2006	.466671
.3	8.5530	.059396	.3	31.1725	.216475	.3	67.9291	.471730
.4	9.0792	.063050	.4	32.1699	.223402	.4	69.3978	.481929
.5	9.6211	.066813	.5	33.1831	.230438	.5	70.8822	.492237
.6	10.1788	.070686	.6	34.2119	.237583	.6	72.3823	.502654
.7	10.7521	.074667	.7	35.2565	.244837	.7	73.8981	.513181
.75	11.0447	.076699	.75	35.7847	.248505	.75	74.6619	.518486
.8	11.3411	.078758	.8	36.3168	.252200	.8	75.4296	.523817
.9	11.9459	.082958	.9	37.3928	.259672	.9	76.9769	.534561

The above table may be used for finding the areas of circles whose diameters are not within the limits of the table. Since the areas vary as the squares of their diameters, the given diameter may be divided (or multiplied) by 10, and the area found from the table under the resulting diameter corrected by moving the decimal point two places to the right (or left). Thus to find the area of a 22-inch circle:

From table, area of 2.2-inch circle = 3.8013 sq in. = .026398 sq ft

Therefore area of 22-inch circle = 380.13 sq in. = 2.64 sq ft

Again, to find the area of a 0.75-inch circle:

From table, area of 7.5-inch circle = 44.1786 sq in. = 0.306796 sq ft

Therefore area of 0.75-inch circle = 0.4418 sq in. = 0.00307 sq ft

It will also be apparent that the *first two* columns in the table may be used for any unit of measure.

Table G-6   Functions of Numbers 1 to 99

No	Square	Cube	Square Root	Cubic Root	Loga- rithm	1000 × Reciprocal	No = Diameter	
							Circum	Area
1	1	1	1.0000	1.0000	0.00000	1000.000	3.142	0.7854
2	4	8	1.4142	1.2599	0.30103	500.000	6.283	3.1416
3	9	27	1.7321	1.4422	0.47712	333.333	9.425	7.0686
4	16	64	2.0000	1.5874	0.60206	250.000	12.566	12.5664
5	25	125	2.2361	1.7100	0.69897	200.000	15.708	19.6350
6	36	216	2.4495	1.8171	0.77815	166.667	18.850	28.2743
7	49	343	2.6458	1.9129	0.84510	142.857	21.991	38.4845
8	64	512	2.8284	2.0000	0.90309	125.000	25.133	50.2655
9	81	729	3.0000	2.0801	0.95424	111.111	28.274	63.6173
10	100	1000	3.1623	2.1544	1.00000	100.000	31.416	78.5398
11	121	1331	3.3166	2.2240	1.04139	90.9091	34.558	95.0332
12	144	1728	3.4641	2.2894	1.07918	83.3333	37.699	113.097
13	169	2197	3.6056	2.3513	1.11394	76.9231	40.841	132.732
14	196	2744	3.7417	2.4101	1.14613	71.4286	43.982	153.938
15	225	3375	3.8730	2.4662	1.17609	66.6667	47.124	176.715
16	256	4096	4.0000	2.5198	1.20412	62.5000	50.265	201.062
17	289	4913	4.1231	2.5713	1.23045	58.8235	53.407	226.980
18	324	5832	4.2426	2.6207	1.25527	55.5556	56.549	254.469
19	361	6859	4.3589	2.6684	1.27875	52.6316	59.690	283.529
20	400	8000	4.4721	2.7144	1.30103	50.0000	62.832	314.159
21	441	9261	4.5826	2.7589	1.32222	47.6190	65.973	346.361
22	484	10648	4.6904	2.8020	1.34242	45.4545	69.115	380.133
23	529	12167	4.7958	2.8439	1.36173	43.4783	72.257	415.476
24	576	13824	4.8990	2.8845	1.38021	41.6667	75.398	452.389
25	625	15625	5.0000	2.9240	1.39794	40.0000	78.540	490.874
26	676	17576	5.0990	2.9625	1.41497	38.4615	81.681	530.929
27	729	19683	5.1962	3.0000	1.43136	37.0370	84.823	572.555
28	784	21952	5.2915	3.0366	1.44716	35.7143	87.965	615.752
29	841	24389	5.3852	3.0723	1.46240	34.4828	91.106	660.520
30	900	27000	5.4772	3.1072	1.47712	33.3333	94.248	706.858
31	961	29791	5.5678	3.1414	1.49136	32.2581	97.389	754.768
32	1024	32768	5.6569	3.1748	1.50515	31.2500	100.531	804.248
33	1089	35937	5.7446	3.2075	1.51851	30.3030	103.673	855.299
34	1156	39304	5.8310	3.2396	1.53148	29.4118	106.814	907.920
35	1225	42875	5.9161	3.2711	1.54407	28.5714	109.956	962.113
36	1296	46656	6.0000	3.3019	1.55630	27.7778	113.097	1017.88
37	1369	50653	6.0828	3.3322	1.56820	27.0270	116.239	1075.21
38	1444	54872	6.1644	3.3620	1.57978	26.3158	119.381	1134.11
39	1521	59319	6.2450	3.3912	1.59106	25.6410	122.522	1194.59
40	1600	64000	6.3246	3.4200	1.60206	25.0000	125.66	1256.64
41	1681	68921	6.4031	3.4482	1.61278	24.3902	128.81	1320.25
42	1764	74088	6.4807	3.4760	1.62325	23.8095	131.95	1385.44
43	1849	79507	6.5574	3.5034	1.63347	23.2558	135.09	1452.20
44	1936	85184	6.6332	3.5303	1.64345	22.7273	138.23	1520.53
45	2025	91125	6.7082	3.5569	1.65321	22.2222	141.37	1590.43
46	2116	97336	6.7823	3.5830	1.66276	21.7391	144.51	1661.90
47	2209	103823	6.8557	3.6088	1.67210	21.2766	147.65	1734.94
48	2304	110592	6.9282	3.6342	1.68124	20.8333	150.80	1809.56
49	2401	117649	7.0000	3.6593	1.69020	20.4082	153.94	1885.74

(*Continued on next page*)

Table G-6 Functions of Numbers 1 to 99 (Continued)

No	Square	Cube	Square Root	Cubic Root	Loga-rithm	1000 × Reciprocal	No = Diameter Circum	No = Diameter Area
50	2500	125000	7.0711	3.6840	1.69897	20.0000	157.08	1963.50
51	2601	132651	7.1414	3.7084	1.70757	19.6078	160.22	2042.82
52	2704	140608	7.2111	3.7325	1.71600	19.2308	163.36	2123.72
53	2809	148877	7.2801	3.7563	1.72428	18.8679	166.50	2206.18
54	2916	157464	7.3485	3.7798	1.73239	18.5185	169.65	2290.22
55	3025	166375	7.4162	3.8030	1.74036	18.1818	172.79	2375.83
56	3136	175616	7.4838	3.8259	1.74819	17.8571	175.93	2463.01
57	3249	185193	7.5498	3.8485	1.75587	17.5439	179.07	2551.76
58	3364	195112	7.6158	3.8709	1.76343	17.2414	182.21	2642.08
59	3481	205379	7.6811	3.8930	1.77085	16.9492	185.35	2733.97
60	3600	216000	7.7460	3.9149	1.77815	16.6667	188.50	2827.43
61	3721	226981	7.8102	3.9365	1.78533	16.3934	191.64	2922.47
62	3844	238328	7.8740	3.9579	1.79239	16.1290	194.78	3019.07
63	3969	250047	7.9373	3.9791	1.79934	15.8730	197.92	3117.25
64	4096	262144	8.0000	4.0000	1.80618	15.6250	201.06	3216.99
65	4225	274625	8.0623	4.0207	1.81291	15.3846	204.20	3318.31
66	4356	287496	8.1240	4.0412	1.81954	15.1515	207.35	3421.19
67	4489	300763	8.1854	4.0615	1.82607	14.9254	210.49	3525.65
68	4624	314432	8.2462	4.0817	1.83251	14.7059	213.63	3631.68
69	4761	328509	8.3066	4.1016	1.83885	14.4928	216.77	3739.28
70	4900	343000	8.3666	4.1213	1.84510	14.2857	219.91	3848.45
71	5041	357911	8.4261	4.1408	1.85126	14.0845	223.05	3959.19
72	5184	373248	8.4853	4.1602	1.85733	13.8889	226.19	4071.50
73	5329	389017	8.5440	4.1793	1.86332	13.6986	229.34	4185.39
74	5476	405224	8.6023	4.1983	1.86923	13.5135	232.48	4300.84
75	5625	421875	8.6603	4.2172	1.87506	13.3333	235.62	4417.86
76	5776	438976	8.7178	4.2358	1.88081	13.1579	238.76	4536.46
77	5929	456533	8.7750	4.2543	1.88649	12.9870	241.90	4656.63
78	6084	474552	8.8318	4.2727	1.89209	12.8205	245.04	4778.36
79	6241	493039	8.8882	4.2908	1.89763	12.6582	248.19	4901.67
80	6400	512000	8.9443	4.3089	1.90309	12.5000	251.33	5026.55
81	6561	531441	9.0000	4.3267	1.90849	12.3457	254.47	5153.00
82	6724	551368	9.0554	4.3445	1.91381	12.1951	257.61	5281.02
83	6889	571787	9.1104	4.3621	1.91908	12.0482	260.75	5410.61
84	7056	592704	9.1652	4.3795	1.92428	11.9048	263.89	5541.77
85	7225	614125	9.2195	4.3968	1.92942	11.7647	267.04	5674.50
86	7396	636056	9.2736	4.4140	1.93450	11.6279	270.18	5808.80
87	7569	658503	9.3274	4.4310	1.93952	11.4943	273.32	5944.68
88	7744	681472	9.3808	4.4480	1.94448	11.3636	276.46	6082.12
89	7921	704969	9.4340	4.4647	1.94939	11.2360	279.60	6221.14
90	8100	729000	9.4868	4.4814	1.95424	11.1111	282.74	6361.73
91	8281	753571	9.5394	4.4979	1.95904	10.9890	285.88	6503.88
92	8464	778688	9.5917	4.5144	1.96379	10.8696	289.03	6647.61
93	8649	804357	9.6437	4.5307	1.96848	10.7527	292.17	6792.91
94	8836	830584	9.6954	4.5468	1.97313	10.6383	295.31	6939.78
95	9025	857375	9.7468	4.5629	1.97772	10.5263	298.45	7088.22
96	9216	884736	9.7980	4.5789	1.98227	10.4167	301.59	7238.23
97	9409	912673	9.8489	4.5947	1.98677	10.3093	304.73	7389.81
98	9604	941192	9.8995	4.6104	1.99123	10.2041	307.88	7542.96
99	9801	970299	9.9499	4.6261	1.99564	10.1010	311.02	7697.69

Table G-7 Two-thirds Powers of Numbers

No	.00	.01	.02	.03	.04	.05	.06	.07	.08	.09
.0	.000	.046	.074	.097	.117	.136	.153	.170	.186	.201
.1	.215	.229	.243	.256	.269	.282	.295	.307	.319	.331
.2	.342	.353	.364	.375	.386	.397	.407	.418	.428	.438
.3	.448	.458	.468	.477	.487	.497	.506	.515	.525	.534
.4	.543	.552	.561	.570	.578	.587	.596	.604	.613	.622
.5	.630	.638	.647	.655	.663	.671	.679	.687	.695	.703
.6	.711	.719	.727	.735	.743	.750	.758	.765	.773	.781
.7	.788	.796	.803	.811	.818	.825	.832	.840	.847	.855
.8	.862	.869	.876	.883	.890	.897	.904	.911	.918	.925
.9	.932	.939	.946	.953	.960	.966	.973	.980	.987	.993
1.0	1.000	1.007	1.013	1.020	1.027	1.033	1.040	1.046	1.053	1.059
1.1	1.065	1.072	1.078	1.085	1.091	1.097	1.104	1.110	1.117	1.123
1.2	1.129	1.136	1.142	1.148	1.154	1.160	1.167	1.173	1.179	1.185
1.3	1.191	1.197	1.203	1.209	1.215	1.221	1.227	1.233	1.239	1.245
1.4	1.251	1.257	1.263	1.269	1.275	1.281	1.287	1.293	1.299	1.305
1.5	1.310	1.316	1.322	1.328	1.334	1.339	1.345	1.351	1.357	1.362
1.6	1.368	1.374	1.379	1.385	1.391	1.396	1.402	1.408	1.413	1.419
1.7	1.424	1.430	1.436	1.441	1.447	1.452	1.458	1.463	1.469	1.474
1.8	1.480	1.485	1.491	1.496	1.502	1.507	1.513	1.518	1.523	1.529
1.9	1.534	1.539	1.545	1.550	1.556	1.561	1.566	1.571	1.577	1.582
2.0	1.587	1.593	1.598	1.603	1.608	1.613	1.619	1.624	1.629	1.634
2.1	1.639	1.645	1.650	1.655	1.660	1.665	1.671	1.676	1.681	1.686
2.2	1.691	1.697	1.702	1.707	1.712	1.717	1.722	1.727	1.732	1.737
2.3	1.742	1.747	1.752	1.757	1.762	1.767	1.772	1.777	1.782	1.787
2.4	1.792	1.797	1.802	1.807	1.812	1.817	1.822	1.827	1.832	1.837
2.5	1.842	1.847	1.852	1.857	1.862	1.867	1.871	1.876	1.881	1.886
2.6	1.891	1.896	1.900	1.905	1.910	1.915	1.920	1.925	1.929	1.934
2.7	1.939	1.944	1.949	1.953	1.958	1.963	1.968	1.972	1.977	1.982
2.8	1.987	1.992	1.996	2.001	2.006	2.010	2.015	2.020	2.024	2.029
2.9	2.034	2.038	2.043	2.048	2.052	2.057	2.062	2.066	2.071	2.075
3.0	2.080	2.085	2.089	2.094	2.099	2.103	2.108	2.112	2.117	2.122
3.1	2.126	2.131	2.135	2.140	2.144	2.149	2.153	2.158	2.163	2.167
3.2	2.172	2.176	2.180	2.185	2.190	2.194	2.199	2.203	2.208	2.212
3.3	2.217	2.221	2.226	2.230	2.234	2.239	2.243	2.248	2.252	2.257
3.4	2.261	2.265	2.270	2.274	2.279	2.283	2.288	2.292	2.296	2.301
3.5	2.305	2.310	2.314	2.318	2.323	2.327	2.331	2.336	2.340	2.345
3.6	2.349	2.353	2.358	2.362	2.366	2.371	2.375	2.379	2.384	2.388
3.7	2.392	2.397	2.401	2.405	2.409	2.414	2.418	2.422	2.427	2.431
3.8	2.435	2.439	2.444	2.448	2.452	2.457	2.461	2.465	2.469	2.474
3.9	2.478	2.482	2.486	2.490	2.495	2.499	2.503	2.507	2.511	2.516
4.0	2.520	2.524	2.528	2.532	2.537	2.541	2.545	2.549	2.553	2.558
4.1	2.562	2.566	2.570	2.574	2.579	2.583	2.587	2.591	2.595	2.599
4.2	2.603	2.607	2.611	2.616	2.620	2.624	2.628	2.632	2.636	2.640
4.3	2.644	2.648	2.653	2.657	2.661	2.665	2.669	2.673	2.677	2.681
4.4	2.685	2.689	2.693	2.698	2.702	2.706	2.710	2.714	2.718	2.722
4.5	2.726	2.730	2.734	2.738	2.742	2.746	2.750	2.754	2.758	2.762
4.6	2.766	2.770	2.774	2.778	2.782	2.786	2.790	2.794	2.798	2.802
4.7	2.806	2.810	2.814	2.818	2.822	2.826	2.830	2.834	2.838	2.842
4.8	2.846	2.850	2.854	2.858	2.862	2.865	2.869	2.873	2.877	2.881
4.9	2.885	2.889	2.893	2.897	2.901	2.904	2.908	2.912	2.916	2.920

From King's "Handbook of Hydraulics."

Table G-8 Square Roots of Decimal Numbers
For Use in Manning's Formula

Number	.−0	.−1	.−2	.−3	.−4	.−5	.−6	.−7	.−8	.−9
.00001	.003162	.003317	.003464	.003606	.003742	.003873	.004000	.004123	.004243	.004359
.00002	.004472	.004583	.004690	.004796	.004899	.005000	.005099	.005196	.005292	.005385
.00003	.005477	.005568	.005657	.005745	.005831	.005916	.006000	.006083	.006164	.006245
.00004	.006325	.006403	.006481	.006557	.006633	.006708	.006782	.006856	.006928	.007000
.00005	.007071	.007141	.007211	.007280	.007348	.007416	.007483	.007550	.007616	.007681
.00006	.007746	.007810	.007874	.007937	.008000	.008062	.008124	.008185	.008246	.008307
.00007	.008367	.008426	.008485	.008544	.008602	.008660	.008718	.008755	.008832	.008888
.00008	.008944	.009000	.009055	.009110	.009165	.009220	.009274	.009327	.009381	.009434
.00009	.009487	.009539	.009592	.009644	.009695	.009747	.009798	.009849	.009899	.009950
.00010	.010000	.010050	.010100	.010149	.010198	.010247	.010296	.010344	.010392	.010440
.0001	.01000	.01049	.01095	.01140	.01183	.01225	.01265	.01304	.01342	.01378
.0002	.01414	.01449	.01483	.01517	.01549	.01581	.01612	.01643	.01673	.01703
.0003	.01732	.01761	.01789	.01817	.01844	.01871	.01897	.01924	.01949	.01975
.0004	.02000	.02025	.02049	.02074	.02098	.02121	.02145	.02168	.02191	.02214
.0005	.02236	.02258	.02280	.02302	.02324	.02345	.02366	.02387	.02408	.02429
.0006	.02449	.02470	.02490	.02510	.02530	.02550	.02569	.02588	.02608	.02627
.0007	.02646	.02665	.02683	.02702	.02720	.02739	.02757	.02775	.02793	.02811
.0008	.02828	.02846	.02864	.02881	.02898	.02915	.02933	.02950	.02966	.02983
.0009	.03000	.03017	.03033	.03050	.03066	.03082	.03098	.03114	.03130	.03146
.0010	.03162	.03178	.03194	.03209	.03225	.03240	.03256	.03271	.03286	.03302
.001	.03162	.03317	.03464	.03606	.03742	.03873	.04000	.04123	.04243	.04359
.002	.04472	.04583	.04690	.04796	.04899	.05000	.05099	.05196	.05292	.05385
.003	.05477	.05568	.05657	.05745	.05831	.05916	.06000	.06083	.06164	.06245
.004	.06325	.06403	.06481	.06557	.06633	.06708	.06782	.06856	.06928	.07000
.005	.07071	.07141	.07211	.07280	.07348	.07416	.07483	.07550	.07616	.07681
.006	.07746	.07810	.07874	.07937	.08000	.08062	.08124	.08185	.08246	.08307
.007	.08367	.08426	.08485	.08544	.08602	.08660	.08718	.08775	.08832	.08888
.008	.08944	.09000	.09055	.09110	.09165	.09220	.09274	.09327	.09381	.09434
.009	.09487	.09539	.09592	.09644	.09695	.09747	.09798	.09849	.09899	.09950
.010	.10000	.10050	.10100	.10149	.10198	.10247	.10296	.10344	.10392	.10440
.01	.1000	.1049	.1095	.1140	.1183	.1225	.1265	.1304	.1342	.1378
.02	.1414	.1449	.1483	.1517	.1549	.1581	.1612	.1643	.1673	.1703
.03	.1732	.1761	.1789	.1817	.1844	.1871	.1897	.1924	.1949	.1975
.04	.2000	.2025	.2049	.2074	.2098	.2121	.2145	.2168	.2191	.2214
.05	.2236	.2258	.2280	.2302	.2324	.2345	.2366	.2387	.2408	.2429
.06	.2449	.2470	.2490	.2510	.2530	.2550	.2569	.2588	.2608	.2627
.07	.2646	.2665	.2683	.2702	.2720	.2739	.2757	.2775	.2793	.2811
.08	.2828	.2846	.2864	.2881	.2898	.2915	.2933	.2950	.2966	.2983
.09	.3000	.3017	.3033	.3050	.3066	.3082	.3098	.3114	.3130	.3146
.10	.3162	.3178	.3194	.3209	.3225	.3240	.3256	.3271	.3286	.3302

From King's "Handbook of Hydraulics."

Table G-9 U. S. Standard Gages for Sheet and Plate Iron and Steel (Black)

Established by Act of Congress, July 1, 1893
(With revisions, 1945)

Number of Gage	Approximate Thickness				Weight		
	Fractions of an Inch	Decimal Parts of an Inch		Milli-meters	per Square Foot in Ounces Avoir-dupois	per Square Foot in Pounds Avoir-dupois	per Square Meter in Kilo-grams
	Wrought Iron*	Wrought Iron*	Steel†	Steel†			
000	3–8	.375	.3587	9.111	240	15.	73.24
00	11–32	.34375	.3288	8.352	220	13.75	67.13
0	5–16	.3125	.2989	7.592	200	12.50	61.03
1	9–32	.28125	.2690	6.833	180	11.25	54.93
2	17–64	.265625	.2541	6.454	170	10.625	51.88
3	1–4	.25	.2391	6.073	160	10.	48.82
4	15–64	.234375	.2242	5.695	150	9.375	45.77
5	7–32	.21875	.2092	5.314	140	8.75	42.72
6	13–64	.203125	.1943	4.935	130	8.125	39.67
7	3–16	.1875	.1793	4.554	120	7.5	36.62
8	11–64	.171875	.1644	4.176	110	6.875	33.57
9	5–32	.15625	.1495	3.797	100	6.25	30.52
10	9–64	.140625	.1345	3.416	90	5.625	27.46
11	1–8	.125	.1196	3.038	80	5.	24.41
12	7–64	.109375	.1046	2.657	70	4.375	21.36
13	3–32	.09375	.0897	2.278	60	3.75	18.31
14	5–64	.078125	.0747	1.897	50	3.125	15.26
15	9–128	.0703125	.0673	1.709	45	2.8125	13.73
16	1–16	.0625	.0598	1.519	40	2.5	12.21
17	9–160	.05625	.0538	1.367	36	2.25	10.99
18	1–20	.05	.0478	1.214	32	2.	9.765
19	7–160	.04375	.0418	1.062	28	1.75	8.544
20	3–80	.0375	.0359	0.912	24	1.50	7.324

By Act of Congress, the gage numbers are based on the weight per square foot in ounce (sixth column) and not on thickness.

*The thickness given in the Congressional table is for wrought iron and not for steel.

†The thickness for steel is from tables compiled by American Iron and Steel Institute, November 1942, based on 41.82 pounds per square foot per inch thick.

Example: A 16 gage sheet of either wrought iron or steel weighs 40 ounces per square foot. The wrought iron is approximately .0625 inch thick whereas the steel is .0598 inch thick.

General Index

The scope of this handbook can best be determined by a look at the CONTENTS, page 5
The chapters, along with sections and prime references, are shown in bold face.

Tables are indicated by T followed by chapter, table no. and page number (T6-1, 51).

NAMES of individuals, places, organizations, colleges and industries are listed at the end of the GENERAL INDEX.

Items listed in the GLOSSARY, page 319, and SYMBOLS, page 325, are partly cross-referenced to this GENERAL INDEX.

(Corrections or suggestions are invited)

Index of Names